WOMEN'S HOSPITALS

in

BRIGHTON

&

HOVE

VAL BROWN

The Hastings Press

British Library Cataloguing in Publication Data:
A catalogue record for this book is available from the British Library

ISBN 1-904-109-98
ISBN 13: 978-1-904109-09-9

Published 2006
The Hastings Press
PO Box 96 Hastings TN34 1GQ
hastings.press@virgin.net
www.hastingspress.co.uk

Set in Garamond
Design: Helena Wojtczak
Cover photo and Windlesham House site plan: Adrian C. Hancock
Map of Brighton & Hove © Lia Segar 2006

Printed by TJI Digital, Padstow, England

To Manon —

Best wishes —

Val   12/10/06

WOMEN'S HOSPITALS

IN

BRIGHTON

&

HOVE

For Elaine

who has put in many long hours
scouring local papers, trawling the world wide web
and always providing much-needed amounts
of cheer, support and encouragement.

CONTENTS

AUTHOR'S NOTE...VII

CHAPTER 1 THE ROAD TO BRIGHTON AND HOVE.......................................1

CHAPTER 2 MRS AND MISS MARTINDALE...10

CHAPTER 3 THE DISPENSARY AND OTHER HOSPITALS...............................19

CHAPTER 4 THE LEWES ROAD HOSPITAL...28

CHAPTER 5 DR LOUISA MARTINDALE...37

CHAPTER 6 MAJOR CHANGES..47

CHAPTER 7 THE TWO BRANCHES...56

CHAPTER 8 THE WAR IN EUROPE...62

CHAPTER 9 THE WAR AT HOME...72

CHAPTER 10 SEPARATION...81

CHAPTER 11 THE OLD VICARAGE...91

CHAPTER 12 ALDRINGTON HOUSE..99

CHAPTER 13 WINDLESHAM HOUSE..110

CHAPTER 14 THE STRUGGLE CONTINUES..120

CHAPTER 15 THE OPENING CEREMONY...135

CHAPTER 16 INTO THE 1920s..147

CHAPTER 17 EPILOGUE...159

APPENDICES

I   LADY CHICHESTER 1926 APPEAL — LIST OF PATRONS AND OFFICERS.................165

II   NEW SUSSEX PAMPHLET 1937 — LIST OF PATRONS AND OFFICERS.....................166

III   YE AUTUMNE FAYRE 1922...167

IV   YE OLDE SUSSEX FAYRE 1922...171

V   TIMELINE..178

VI   PLACES, PEOPLE AND CONNECTIONS..179

MAP...194

SOURCES...195

INDEX..197

Acknowledgements

I would like to thank David and Richard Boyle for their advice, support and wonderful contributions; John Goodchild for his detailed knowledge about George Wilton Chambers; Gary Haines for his help with information about the Canning Town Women's Settlement and Mission; T. M. Houston for his informative letter about Windlesham House. I am also deeply grateful for professional efforts on my behalf to Alison Leggatt of Brighton & Hove High School; the archivist at St Mary's Hospital, London; Lee Sands at the BMA; Victoria North and Vicky Rea at the Royal Free Hospital Archives Centre; Michael Stephens at the Glasgow Royal College of Physicians and Surgeons; the archivist at the Royal College of Physicians; Robert Mills at the Royal College of Physicians of Ireland; Sue Symonds of the National Association of Women Pharmacists; Ann Thompson at Newnham College Archives; the staff at the East Sussex Records Office, Hove Library and Brighton Museum Local Studies Library; and the Business and Professional Women's Association.

For their valuable assistance and interest I am deeply grateful to Lord Chichester; Mrs Pamela Brotherton; Helen Davitt; Harry Gaston; Dr Lesley Hall; Andrew Holmes-Siedle; Dr I. M. Ingram MD, FRCPsych, DPM; H. Melville, FRCS (Ed), FRCOG; Emma Milliken; Linda Pointing of Brighton Ourstory Lesbian, Gay and Bisexual History Centre; Mrs J. C. Pollock; Charlotte Ridings; Sarah Tobias; Dr Gerry Holloway and Dr Louise Westwood of Sussex University; the contributors to the mybrightonandhove egroup; and Adrian C. Hancock and Helena Wojtczak of the Hastings Press. Special appreciation for demonstrating great patience with me at all times goes to Hilary Anderson and Dr Jenny Beckett-Wood.

If I have omitted anyone I am truly sorry, please accept my sincere apologies.

AUTHOR'S NOTE

Researching the two women's hospitals in Brighton and Hove necessitated learning about the long battle which women fought in order to practise medicine in the nineteenth century, trying to reduce a long and complex drama into easily readable chunks and then pasting them onto a background of life in Brighton and Hove — and indeed further afield — in late Victorian and Edwardian times. The women's movement embraced long campaigns not only for the right to vote, but for married women to have financial independence and for entry into higher education and into the professions. This ceaseless activity spun a vigorous and complex social web of friendships and connections, bonds and relationships amongst middle class women — the women who founded their hospitals in this small seaside town could rely upon an energetic feminine network that stretched from London to Ireland, from Scotland to India and around the institutions of Cambridge, Oxford, London and Glasgow. Their lives embraced connections with other women in hard-core social reform affecting schools, prisons and workhouses, and included a lively involvement in science, psychical research, journalism and literature. Even during the First World War Miss Mary Sheepshanks and Mrs Helena Swanwick (née Sickert), dedicated pacifists and members of the National Union of Women's Suffrage Societies, came to Brighton to lecture on pacifism, receiving for their trouble much heckling and subsequent angry letters to the local papers. As those of us who live here know, Brighton and Hove is the centre of the world and what happens in London gets off the train only an hour later here. It was no different a hundred years ago.

I am very conscious that Dr Sophia Jex-Blake, unlike Dr Elizabeth Garrett Anderson, has been given no substantial role in this narrative although her contribution to women's history is phenomenal and her association with Sussex considerable. Nevertheless she was not at any time associated with the two women's hospitals in Brighton and Hove (although her friend and biographer Dr Margaret Todd was fleetingly associated with the New Sussex in a literary capacity) and so must reluctantly be put to one side.

A modest sidetrack into the history of women in dentistry and pharmacy became both necessary and interesting. Women dentists also benefited from the 1877 Enabling Act and their story has not yet been told; hopefully someone will do so in the near future. The history of women veterinary surgeons also awaits study.

There is much interest, in academic circles (particularly by my good friend Helena Wojtczak and Dr Gerry Holloway) in working-class women who laboured long and hard all of their lives and yet remain almost invisible in the literature of their time. The voluntary work of the leisured middle-class married woman and her daughter is even more invisible since it is also unfashionable, and this narrative may well be among the few that pay tribute to their unsung work. The women doctors who were the driving force behind the Lady Chichester and the New Sussex Hospitals depended enormously upon a well-functioning, efficient and well-connected raft of non-professional women putting in many hours of unpaid work attending committee and council meetings, organising complex entertainments, standing tirelessly behind stalls during the incessant flow of bazaars, sales of work and jumble sales, and simply giving time to provide refreshments for callers at outpatients'. These women were clever and determined, and they learned how to function as a team in the rapidly changing world of the twentieth century. Frequently they were snobbish and class-conscious (they did not embrace the principle of social mobility) and they could be harsh and unkind in their judgements. But they put in the hours, the slog behind the scenes, the passionate commitment that was needed to keep the hospitals open and the patients treated.

In their defence I have included full accounts of the two magnificent bazaars organised in 1922 by the ladies affiliated to both women's hospitals and lengthily reported at the time in the *Sussex Daily News* (a newspaper regretfully long defunct). The time and the painstaking trouble, the intense planning detail, the complexity of teamwork and organisation and the breadth of artistic effort involved in staging these spectacular events does their abilities enormous credit.

I had hoped originally to take the story up to the late 1940s but circumstances and poor health have precluded this. However, drawing a line beneath the story in the 1920s, give or take a few years, with a few later bits and pieces stirred in for good measure, still makes a good narrative. I do apologise for not offering a detailed history of the beginnings of the National Health Service from the passing of the Act in 1945 to its arrival on the ground in 1948; its tectonic administrative reorganisations, its ceaseless struggle to find enough funding and the recent growth of private hospitals as commercially viable ventures could provide ironic interest when the days of Lady Chichester and the New Sussex have long passed. This is beyond my scope and will require more than a few volumes, the number multiplying daily, all of its own.

1

THE ROAD TO BRIGHTON AND HOVE

On Wednesday, 1st November 1899 the *Sussex Daily News*, always avid for fresh local copy, announced the opening of a new dispensary for women and children at 145 Islingword Road, just off the Lewes Road, out to the north of Brighton. A medium-sized house on the end of a terrace and happily right next door to the pretty Percy and Wagner Almshouses for Elderly Widows and Spinsters — which to this day continue to look out over The Level — it was conveniently situated near the busy shops, dwellings, churches and public houses of Lewes Road and had a good electric tram service nearby. A few alterations had had to be made to the ground floor to provide waiting, consulting and dispensing rooms and to a top floor that could be usefully let to provide accommodation for a residential caretaker.

This was a poor district of Brighton but one that was heavily populated. There were streets of houses tucked closely together in a muddle of Victorian terraces, small and overcrowded, rented rather than owned, that were home to the working and poorer families of Brighton. For affordable medical care the people of the area mostly relied on the services of the Brighton, Hove and Preston Dispensary, a charitable institution founded in 1809 that had a small northern branch situated on the other side of The Level at 26 Ditchling Road.[1]

In the late nineteenth century medical care was provided by a doctor's home visit; the visit was always expensive and was avoided by working men and women except in cases of extreme urgency or impending death. In earlier days bumps, boils, bruises, coughs, digestive disorders, deafness, loss of sight, scalds, sprains and other afflictions, which impaired daily life but did not immediately threaten its extinction, had been taken care of by recourse to the local apothecary or druggist, a less expensive — although by no means reliable — recourse. A visit to the local dispensary had taken the place of the visit to the druggist: a dispensary offered modern and up-to-date medical care by a skilled and qualified physician and the visit was always affordable, so there was no heavy bill to worry about afterwards. The convenience of regular and fixed consulting hours was agreeable and the privacy of the consulting room was particularly welcomed by women.

The physicians at the dispensaries were local doctors who gave their services freely and voluntarily for a few hours each week. They were known as 'honorary' medical officers. The pharmacist — or dispenser — was also voluntary as was the secretary and any other clerical assistant. Sometimes a small charge was made for a patient to consult the doctor; sometimes not, although a small charge for medicines provided by the dispenser from the doctor's prescription was frequently made. Because the dispensary served working people there was usually an afternoon 'calling time', which suited many women at home with their children, and an evening calling time for their working sisters and menfolk.

A dispensary was a charitable institution, managed by a competent committee or board of management, which was responsible for securing its funds from regular (or more often intermittent) subscriptions from wealthy patrons. The honorary physicians were automatically given a place on the board but most members were local businessmen and political dignitaries: wealthy, middle-class men who also gave their time and business expertise voluntarily and who, by the turn of the nineteenth century, were often joined by their wives, daughters and sisters. There was never a time when funds were not needed and the women became skilled at organising fundraising events and creating catchy publicity that would draw in regular subscriptions.

The subscriber was an important bird to catch and hold on to: he or she could be relied upon to make a reliably regular donation to the dispensary by means of a yearly standing order at the bank, and local dignitaries, mayors and mayoresses of Brighton and of Hove, MPs, aldermen and all varieties of businessmen were approached. Potential new subscribers were courted energetically and might well look for privileges in return for their patronage. Introductions to and socialising with the local wealthy classes (the Earls of Chichester had always nobly headed the Brighton and Hove Dispensary as president) became possible, a seat on the board of management might even become available, and in any case a vote at the annual meeting was ensured. But even more useful, if the subscriber was a businessman, was the ease with which his workmen or servants could get medical treatment if they were ill because seeing the doctor at the dispensary was not that easy. The prospective patient first had to obtain a letter of introduction (usually called a 'ticket') before she or he was allowed in to consult the dispensary duty doctor. All subscribers had the privilege of issuing these 'tickets'. The businessman who was a regular subscriber to a dispensary naturally could write, or even sell, regular 'tickets' to his workforce. In fact, by 1898 a general unease about the system had become apparent; although the subscribers were normally men and women of the highest moral calibre, at least one subscriber — a clergyman — had recently been criticised for 'selling' tickets to the poor.

In 1898 Dr Helen Boyle, then aged 29, along with her associate and medical partner Dr Mabel Jones, probably born in 1870 and of much the same age, came to Hove to set up in general practice. They had met at the London School of Medicine for Women* where both had studied during the 1890s and, after some time working in and around London where they could, joined forces, left the capital, and arrived in summery but perhaps sedate Hove. They took a lease on a good house, 3 Palmeira Terrace (now 37 Church Road) in a reasonably well-to-do area; a tall and ornate property built in the early 1880s, not too far from the beaming faces of the great town hall clock tower beneath its slender gothic cap, and facing the flinty sides of St John's Church immediately across Church Road. It was hardly a stone's throw from the grassy stretch of Palmeira Square sloping down to the sea and the ponderous white porches of expensive Adelaide Crescent with its much larger houses which — with luck — would furnish an excellent supply of potential clients. Good shops were not too far away and the frequent arrival of horse-drawn (but shortly to be motorised) trams on their way to The Steine with their cream and maroon liveried drivers, made travelling fairly easy. They affixed their brass plate next to the dentist at what is now number 35 and, with a cook and a maidservant to look after them, awaited patients, made their plans for the future and, as the nineteenth century hurtled to its close, like all newcomers looked eagerly around at the nearby roads of Hove and the more noisy streets of its neighbour Brighton a mile away along Western Road.

The two towns had rubbed along well together for years: Brightonians travelled along Church Road to work on the seemingly endless building sites in Hove which were pushing up from the dark soil of the Wick, Vallance and Cliftonville estates; and Hoveans went the other way along Western Road for their daily and weekend entertainment. There were theatres, music halls and two moving picture establishments; and if those were perhaps not quite to one's taste, between them Brighton and Hove boasted at least twenty societies for more genteel recreation, including ladies' archery, music, swimming and cycling, along with Liberal and Tory ladies' associations for the more serious-minded. Temperance groups and

* The London School of Medicine for Women (LSMW) opened in 1874, but changed its name to The London (Royal Free Hospital) School of Medicine for Women in 1898 when the Royal Free Hospital allowed women onto its wards for clinical studies. In 1900 the name was changed again to the London (Royal Free Hospital) School of Medicine for Women (University of London). This cumbersome title was rarely, if ever, used in full, and for the purposes of brevity and clarity the name London School of Medicine for Women (usually abbreviated to LSMW) has been retained throughout this work.

the Band of Hope scratched no few supporters. The green crevasse of Devil's Dyke was a favourite place for picnics and could be easily reached by train; bandstands belted out favourite melodies in the sunshine by the beach and there were large numbers of public houses, pimps, pickpockets and prostitutes of both sexes. The Brighton electric tramway system, begun in the 1880s, was nearly complete and along with the chunky, horse-drawn trams of Hove the pleasure seeker could be ferried anywhere for a few pence. Gas lamps illuminated the streets at night and horse-drawn hackney cabs for hire trawled the roads should the revelries go on just a little too long.

Since the railway had arrived in Brighton in 1845 the holiday culture and the numbers of gaudy day-trippers had boomed, and some of the massive and hard-to-heat homes built much earlier in the century to accommodate the itinerant wealthy classes had become plain and simple boarding houses for ordinary folk as well as private schools and nursing homes. Some had even turned into unsavoury tenements, but many still housed the permanently resident — and frequently sickly — rich. The army lingered in barracks along the Lewes Road and Hove batteries still pointed their guns out to sea where the broad-beamed fishing boats with their plump sails dotted the Brighton seas between the two stalky thrusts of the Palace and West Piers. Business was excellent all round and fortunes were made from departmental stores, theatrical entertainments and the practices of law and architecture. The other classes did very well from the boarding establishments, shop keeping, railways, domestic service, road transport and the building and traditional trades of every description and variety.

There were areas of wealth which bordered on areas of poverty and more than one red light district crept uncomfortably close to a tightly-knit local 'high society' made up of members of the local middle-class and lesser nobility. Many businessmen became very rich, and went on to do their civic duty as local councillors, aldermen and magistrates whilst their wives, daughters and sisters interested themselves in associations founded to improve schooling, housing, public sanitation and the welfare of orphans and distressed servant girls. There were over forty charitable institutions to choose to support, societies for the care of sick children, sick animals and sick people.

The town was then, as now, odd and eccentric. A strong liberal and philanthropic vein coursed energetically through its public life, its citizens admired themselves for being giddily cosmopolitan, but by 1898 the MPs returned were Tory and the Primrose League for Conservative women attracted many supporters. There was a strong movement already in place amongst the middle-class women of Brighton and Hove who ardently supported the nationwide struggle for the women's franchise. Millicent Garrett Fawcett, president of the National Union of Women's Suffrage Societies, was well-known and respected in Brighton: she had married the blind Liberal MP Henry Fawcett (1833–1880) who represented the town in the 1860s.

How would two women doctors freshly arrived from London fare in such a place? In fact with such an aggressive and energetic mixture of liberalism, wealth and gaudiness flowing through its streets and with an active resident middle class as well as an extensive working population, the chances for a good career might turn out to be very favourable indeed. Brighton and Hove in 1898, then as now happily blessed with frequent trains to and from London, could possibly be just the right place. A repository of health and wealth, disease and poverty for over a century, the towns sported a fine selection of over a hundred practising physicians as well as an assortment of dispensaries and specialist hospitals, and away to the hilly east the Sussex County Hospital had been long established and was already flexing the tentacles of its ambitious growth. As was customary, Drs Boyle and Jones called on the local doctors, and seemed to have received no overt opposition, although one local physician had expressed at a meeting of the Brighton & Sussex Medico-Chirurgical Society a rather bewildered opinion: 'In all my years of practise I have never been asked by a patient to consult a woman.'

Queen Victoria could not last much longer, and the prejudice against middle-class women from good families taking up a profession of any kind was slowly draining away as the 'New Woman', working and living alone, smoking and entering restaurants by herself, was making her appearance in late-Victorian society. But women's involvement in the often bloody and always indelicate nature of medical practice had aroused much (and often vicious) hostility from the medical and surgical masculine establishment, although against the rising demand from women to be treated by other women at times of illness (or during the unconsciousness thankfully induced by the new chemistry of anaesthesia, now easily available) there could be only feeble argument.

Some fruits of the industrial revolution — the typewriter and the telephone recently instituted in offices and public buildings — were beginning to provide an abundance of new types of work for the daughters of fairly well-off tradesmen and the more comfortable daughters of independent businessmen. The work was clean, respectable, and not taxing of feminine strengths. A rung or two up the social ladder, their middle-class sisters from professional families were beginning to look with jaundiced eyes at the family money being automatically invested in their brothers' education, which would be followed by prompt entry into a rewarding profession, bringing them both independence and prosperity at an early age. These women knew that their own capabilities equalled — and not infrequently exceeded — those of their brothers. Had they not lived and studied together as children? Why should the son, who by no means was possessed of any greater intelligence than his sister, go off to school, then university and become a wealthy lawyer, architect or physician, whilst she was kept fretful at home with neither occupation, independent income nor the means to achieve either?

Forty years previously, in 1860, Elizabeth Garrett Anderson, on seeking advice from an eminent physician about training to become a doctor, had been patronisingly asked: 'Why not become a nurse?' Her reply: 'I prefer to earn a thousand rather than twenty pounds a year', although possibly indiscreet at the time, was scornfully accurate.[2] By 1890 the obstacles a woman needed to surmount in order to become qualified as a doctor had crumbled; the main hurdle then (as indeed it often is now) being the acquisition of a high standard of education that would enable acceptance into a medical school. For women who had been educated by governess and finishing school, the study of maths, Latin, Greek, algebra, botany, chemistry and other academic subjects needed to pass a public examination was formidable.

The most serious, last-stand opposition to women becoming physicians and surgeons had finally been overcome in 1876. The Medical Act of 1858 had established the General Medical Council, which would oversee desirable standards of education and training in the medical profession and maintain and publish annually a register of all qualified physicians and surgeons.[3] To get onto the register the medical student had to obtain either the appropriate degree from a university, or to become a licentiate member of one of the medical corporations, such as the Royal Colleges or Faculties of Medicine and Surgery, or the Royal Society of Apothecaries, by sitting — and passing — one of their professional examinations. In 1876 no university would yet grant a degree to a woman, so entry into the profession would have to be by this route: sitting for, and passing, one of the Royal Colleges' and Faculties' 'in house' licentiate examinations.[4] But the powerful physicians and surgeons who made up the Royal Colleges and faculties, fathers of their science, successfully managed to stop women doing this — and so inhibited their entry onto the medical register — simply by not allowing them to sit the examination at all! This they did by smugly quoting the texts of their ancient Royal Charters, which declared that they were able only to examine men — and not women — for admission to the profession. And from this stance they simply would not budge.[5]

It had taken an Act of Parliament to defeat them. In 1876 Russell Gurney, an MP and supporter of women doctors, successfully steered through parliament a bill that would enable the medical corporations to examine women, 'notwithstanding any restrictions to be found in their Charters'. In effect, the medical corporations could now examine women — if they so chose. Some did immediately, some didn't for many years, but the final barrier went gently, though purposefully, down. This was called the Enabling Act, and it was followed — somewhat tardily — in 1919 by the Sex Disqualification (Removal) Act allowing women to enter all professions.

By no means did all male doctors disapprove of women entering their profession; many were progressive men who actively supported the women's struggle and as early as October 1878 the King and Queen's College in Dublin did choose to examine women medical students, and it was followed in 1885 by the Colleges of Physicians and of Surgeons in Edinburgh and the Glasgow and Edinburgh University Faculties of Medicine, Surgery and Midwifery. In London, the Royal College of Physicians and the Royal College of Surgeons established a conjoint qualifying examination (Medicine and Surgery) in 1885, but stubbornly declined to allow women to sit for it until nearly twenty years later, in 1908. However by this time London University had (since 1878) agreed to grant degrees of Bachelor of Medicine and Bachelor of Surgery to women, which allowed direct entry onto the British Medical Register along with the second and more prestigious degree, the Doctorate of Medicine.[6]

The problem of gaining practical training in hands-on ward work at a teaching hospital had also been successfully overcome by the admission of women student doctors to the wards of the Glasgow Royal Infirmary and, in 1877, to the Royal Free Hospital in London which, alone of the London hospitals, had no medical school attached to it.[7]

Dr Boyle and Dr Jones had come in headily on the crest of the wave. By 1890 over two hundred women had qualified as doctors: Lillie Mabel Agnes Jones, originally from Newfoundland, entered the London School of Medicine for Women in October 1887 as student no. 187 and she qualified MB (London) in 1893. Alice Helen Anne Boyle entered the school in October 1889 as student no. 249

and qualified in 1893 by sitting and passing the Triple Qualification of Medicine, Surgery and Obstetrics offered in Glasgow by the Royal Faculty of Physicians, and immediately went on to obtain her MD, with distinction, in Brussels in 1894. Born in Dublin in 1869, having spent most of her childhood on the continent she was fluent in French and German. A year later, in 1895, Mabel Jones gained her MD at London University and, in 1898, with a few years of practical everyday work experience under their black, tightly buttoned-up corseted dresses — de rigueur for a woman doctor, of whose body only the hands and face should be visible to the patient — they had teamed up and entered general practice together in sunny and salty Hove. A year later, with Dr Helen Boyle and Dr Mabel Jones at the helm as honorary medical officers, the Lewes Road Dispensary for Women and Children opened in Islingword Road.

Notes

[1] The Brighton, Hove and Preston dispensary building, opened in 1850, was in downtown Brighton at 113 Queens Road; it has gone now, having been replaced by a rather nasty blueish office block. A western branch in Hove had been upgraded in 1885 to a handsome red-brick hospital in Sackville Road, survived as Hove Hospital for many years but is now a prestigious set of apartments named Tennyson Court. Sadly, the developers of neither site have seen fit to remember the Brighton, Hove and Preston Dispensary that for many years provided a large proportion of health care for the working and poorer people of the town.

[2] Manton, J. (1965) *Elizabeth Garrett Anderson*. p.76.

[3] It was not a criminal act to practise medicine without registration (some women followed that road in the early years) but it was not in their long-term interests to do so since this choice would lay them wide open to accusations of ignorance, quackery and fraud.

[4] In the 1880s only a minority of registered medical practitioners held a university degree. Peterson M. J., (1978) *The Medical Profession in Mid Victorian London*.

[5] Elizabeth Garrett Anderson had managed to become registered with the BMC in 1866. She was able to submit herself to be examined by the Royal Society of Apothecaries — a Licentiateship of the RSA (LSA) qualified for entry into the British Medical Register — because its charter had specified 'person' rather than 'man'. She was aided considerably by a successful lawsuit brought by her father to insist that 'person' did not exclude women. After her successful entry to its examinations and the award of a licentiateship which enabled her to practise as a GP, the Royal Society of Apothecaries hastily changed its charter to read 'man' instead of 'person', thereby blocking that route for other women until the Enabling Act of 1876. The Society is not nowadays proud of that decision.

[6] Elizabeth Garrett obtained her MD in Paris 1870, and Sophia Jex-Blake obtained hers in Berne in 1877. Both had to learn French in order to do so. The first woman to

obtain the MD in London was Mrs Scharlieb in 1888.

[7] Interestingly, in the late nineteenth century there were medical schools in Poona and Madras in India that would admit women. Dr Mary Scharlieb qualified in Madras as Licentiate of Medicine, Surgery and Midwifery in 1875 before returning to study at the LSMW and is credited with being the woman who caused Queen Victoria to change her opposition to women doctors. When speaking to Her Majesty about the millions of her women subjects living in purdah in India with no hope whatsoever of expert medical care unless women became qualified, the Queen, who genuinely cared for her subjects in India, came to agree and spoke out no more against the qualification of women. Dr Scharlieb was the first woman to be awarded the specialised degree of Master of Surgery from London University in 1897.

2

Mrs and Miss Martindale

There were three generations named Louisa. The first, Miss Louisa Edwards of Denmark Hill in south London, married Mr James Spicer in 1838. Their first child, a daughter, the second Louisa, was born on 25th June 1839 at his house 'Harts' in Woodford Green, Essex. The house was fine, originally Elizabethan, painted white, but unfortunately encumbered with a classical front that had been added by a previous owner in the nineteenth century. In its extensive grounds there were trees, a shrubbery, lawns, flower-beds and ponds; it was a Victorian garden at its best, a magical place for children of all ages. The family of James Spicer could have been written from a Victorian script for ideal family life. Mr Spicer was a wealthy businessman who had made a fortune in the paper trade in the City of London. He was deeply religious, a nonconformist and Congregationalist by conviction (as had been his father, John Edward Spicer) and a fervent believer in homeopathy. The Victorians had no qualms of conscience with this way of life; in the Midlands and the north of England several Quaker families had over the years established vast fortunes and fathered extended dynasties by the middle of the nineteenth century, and in the manner of his times James Spicer presided grandly at the head of a growing family which would eventually number ten children.

Two years earlier, in Whitechapel, east London, another family had been blessed with the arrival of a second daughter. Born on 9th June 1836 to Newson and Louisa Garrett, little Elizabeth Garrett could have had no idea how her own life, and the fortunes of her equally extending and prospering family, which would eventually number nine children and move to Aldeburgh in Suffolk, would weave itself into that of little Louisa Spicer and her daughter-to-be, the third Louisa.

As the first-born daughter of a rich, middle-class, professional father, there was only one future for Louisa Spicer: home and family. Looking after the younger children as they arrived, and assisting her mother (who would spend much of her married life expecting her next confinement), caring for servants, cherishing the expensive furniture and organising the prompt arrival of meals. Her education consisted mostly of lessons in ladylike deportment, the acquisition of serene manners and the cultivation of a graceful demeanour. There was much emphasis on punctuality, neatness and the avoidance of making noise. But Louisa Spicer was made of sterner stuff than her teachers expected. She learned her lessons avidly but improved upon their strictures. She became determined to acquire the habit of doing everything not only well, but more than well: to learn something from every person she met and to strive continually to improve herself. She began to read widely — books, magazines and religious tracts — and strove to improve not only herself but the lives of those surrounding her.

She also acquired and maintained throughout her life the profound and deeply religious faith in the congregational, nonconformist tradition of her father, and also came to support his lifelong attachment to the Liberal Party. She loved all children and, as well as caring for her younger brothers and sisters, she started a Sunday school for poor children in Woodford Green and became a visitor to the Ragged Schools in the East End of London.

Louisa Spicer's life at home as she approached her thirtieth year was full and satisfying in the tradition of the private world of the middle-class Victorian woman. Her life was busy and occupied with home-based and charitable activities; she interested herself in the lives of the poor, she occupied spare moments with intense reading and developed a keen interest in art and travel. Her life was rich and rewarding — or was it? In the 1860s a father's authority over his daughter was severe; he could read her letters; his approval had to be sought at all times for decisions concerning her welfare; he could, in short, direct every aspect of her life. She did not, it would appear, ever actively oppose her father's will; she sought no independence from him and throughout her life Louisa Spicer, although tirelessly active, ever vigilant for injustices to be righted, ceaselessly occupied in improving the lives of women, a planner and great mover of obstacles, preferred to be a woman who remained, apparently passive, in the background. She was a mover behind the scenes rather than seeking centre stage, choosing modesty, religion, and the private rather than the public life. And yet Louisa Spicer was determined, energetic and intelligent. By the middle 1860s her abilities had refined into those which might well have been admirably suited to engage in the long, drawn-out battle being fought at that time in London by an equally determined and fiercely ambitious Elizabeth Garrett, as she battled for ten years, using all of her considerable intellect, patience and cunning, to become a qualified and practising doctor of medicine. Elizabeth Garrett eventually succeeded, but she would not have done so without the support of her father, Newson Garrett. A wealthy man, he could afford to sue the Apothecaries' Society when that body of gentlemen refused to examine Elizabeth after her years of study; a self-made man of intense pride, he would not accept, on principle, their rejection of his favourite child. The sons of Newson

Garrett were known to complain that their sister took up too much of their father's attention.

James Spicer seems not to have had that manner of relationship with Louisa. He did not stint the education of his sons: both Evan and Albert went on to have successful public careers and both achieved knighthood. But it would seem unlikely that he would have been sympathetic to the wishes of a daughter who might desire to leave the home that he had provided for her, in order to seek an independent life when such a notion was rare and even shocking. But it does seem likely that Louisa later came to regret her uncontroversial choice of the homely life. Reading even more widely and deeply, she became increasingly aware of the rising tide of the women's rights movement, which was demanding for women the equal education so necessary to achieve an equal right to work. Elizabeth Garrett's struggle was widely — even salaciously — reported in the newspapers of the 1860s and, as Louisa Spicer approached her thirtieth year, Barbara Leigh Smith (later to become Madame Bodichon) and Bessie Rayner Parkes were seeking to amend the iniquities of the marriage laws which decreed that, in law, the married woman did not exist as an individual.

Their activity began after Caroline Norton's bitter struggle in the courts to keep her children, following a scandalous divorce from her abusive husband. There was also Josephine Butler's campaign against the injustice of the Contagious Diseases Acts to read about[1] and Emily Davies's patient determination to break into the universities and open up advanced education for women. Reports of these campaigns were splashed heartily — and by no means without sympathy — across the pages of the daily newspapers, along with the sinister approach of the feminine demand for parliamentary suffrage.

It would seem to be time to move on and in 1871 Louisa Spicer, probably to her family's surprise and discomfiture, left her father's house for ever. At the age of thirty-two she married William Martindale, a businessman and merchant nearly forty years old, a widower with four children. He was a cultured man; a Fellow of the Royal Geographical Society and not exactly a nonconformist but, acceptably, a supporter of the low church. Their first child — the third Louisa — was born at their home, Gainsborough Lodge, Leytonstone, on 30th October 1872. A second child, Mary, followed soon after and, by the summer of 1874, a third was expected. The marriage was happy and the step-children comfortable with their new mother, but Mrs Martindale seems to have been impatient with her new round of domestic duties. Not the first woman to do so, possibly she had found that marriage, far from opening the door to wider opportunities, had in fact slammed more tightly shut. In her father's house she had enjoyed as much freedom as would have been possible for an unmarried daughter; as a wife and mother her energies and activities became even more confined to being indoors, caring for her daughters and her husband's failing health. In early August 1874 he became ill with a heart condition and his wife nursed him devotedly, but her strength, energies and, indeed, religious faith were to be tested to the limit. On Sunday, 30th August 1874 little Mary Martindale died and together her parents buried her on 4th September. On the following day William Martindale himself was claimed by his heart condition; he collapsed suddenly then he, too, died.

After only three years of marriage Mrs Martindale's life was broken apart. Within a week she had lost a child and her husband, and had become a widow with a large family to care for. She had a child of her own (little Louisa), four older step-children and was three months pregnant. It was at this time that the forceful and independent woman that Mrs Martindale was to become made her entrance. After the birth of her third daughter, whom she named Hilda, she promptly placed her step-children in boarding school and moved to Penzance, far away from her father and family. She followed this separation with a move abroad to Eisenbach in Germany, taking all six children with her, and in 1879 the family moved on to Switzerland, to a house overlooking Lake Geneva.

They returned to England in 1880, to the county town of Lewes, with its cobbled cottages and flint-faced houses bordering the steep, winding streets and paved dark alleys that still shelter beneath the chalky, grey-green hills of East Sussex. Mrs Martindale took a house for her family in the centre of town: 212 High Street, a large, double-fronted, terraced, red-brick property. The house had a large garden with a good tree to climb, but it was perilously close to the River Ouse, which had a tendency to flood regularly. The Martindale family stayed in Lewes until 1886, when it was time for Louisa and her younger sister Hilda to begin their education. By one of those strange coincidences, at that time there was a powerful connection between Lewes and the distant feminine ferment far away in London, at the heart of the London School of Medicine for Women.

In 1869 seven women, led by Sophia Jex-Blake (whose mother lived in Sussex Square, Brighton) had travelled to Edinburgh to seek entry to the university in order to study and qualify as physicians and surgeons. Scotland had always enjoyed a more liberal approach to education than the stuffy universities of England (it had four universities to England's two until the University of Durham was founded in 1815) and Miss Jex-Blake had been led to believe that the chances of women entering the medical profession via an academic institution north of the border were greater.

One of the seven was Mrs Isabel Thorne. Born in 1834, she was a contemporary of Mrs Martindale and Elizabeth Garrett and was married to Joseph Thorne, an industrious and wealthy businessman and one time master of the Cutlers' Company, who had made his money abroad in China. Their first child, Thomas, had died as a baby in that country; convinced that he would have lived had better medical care been available, Isabel Thorne decided to attempt to enter the profession. Her husband supported her fully, but to no avail. In 1874, all seven would-be doctors left Scotland, defeated, and their campaign was resumed in London with the opening of the LSMW in that year. Mrs Thorne was the first student to enrol; however, by 1877 she had taken up the prestigious and important post of Organising Secretary for the LSMW, which meant in reality that she would not be able to qualify. Mrs Thorne's husband, retiring from the world of business and the years abroad, had wanted to live in the English countryside and in 1878 he bought Southover Grange, a beautiful, rambling, stone-built house situated just outside the old walls of Lewes, and moved in his wife, four sons and two daughters. He became a hunting and shooting local gentleman and took up local politics, soon becoming an alderman, and in 1884 serving a term as Mayor with Mrs Thorne as his Mayoress.[2] Mrs Martindale, living in Lewes at the same time, a mother of two and step-mother of four, would have known Mrs Thorne well and been fully aware of her past adventures in Edinburgh with Sophia Jex-Blake and her current close association with the London School of Medicine for Women. It is hardly surprising that Mrs Martindale decided very early that little Louisa should eventually come to embrace the medical profession and become a doctor, as did Isabel Thorne's younger daughter, May, and one of her sons, Atwood.[3]

Mrs Martindale had to consider the education of her daughters very carefully. Both should receive the best that was obtainable for girls in order to enable them to take up careers with professional status when the time arrived. Now placed in that most enviable situation for women, the wealthy widow free from the interference of a husband, father or brother, Mrs Martindale could choose where and how to begin to construct her daughters' careers. She had always been interested in the secondary education of girls and had heard of the Girls' Public Day School Trust. The education offered was wide ranging; the teachers were professionally trained women who had studied at the recently formed women's colleges in Cambridge:

Girton and Newnham. Classes at Brighton High School were comparable to those in boys' schools: English, French and botany, which were usually taught to girls, but also mathematics, geography, physics and chemistry, which were not. With all these subjects under their schoolgirl belts, the girls could go on to study at other colleges of education and, at age eighteen, could enter the London University Matriculation Examination, which could lead to a place at London University.[4] For little Louisa this was essential, since the London University Medical degree (available since 1878) had the highest status. Girls of all backgrounds could attend the schools of the Trust daily and mix freely with each other, and it so happened that there was just such a school in Brighton, recently opened in Montpelier Road, south of Preston and on the way out to Hove. So in 1885, Mrs Martindale made her decision and the family moved away from Lewes and into Brighton, to a smaller house at 2 Lancaster Road, and little Louisa and her younger sister Hilda were immediately enrolled in Brighton High School for Girls.[5]

Whilst Louisa and Hilda went off to school, escorted daily (to their dismay) by a governess, Mrs Martindale plunged into new involvements with voluntary work in Brighton on a scale that would not have been possible in Lewes. She became active in the British and Foreign Bible Society and was President of the Brighton Women's Liberal Association and of the Women's Co-operative Movement. She was one of the founders of the Brighton branch of the Pioneer Club, a women's association with headquarters in London that maintained the campaigning issues of the battle for the parliamentary franchise and education high on its agenda. (Its premises were rooms at 4 New Road, a step away from the Theatre Royal.) She was active in the German Church in Brighton and opened her home to German governesses working with local families as a place to rest and relax on two Saturdays a month. On the other two Saturdays she held open house for young working women, one of whom, Margaret Bondfield, later became an MP, the first woman Privy Councillor and the first woman cabinet member when she served as Minister of Labour in the Labour government of 1929.

Other young women living away from home were also welcomed on those Saturday afternoons. One was Rukhmabai, an Indian woman who had fought to free herself from the consequences of early widowhood following an arranged child-marriage in India, and who had come to England to study medicine at the London School of Medicine for Women. Almost certainly another was the young Dr Mary Murdoch (born in Scotland in 1864), who would later become a good family friend and young Louisa's first employer. Dr Murdoch, known as Murdie to her friends, entered the London School of Medicine for Women in 1888 and travelled through the Scottish Triple Qualification examination set by Glasgow and Edinburgh Faculties of Physicians and Surgeons in order to qualify (since she had not passed the London matriculation and could not sit for the London University degree). She came to Brighton to gain midwifery training and experience, probably at the Brighton Lying-in Institution and Hospital. Almost certainly the only woman medical student in Brighton and living a long way not only from Scotland but also from her friends in London, Mrs Martindale's 'open Saturday afternoons' would have been very welcome, and her hostess more than pleased to entertain a woman medical student. Mrs Thorne, secretary of the London School of Medicine for Women, may well have encouraged her.

Mrs Martindale's philosophy of life had matured and crystallised over the years. She believed steadfastly that women must be allowed to 'further themselves' and be given the opportunity to learn, to achieve all manner of privileges, to be trained for interesting and worthwhile work, to be able to earn well, to be independent and to lead rich and rewarding lives. She was determined that her daughters would do all these, and so, in September 1893, her twenty-year-old daughter Miss Louisa Martindale entered the London School of Medicine for Women, having matriculated from Royal Holloway College in 1892.

It is very possible that it was Mrs Martindale who first imagined the setting up of a Dispensary for Women and Children in Brighton, and she was well placed to bring such a dream to reality. She was well known in the local Liberal and voluntary women's circles, ideally placed to seek out and cajole reluctant ladies — and indeed gentlemen — into assuming positions either of responsibility or generosity. But she would have needed at least one woman doctor in order to provide the medical services. No personal papers have survived that describe the setting up of the Lewes Road Dispensary, yet it is surely beyond coincidence that Drs Boyle and Jones simply hopped off a train at Brighton or Hove station and had the amazing good fortune to find Mrs Martindale ready and waiting for them on the platform. It seems more likely that their choice of Brighton and Hove may well have been made after an approach from Mrs Martindale: the decision to set up their brass plate in Hove was so good and became so successful that it is unlikely to have been simply a lucky choice on their part.

The Lewes Road Dispensary for Women and Children opened in 1899 when Drs Boyle and Jones had been living in Hove for only a year. During that time they had had to set up the mechanics of their practice, to find a suitable house to live in and work from, meet up with other Brighton and Hove doctors, dentists and pharmacists, publicise their presence in Hove and locate and treat new patients without cavilling at after hours call outs. They would have joined up with local women's voluntary societies for both leisure and potential business, probably suffered stressful visits to the bank manager and from worried family members, and generally started to get to grips with making a living. To have found, on the far side of a strange town, a building suitable to accommodate a dispensary, to woo a throng of potential subscribers, to put together a managing council, to interview and then employ a nurse, a dispenser and a resident caretaker, and at the same time make arrangements for the building to be modified, all in one year, seems hardly likely. They could not have done it by themselves, there are just not enough hours in a week. They had to have had help, help that was already in place.

Mrs Martindale could have been putting out feelers at the London School of Medicine for Women for one or two qualified women to make their homes and practice in Brighton or Hove and at the same time commit themselves to taking up posts as honorary physicians at a local dispensary. Two women who in return for their commitment could happily anticipate considerable assistance with setting up their practice; help in finding accommodation and very useful introductions to prospective female clients. A golden opportunity for the right young women; not without risk, certainly, since the general practice would also need a lot of hard work put into it, but as good as anything that might come along if not a hundred times better. Mrs Martindale would have had the ear of Mrs Thorne, secretary of the LSMW, from their days in Lewes; telephones were not uncommon and May Thorne, Mrs Thorne's daughter, had graduated from the LSMW in 1895, a contemporary of Dr Boyle and Dr Jones.

Meanwhile, in London, Miss Louisa Martindale qualified as a doctor in 1899.

Notes

[1] In fact Elizabeth Garrett made one of the few bad publicity decisions of her professional life at this time. The only qualified woman doctor at that time, she supported the Contagious Diseases Acts, arousing scorn and fury from other women who were agitating to have them repealed. Dr Garrett later withdrew her support for the Acts.

[2] Alderman Thorne died suddenly in 1885 after returning from a meet of the Brookside Harriers. Elizabeth Garrett Anderson attended his funeral. *Sussex Express* 21 November 1885.

[3] Mrs Thorne served as honorary secretary to the LSMW until 1908, when she was succeeded by her younger daughter Dr May Thorne, who had qualified in 1895.

[4] Schools in Brighton and Hove entered their pupils for the Oxford and Cambridge Local Examinations. However, in order to graduate from London University, the London University Matriculation examination was required (or the Preliminary Science or Preliminary Arts Examination if the candidate was of mature years; Dr Scharlieb, who had had no opportunity to study for and obtain the Matric., took the Prelim. Science — it was a long, hard and expensive slog). This is probably the reason why Louisa and Hilda Martindale went on to the Royal Holloway College after their schooldays.

[5] Brighton High School for Girls opened in 1876 and in 1880 moved to The Temple, built by Thomas Read Kemp in 1819/20 supposedly to the exact measurements of King Solomon's Temple in Jerusalem. The building, which included a great dome, pillars and a grand spiral staircase, was sold by him in 1827. Although once isolated on a hill outside Brighton, it was soon surrounded by streets and houses and remains, much altered, in Montpelier Road to this day. In 1922 the school acquired the building 'The Old Vicarage' in nearby Victoria Road (now Temple Gardens) which is used as the sixth-form building.

3

THE DISPENSARY AND OTHER HOSPITALS

Estimates of Brighton's population in the nineteenth century indicate a rapid increase in numbers from 40,000 in 1828 to 136,000 in 1899.[1] There was by no means a shortage of medical practitioners; the arrival of the well-heeled classes seeking sea water and sea air cures so punchily publicised by Dr William Russell and his followers a century before had lured a good crop of physicians and surgeons to the town who were eager to make both their private and public fortunes.

The rich, noble and other affluent classes, when ill, had always been treated in the comfort of their own homes and beds. Servants were hired for the duration of an illness and the services of unmarried sisters and daughters could be relied upon until the patient either recovered or died. The hospital was a place where the sick could be gathered together for ease of both nursing and immediate medical care by the doctor. For many centuries the hospital remained the province of the poor, who could not afford the fees which went along with home care supervised by visits from the physician. Hospitals were also introduced for the isolation of 'contagion': without fathoming exactly why it was so, physicians knew well that contagion could cause disease to jump across a room from one patient to another, more often than not with deadly results. Isolation of the patient was the only effective remedy, and, interestingly, one of the first contagions to be recognised was puerperal fever, the scourge of childbirth. Lying-in hospitals were among the first isolation hospitals to be set up; indeed the Brighton Lying-in Institution (entry by a 'lying-in ticket') in the late eighteenth century was the first recorded organised medical facility set up in Brighton. Fever hospitals, built for the mandatory treatment of contagious and debilitating diseases such as tuberculosis, were built well away from the bustling and overcrowded city streets; they were maintained by the local town councils and corporations and were always free at point of entry. They had to be, since mandatory removal and isolation of a breadwinner by the order of a conscientious (or busy-bodying) town medical officer could be devastating for poorer families.

By the end of the nineteenth century major advances in medical science, alongside the stringent new academic requirements for the training of doctors, had resulted in the arrival — not out on the far reaches of towns but frequently more close to the swarming centres — of general and other specialist hospitals offering the latest surgical and medical treatment. Treatments did not come cheaply; fees were charged. For those less well-off, insurance schemes were often available for a few pence a week and for others even more generous charitable arrangements could be made.

The wealthy classes, instead of staying at home when they became ill, now quickly took themselves off into comfortable and clean hospital wards where they were looked after by Miss Nightingale's sometimes severe but always spruce and tidy nurses; after discharge all they had to do was to pay their bills — with or without complaint. These were the voluntary hospitals; hospitals which had been kick-started in years past by an initial gift of a large sum of money, the endowment, which, suitably invested, provided a decent income to keep the hospital going. However, as time went by it became more and more necessary to augment the income from the endowment, and a rich variety of ongoing and indeed a ceaseless round of fundraising activities — donations, annual subscriptions, testamentary bequests — was instituted. Charitable status became important because of tax privileges.[2]

In later years not all voluntary hospitals had endowments, and dispensaries probably not at all. All voluntary hospitals were autonomous and independent and each had their own rules for admissions and the employment of staff. They could select members of the management board as they pleased, either for expertise or decoration, and the local aristocracy and minor nobility were always in great demand to grace councils and committees with their illustrious names, albeit often in a position which required little or no actual work.

Fundraising was the particular sphere of the moneyed wealthy women of the town; wives, sisters and daughters who were skilled at merging desirable social gatherings with fundraising activities. Entry to an afternoon tea held in a fashionable drawing room and featuring a well-known guest speaker or singer (persuaded to forgo her normal fee) could be cheerfully offered at a price, all profits going to the hospital of choice. They organised sales of work, bazaars, raffles, garden parties and concerts, and new ideas to raise money were eagerly sought and imaginatively put into practice.

By 1898 all nurses, sisters and matrons in all the hospitals were professionally trained and certificated. They were mostly employed full time and usually lived in the nurses' home at the hospital. The junior physicians were also full-time and salaried, working on a six-month contract, and known as 'house physicians'. They were invariably young, fresh out of medical school and eager to gain wholesale medical experience. It was at this point in their careers that young women doctors had come across the latest professional difficulty: prejudiced and entrenched senior consultants who served on the boards and medical committees of the voluntary hospitals frequently remained resolute in their opposition to medical women working on the wards.

Women could apply for jobs as salaried house physicians, they were just not appointed; and in this respect the Sussex County Hospital, the most prestigious in Brighton, was no exception.[3] Even as general practitioners women were not allowed positions as 'honorary' physicians — local GPs of repute who were given access to a certain number of beds in a voluntary hospital for their own individual patients — and this was particularly painful. The honorary physician would care for and treat 'his' patient, coming into the hospital daily or as required, directing overall treatment and nursing care. He was, in fact, paid but by the patient, not the hospital, and was appointed in various degrees of seniority by the management board. A seat on such a board — which might well be accompanied by a productive influence on the direction of hospital policies — would often be included in the package. A similar access to hospital beds was invariably denied to local women GPs by the board members for many years. The women were able to refer patients for in-hospital treatment, but only into the care and beds of a male doctor. The Sussex County Hospital in this too was no exception.

Admission to the voluntary hospital for treatment usually meant, as with the dispensary, locating a subscriber and acquiring a 'ticket'. The prospective patient then had to hand over the ticket to the hospital admissions' officer.[4] In Brighton the numbers of voluntary hospitals and other medical institutions had increased as the nineteenth century drew to its close. They expanded, moved site, reopened and were renamed, always trying to meet the demands of the growing population and to practise the latest advances in medical science. The Sussex County was the most prominent voluntary hospital in Brighton and Hove. It had opened in 1828 under the patronage of the Earl of Egremont and immediately launched into a period of growth which continues, under the name of the Royal Sussex County Hospital, to this day. Like many hospitals it admitted medical students, for a fee, after approval by the appropriate medical and governmental bodies had been granted. The Lying-in Institute also trained midwives for a payment of £5 and was able to award its successful candidates the valuable Diploma of Qualification from the Obstetrical Society of London.

Before the Sussex County there had been the Sussex General Infirmary, founded in 1809 as part of the Brighthelmstone Dispensary; however, it closed when the Sussex County Hospital opened in Eastern Road; although the Brighthelmstone Dispensary — renamed the Brighton, Hove and Preston Dispensary — remained busy and was, of course, much easier to get to. It moved in 1847 to extended premises in Queen's Road, on the corner of North Street (see Chapter 1).

In 1899 the Queen Alexandra Hospital for Children on Dyke Road boasted the Earl of Chichester as its president and there were two homeopathic dispensaries in town to cater for the more daring adult inhabitant. There was the Eye Hospital, the Throat and Ear Hospital and the Dental Hospital, and the hunt for an adequate flow of funds in order to keep them all going never stopped. It was a cut-throat business and every hospital and dispensary continually and jealously vied with the others to pick up committed subscribers and collect intermittent large or off-the-cuff small donations; loyalties were eagerly sought and the subscriber who pledged a certain amount per year could have the satisfaction of seeing his or her name neatly printed on a subscribers' list, published (and enthusiastically perused) annually. There were never enough regular subscribers and in order to attract the new and plenteous money of the middle classes, the patronage of a member of the nobility, the higher the better, was always sought eagerly. The Royal Alexandra Hospital at one time boasted no fewer than four HRHs as patrons. If a standing order at the bank could not be gently extracted, intermittent donations would have to do and were regularly collected by a named 'Collector of Subscriptions', a volunteer man or woman of steely determination as well as impeccable honesty, who knocked on doors and collected cash. His or her name was always well publicised so that generosity promised needed no effort to locate its destination. The private insurance society — the Brighton and Sussex Mutual Provident Society — which provided payments during sickness for its members also provided door-to-door collectors (the Society was also advertised as a generally profitable fund for investors).

The Sussex County Hospital became the most successful of the voluntary hospitals in Brighton. In the fullness of time it ingested most of the smaller specialist hospitals in Brighton, probably because its location — up on the hills outside the narrow streets and beyond the fine houses of the town, but not too far away — afforded ample room for expansion.

Women doctors desired passionately to enter hospital service and, by the turn of the century, some 'hard to fill' jobs, spurned by male applicants, were drifting their way. But most did not persevere and the majority set up their brass plates in private practice. Often this was with another woman doctor: it made admirable sense both financially and professionally to have a partner under the same roof. Night calls could be shared, surgeries and home visits staggered, and in the days when GPs could — and did — perform small surgical operations in their surgeries, one could operate and the other administer the anaesthetic, thus prudently saving time and an anaesthetist's fee. And there was always the company and support of a woman friend in the evenings if any spare time could be found.

Elizabeth Garrett Anderson, although initially opposed to the idea, had come to realise that opening independent dispensaries and hospitals solely for women and children might be a good answer to the scarcity of hospital appointments for women doctors. 'Officered solely by medical women' would be the flagship cry and with luck and in the fullness of time a women's dispensary might well blossom into a fully-fledged hospital employing young women doctors, allowing them to gain the knowledge and experience they needed, and boosting their status in the eyes of those male colleagues who were not yet convinced of women's suitability for the profession. A women's hospital, officered by women doctors, could even be gently underlined by delicate hints that it was a woman's role to carry out her Christian duty: to nurture, nourish and care for the sick and needy, and to be charitable. To take the image of womanhood out of the home and into the houses of the poor. The newspapers loved it. [5]

In the late nineteenth century several dispensaries for women and children had opened in England and Scotland, and all were overwhelmingly successful. Dr Mary Murdoch presided over one in Hull as did Dr Elsie Inglis in Glasgow and Dr Jex-Blake in Edinburgh. In London, Dr Elizabeth Garrett Anderson — the essential 'Subscriber's List' conveniently already at her fingertips — had started the St Mary's Dispensary for Women and Children.

In Brighton, the Lewes Road Dispensary for Women and Children opened on 31st October 1899, the founders having provided themselves with a ringing objective: 'To afford to poor women of Brighton and the neighbourhood the opportunity of free consultation with doctors of their own sex.' A small but welcome paragraph appeared in the *Sussex Daily News* on 1st November:

The Lewes Road Dispensary, No 145 Islingword Road, Brighton, which provides gratuitous medical aid for women and children was opened on Monday, the times of attendance being from two to three o'clock. Gratifying appreciation of the new institution was shewn by the attendance of a good number of patients.

The patron was the Countess of Chichester, the wife of the fifth Earl; the honorary secretary was Mrs C. S. Ashton of 3 Chatsworth Road, Brighton; the honorary auditor was Miss Harvey of 16 Eaton Place, Brighton; and the honorary dispenser was Miss Gates.[6] Eight other women made up the Dispensary Council:

> Mrs Charles Corbett, Danehill, Sussex
> Miss M. Gates, Chesham House, Brighton
> Mrs Paget, 1 Percival Terrace, Brighton
> Mrs Bernard Roth, Wayside, Preston
> Miss Ritchie, 165 Clapham Road, London
> Mrs Taylor, 10 Brunswick Place, Hove
> Miss M. E. Verrall, 26 Gloucester Place, Brighton
> Mrs Watson Griffin, 68 Brunswick Place, Hove

The Council leased 145 Islingword Road for three years and sublet the top floor to a tenant who would also act as caretaker. Two consulting rooms, a waiting room and a room for the dispenser were fitted up. Drs Boyle and Jones had given £200 initially and the rent from the tenant would be useful, but the task of raising money to pay for the dispensary started then and there and would continue ceaselessly.

A simplification of the procedures to enable women to consult the doctor was instituted: the traditional initial production of a 'ticket' from a subscriber was abolished. The Lewes Road Dispensary Council, aware of the time-consuming difficulties that faced working women who would have little time to locate and then petition a subscriber before getting along to the dispensary, sliced through this tangle of accepted procedure and decided that any woman who presented herself at the waiting room during opening hours would be registered by the secretary. After completing a few details on a form — name, address, symptoms — the secretary would hand over a Card of Admission on the spot which was to be given to the doctor. A record of treatment would be maintained. Opening hours were to be Monday and Wednesday in the afternoon and Thursday and Saturday in the evenings, to provide employed women with the opportunity to attend. The change of admission procedure was a badly needed and welcome reform and it goes a long way to explaining the success of the Lewes Road Dispensary. There is a certain innovative feminine practicality about the new system since it also discontinued the subscriber's privilege of issuing the ticket in the first place, and possibly other dispensaries for women also did away with such a cumbersome and potentially profiteering process. Although consultation was free, a charge of 3d* was made for prescribed medicines, which was intended to plump up the income needed to maintain the dispensary and make ends meet.

All Lewes Road Dispensary Council members were charged with the endless effort to rake in subscribers from wealthy local and county women and their husbands. One of the first fundraising efforts, in March 1900, was a series of six free lectures given by Mrs Congreve of the Women's Health Society, where a collection was to be made with the audience pointedly cajoled into giving generously. Over the years the Dispensary Council would become highly proficient in inventing and presenting polished fundraising performances; sadly, on the other sides of the coin, money-saving techniques, cheeseparing and even downright meanness would also not be too far away.

By the end of its first year the dispensary had clocked up 1,019 treated patients, who had come from not only Brighton but also from further away, its neighbours Preston and Hove. An income of £152 3s 9d had been raised. The Council met every three months to agree upon and pay bills; donations high and low were continually scrutinised and recorded — for example, Mrs Martindale donated five guineas* and Miss Olive Boyle (Dr Boyle's younger sister) gave five shillings. The books balanced.

However, change was coming. During the first year the honorary dispenser, Miss Gates, left and was replaced by Miss Hackney, formerly dispenser at the Alexandra Hospital. And after one year as president and treasurer, Mrs Martindale resigned: now reaching sixty, she was planning a year-long voyage around the world, accompanied by Louisa junior and her younger sister Hilda, both now grown up and ready to make their inevitable mark upon the world. This had long been an ambition: Mrs Martindale was an intrepid traveller and the long trip would be combined with an opportunity for the recently-qualified Louisa Martindale (MB BS Lond.) to gain a splendid knowledge and even experience of worldwide medical practice, and for Miss Hilda Martindale, destined for a career working with children, to take a

---

* 3d= three pence. There were twelve pence in a shilling and twenty shillings in a pound. A guinea was one pound and one shilling.

closer look at the missions, orphanages and reformatories set up in many countries for the relief of their poor and abandoned children. On their return Mrs Martindale would re-join the Dispensary Council as a member, but without office.

The first year was a taste of the practicalities of the business of running what we would call a service; the worry about the arrival — from somewhere — of the necessary funds to continue, would never go away. Rent, rates, drugs, dressings, gas, electricity, coal, mending the roof, looking after the drains and carpenters' bills all had to be paid for out of a shoestring budget. A quiet life without pressure it was not; and there was also the ambition of the two doctors, Dr Boyle in particular. Mindful of the poor opportunities for professional advancement of women doctors as consultants, Helen Boyle seems to have always been very clear that her career in Brighton and Hove would include opening her own hospital.

With the dispensary up and running, firmly established and accepted as a success in Brighton, it would not be long before she would do just that.

Notes

[1] *Pike's Directory of Brighton* 1899.
[2] There was another hospital in Brighton in 1898; supported not by voluntary contributions but entirely by money from the local ratepayers, and situated inside several acres of gaunt and chilly buildings overlooking Brighton from the green and windswept heights of Race Hill. This was the workhouse infirmary. The Poor Law Amendment Act of 1867 had required the Boards of Guardians to establish infirmaries; admission and free treatment for the local sick and poor who were not inmates, was allowed by the 1883 Diseases Prevention (Metropolis) Act. No subscriptions were raised, salaried professional medical officers and nurses cared for the sick inmates. A prospective patient who was not an inmate could seek admission by going to the police, then being sent on to a designated admissions' officer who would hand out a ticket. It was a source of great shame to many working men and women to be reduced to being treated at the workhouse infirmary: however a pregnant but unmarried woman, in need of hospitalisation, had no other recourse since the Brighton Lying-in Institution did not accept unmarried women as patients.
[3] In 1911 King George V granted the Sussex County the privilege of prefixing itself 'Royal'.
[4] Working-class and poorer patients might be asked to pay what they could afford, but a doctor coming across an interesting or unusual case would not deny admission to a prospective but poor patient.
[5] Generally speaking, the press was not unkind to the efforts of women to obtain a medical education. This may be because of a genuine desire to support women

in their preference to be treated by doctors of their own sex (Elizabeth Garrett Anderson played this trump card all her life) or simply a journalistic nose for high drama, a certain love of puncturing pomposity or a genuine British feeling of warmth and sympathy for the underdog.

[6] The Pharmacy Act of 1868 required all hospital dispensers to be registered with the Pharmaceutical Society. As might be expected, women pharmacists had a rocky ride. Because of a loophole in the wording of the Act the Pharmaceutical Society had permitted women to sit for its Preliminary and Minor examinations to obtain the qualification of Chemist and Druggist, which would allow women to take up work as a hospital dispenser. They could then progress on to the Major certificate to be designated Pharmaceutical Chemist. Initially the Pharmaceutical Society did not allow them access to its lectures and, although this was granted in 1872, they were still not permitted to attend practical sessions. Qualifying as a Pharmaceutical Chemist should have entitled women to full membership of the Society, but this was denied until 1879, when their repeated applications, championed by Robert Hampson, a Society Council member, were finally successful. In 1905 women pharmacists founded the National Association of Women Pharmacists, which is still in existence, celebrating its centenary in 2005. Thanks to Sue Symonds of the National Association of Women Pharmacists <www.nawp.org.uk>.

4

THE LEWES ROAD HOSPITAL
FOR WOMEN AND CHILDREN

Alice Helen Anne Boyle, a small and frail child suffering from poor eyesight throughout her life, was born in Dublin on 19th November 1869. She was the eldest child of Richard Warneford Boyle, a Dublin banker, and his wife Alice Mary, the daughter of George Wilton Chambers, a wealthy industrialist from Yorkshire, who had married in Rotherham in 1868. Little Helen was soon followed by another daughter, Olive Wilton, and then two boys, Alexander George and Charles Vicars. A third boy died in infancy. Their happy family life by the sea in one of the fashionable suburbs north of Dublin was torn apart when Richard Warneford Boyle was declared bankrupt in about 1884 and left Ireland to live permanently on the Continent. There seems to have been a family scandal connected with his flight but after more than a century no details have survived. While the boys attended public day school in England, living with their mother in Bristol, Helen was sent abroad and was educated at Hohere Fochterschule in Bonn-auf-Rhein, Germany, and probably also in Brussels, becoming fluent in German and French. In 1887 her parents formally and finally separated and the young Helen returned to England, also to live in Bristol, boosting her education with private tuition and sitting preliminary exams in religious knowledge, English, history, geography, French, German and Latin, with geometry, algebra and mechanics thrown in for good measure.

In July 1889 she applied for entry to the London School of Medicine for Women. She was clearly an exceptional student with both charm and determination. Dr Elizabeth Garrett Anderson, Dean of the school at the time (1883–1903), had always been very particular indeed that applicants to the school should be proven to have been educated to no less a high standard than their male counterparts. At the beginning of their studies her students should have held the correct number of preliminary public examination passes which would allow them eventually to sit for either university degrees in science and medicine, or non-university licentiateships at the medical and surgical professional societies and colleges. Helen Boyle was accepted as a student by Dr Garrett Anderson before her results were known. This was very unusual, but there is a possible explanation: her application to enter the London School of Medicine for Women was accompanied by a testimonial from Dr Thomas King Chambers, a well-respected doctor and senior physician at St Mary's Hospital, who had long supported the entry of women to the medical profession. An old friend of both Elizabeth Garrett Anderson and Sophia Jex-Blake, he had been instrumental in setting up the London School of Medicine for Women and taught Materia Medica as an honorary lecturer at the school until 1879. Dr Chambers just happened to be Helen Boyle's great uncle, the younger brother of her grandfather, George Chambers of Rotherham. Recommending young Helen to the school in his testimonial he added, with accurate foresight, his belief that she would be 'a credit to the school.'

If Elizabeth Garrett Anderson took a chance on admitting Helen Boyle by way of pleasing the elderly Dr Chambers (she was never one to take a risk) she would not come to regret it. After only three years of study Helen Boyle, then aged 24, unable to enter herself for a London University medical degree since she did not hold the Certificate of Matriculation from London University, successfully sat the joint examination for the Triple Qualification in Medicine, Surgery and Obstetrics at the Faculties (later, Royal Colleges) of Physicians and Surgeons in Glasgow and Edinburgh. She passed and was awarded the Licentiateship of the College and was able to place the wonderful letters 'L.C.P.S Glas. & Edin.' after her name.[1] She could now sign up with the British Medical Register and gain her licence to practise as a physician in Great Britain and Ireland.

This was an amazingly short period of study, four years would have been accounted good, but it was followed by better: only a year later she was in Brussels obtaining her second degree, with distinction, as a Doctor of Medicine. Later, Dr Boyle would say that she chose this road because it was the cheapest. There is no record of her financial situation during her surprisingly short time of study, a time which then, as now, was as a rule long, gruelling and expensive. Her immediate family was not well off, probably because of her father's circumstances, but she had a score of rich relatives and it is unlikely that they would have allowed her mother and the junior Boyles to starve. Yet financial prudence was clearly important.[2]

A fast track to earning power, however, is generally preceded by some form of paid apprenticeship. From 1895 to 1897 Helen Boyle worked as an assistant medical officer at Claybury Mental Asylum, where Mabel Jones acted as her locum from time to time. Claybury was a large psychiatric hospital near Ilford in Essex, placed as was usual in wide green countryside well outside London's borders, and funded by the London County Council, which also supplied most of its inhabitants.[3] It was at Claybury that she met Dr (later Sir) Robert

Armstrong-Jones, the superintendent, and it was here that she began her association with the relief of mental illness that would later become her specialisation. A medical officer's job in a large county asylum was one of the few salaried hospital posts which women could obtain since most young male doctors were reluctant to apply for them. However, the move to Claybury was crucial for Dr Boyle and would shape her future career. In 1895 (and possibly in other years) she combined her work at Claybury with a part-time appointment in the impoverished East End of London as the medical officer — or superintendent — of the small women's hospital attached to the Canning Town Women's Settlement.

It was at Canning Town that Helen Boyle saw that here, in their homes, struggling against overwork, poverty, repeated childbearing and lack of skilled medical care, were sown the seeds of later severe mental breakdown and illness in women:

> I saw the impecunious and harassed mother of five (or ten as the case may be) with a nervous breakdown after influenza or possibly childbirth, getting up too soon, with bad air, bad food, noise and worry. I saw her apply for treatment, wait many weary hours and get a bottle of medicine and the advice not to worry and to go home and rest. No hospital would take her because she had no organic disease; no asylum because she was not certified. I saw mental patients being manufactured in the rough, as it were. I met them every day at the Dispensary and in people's houses. I saw them to my mind, neglected and maltreated until after days, months, years, according to their resisting power, they were turned into the finished product — lunatics — and were certified.[4]

She became deeply interested in what she would later term the 'borderland' state between the beginnings of mental failure and its final eruption into incurable insanity; a crucial time when intervention and treatment could halt the slide into complete breakdown and subsequent removal from society, into either the workhouse infirmary or the local county lunatic asylum.

She knew that this condition was already recognised and termed 'melancholia', 'exhaustion', 'nervous collapse' and, later, 'neurasthenia', and was a common condition frequently affecting middle-class and upper-class women. Recovery after diagnosis could be made with prolonged rest and gentle care until full health was restored — the 'rest cure' — but the treatment was long and expensive. For working and poor women with a similar condition there was no provision;

even if the illness was spotted by the physician in its early stages there was nothing that could be done. Psychiatric treatment was only available after a Certification of Insanity had been made and a mandatory stay for the patient in one of the big county asylums undergone. By then, of course, the removal was frequently too late and the patient made no recovery.

Change was in fact on its way, but too slowly and too hesitantly. The idea of provision of outpatient and pre-certification care for the mentally ill was beginning to surface, though mostly in London. Outpatients' clinics for mental disorders had been created at St Thomas's and Charing Cross hospitals and another was opened in Euston Road by Dr L. S. Forbes Winslow; all were new and experimental.[5]

The separation of the chronic and unrecoverable patient shut away in the institution, and the recoverable and temporary sick remaining and being treated in the outside world was both very new and highly controversial. As was to be expected, many powerful physicians were adamantly opposed to any change in the lunacy laws but Helen Boyle would make the provision of care and treatment for cases of early —or borderland — nervous disorders in women and children her life's work. She would provide in-hospital care for chronic cases, followed by careful outpatient care as required, for women who otherwise would have to slide into insanity before any treatment could be offered.

By 1905 the Lewes Road Dispensary was flourishing. There was no lack of clients coming to the house in Islingword Road, although the constant struggle for funds to pay for utilities was never far from anyone's mind. Since first opening the door, 1,642 patients had registered and there had been 4,908 callers from all over Brighton, Hove and Preston. That there was a niche in Brighton for a dispensary wholly devoted to the care of women and their children was becoming apparent.

Miss Harvey and Mrs C. Ashton remained as honorary auditor and secretary respectively, but Miss Florence Pickworth, a music teacher, ceased to be honorary secretary to the dispenser retaining, nevertheless, her place on the Council. The Council itself had seen a few changes; back from her world tour Mrs Martindale (now retired and living in a new house, 'Cheeleys' in Horsted Keynes, a village in the leafy northern parts of West Sussex)[6] was back on the Council but without office. Miss G. Cohen of 68 Great Russell Street, London, Miss Gates of Chesham House in Brighton, Mrs Bernard Roth, now giving her address as 'Kingswood', Enfield, and Mrs Watson Griffith of 68 Brunswick Place, Brighton, made up its numbers. The treasurer was by then Miss Marian E. Verrall, a sister of Dr (later, Sir) Thomas Jenner Verrall, both part of the extended Verrall family which had a distant branch in Lewes — and into which Miss Isabel Thorne had married in 1890. Miss Verrall and her elder sister, Annette Sarah, were well-known, influential figures in the middle-class, leisured women's strata of Brighton society. Energetic, clever and confident, they were an asset to any board of management and gave freely of their time and skills to many charitable institutions in Brighton.

There was news at the annual meeting for subscribers in 1905: Dr Boyle had taken a major step towards achieving her ambition to open her own hospital. In February 1905 the Dispensary Council acquired a seven-year lease at £50 p.a. on a property at 101 Roundhill Crescent. It was to be a proper hospital, a house nicely placed just off the Lewes Road, a little further to the north of the dispensary. At the beginning it was called the Lewes Road Hospital for Women and Children and was to serve

> a class not now admitted to any hospital in Brighton or indeed in England: cases of serious nervous breakdown amongst poor women and children. These patients cannot afford an expensive rest cure, neither can they be properly treated at home where worry, overwork and insufficient food aggravate the trouble so that they fall out of the ranks of workers and so often end by becoming a burden on the rates. By the removal for a time from associated and depressing environment, and by the provision of skilled treatment, care, rest and good feeding, many such patients may be permanently cured and made fit to resume work.[7]

On the corner of Ashdown Road at the sloping end of Roundhill Crescent, the house was of fair size, three storeys and a basement, square and white-painted with a trim, iron 'Juliet' balcony in front of the large first floor windows. There was a secluded, lawned garden with a side entrance. Offering twelve beds, full time nursing was provided by a matron and two probationer nurses. The matron would have been a trained, professional nurse and the two probationers possibly young women looking for a career but as yet untrained, and so by no means entitled to a generous salary. A house committee had been appointed and would meet monthly to take care of the administration and medical needs. Most importantly, all of the patients were voluntary and not confined by a certification of insanity. A patient could be referred by her own GP or, more importantly, ask for admission herself by writing directly to the matron, and she could leave as and when she felt ready. Dr Boyle's lifelong work in the treatment of borderland nervous disorder had begun. Mabel Jones's input is a little more shadowy. She must have shared, in some part, either Dr Boyle's drive and interest in this little-known branch of psychiatry, or been concerned with the relief of distress and illness affecting poorer women. But she is never described as an honorary physician at the hospital and, with the afternoons and evenings at the dispensary to be put in, it would seem most likely that to her fell the job of building up the general practice, keeping the numbers of patients knocking on the door of 3 Palmeira Terrace, thereby securing the home income.

In the following years the number of patients at the hospital increased and it became necessary for a full-time house physician to be employed. Dr Boyle had found that the treatment of any lingering physical ailment would often give such relief that the nervous disorder would be wonderfully reduced. She was fond of quoting a case where immediate dental treatment for previously ignored chronic pyorrhoea of the teeth and gums almost by itself completed the cure! A rigorous health check of all patients on admission could be instituted, the patients had on-the-spot health care and one more post was opened up for recently-qualified women doctors to gain clinical experience, and of course to consider a career in the treatment of nervous disorders. The house physician at Lewes Road Hospital was always a woman, probably straight out of the London School of Medicine for Women. The first incumbent was Dr Gertrude Grogan, who was followed the next year by Dr Ada McLaren. The appointment was always for six months initially, a tradition observed by new doctors even today.

Meanwhile the Lewes Road Dispensary continued to be very busy dealing with knocks, bruises, spots, diseases and the usual ailments needing medical opinion, attention and treatment. It was becoming well-known up in London at the London School of Medicine for Women, and the benefit of Brighton's proximity to London and the frequency of trains from Victoria and London Bridge became apparent as mature women doctors began to offer their voluntary services in Brighton, a trend which, happily, was to continue. Julia Cock, who held the very powerful and influential position of Dean of the London School of Medicine for Women from 1903 to 1914, added her name as honorary consulting physician at the Lewes Road Dispensary. Nothing much is known about how much time she actually put in, probably she visited from time to time since then, as now, most people are very happy to have the odd trip to Brighton away from the grimy streets of London. From the Council's point of view, as honorary consulting physician she might well have paid her own expenses and received no fee, which would have been most satisfactory to the treasurer, Miss Verrall.

The more well-known and high-ranking the patrons giving money, or the honorary physicians handsomely putting in some shifts — or even simply lending their names in either case — the easier it was to attract subscriptions. Class, either professional or noble, would always be required. Regular subscriptions to the hospital by yearly standing order were encouraged by the usual blank bankers' form being tucked into each published copy of the proceedings of the annual meetings. But gifts in kind were also very welcome and would continue to be so. Old magazines were always sought, and in 1905 Miss Cohen had given a bicycle while Mrs Carey, Miss Stores and Miss Jones had donated furnishings and fittings.[8] Miss Image had marked the bed linen with a monogram, Brighton and Hove Teachers' Association gave two guineas and Brighton Women's Co-operative Society gave five shillings. Dr Boyle herself, although busy with the hospital, donated nine guineas, while Dr Jones gave £1 12s and Mrs Martindale, £3. A concert, always popular, had raised £4 10s.

However, in 1906 a small deficit began shyly to rear its head. The rent for the hospital building at 101 Roundhill Crescent was £50 p.a. and that for the dispensary at 145 Islingword Road was £35. The Lewes Road Hospital had managed to raise only £445 against £465 expenditure, while the corresponding figures for the Lewes Road Dispensary were £133 and £154. Although the accounts of the two endeavours were reported and published separately, clearly there was no room for complacency and, sadly, and probably against Dr Boyle's desires, patients had had to be asked to pay a little if they could although no records survive of how many patients managed to put in some cash. The patients were not idle; unless physically ill they were not confined to bed and therapeutic activities, mostly communal, were prescribed once recovery was in progress, all designed to make life 'bright and interesting'.[9] These included helping with the housework and doing some cooking but these routine tasks were offset by much more jolly games and piano music in the evening. There was basketwork, tennis, visits to the beach and to other places of interest during the day. The Lewes Road Hospital also broke new ground by offering aftercare so that following discharge former patients could voluntarily maintain their links with the hospital. A guild was formed to carry out a little fundraising or needlework, which meant that the one-time patient could keep in touch with friends and nurses

— or even the doctor — and talk over any niggling problems or symptoms. Outpatients were, of course, less expensive to maintain and any fundraising effort would always be very welcome.

Both the Lewes Road Dispensary and the Lewes Road Hospital proclaimed that they were 'Officered by Medical Women', and in the early years of the twentieth century both were up, running, and well-used. To Dr Boyle's delight, patients to both institutions came not only from Brighton and Hove but from wider Sussex and even from other counties. Dr Garrett Anderson's motif, that women preferred to be treated by women doctors, was being verified daily by the steadily increasing march of female feet towards the doors of Islingword Road and Roundhill Crescent.

The original, three-year lease for the former was renewed in 1903; however, by 1906 the building was straining at the seams and more change was on its way. Business was booming and, with Helen Boyle's increasing responsibilities at the hospital and her essential work in her general practice, the hours — like the money — still did not stretch far enough.

At the end of 1906 Dr Louisa Martindale who, since her return from the round-the-world trip with her mother and sister Hilda in 1901, had been working as a paid assistant in Dr Mary Murdoch's general practice and dispensary in Hull, was examined for her Doctorate of Medicine at London University. Successful (although the outcome was, of course, never in doubt), in 1907 she prepared to leave the north of England. Now in secure possession of the highest status of medical degrees, she decided to return to Brighton.

Notes

[1] Licentiate of the College of Physicians, Edinburgh, 1893; Licentiate of the College of Surgeons, Edinburgh; Licentiate of the Faculty of Physicians and Surgeons, Glasgow.
[2] Helen Boyle always spoke highly of the benefits of family life and remained in close and happy contact with her mother, sister, brothers, and her brothers' families. Interestingly her father's cousin, the Reverend Vicars Armstrong Boyle, with his sister Miss Louisa Courtney Boyle, came to Portslade vicarage in 1899 where he was Vicar of Portslade and Rector of Hangleton. Both are buried in St Helen's Church, Hangleton. There is a marble memorial to Miss Boyle in the church of St Nicholas & St Andrew Portslade, and in the corner of the east window at St Helen's.
[3] Opened in 1893 and covering twelve acres, Claybury Asylum (Middlesex County) was large and set in pleasant park-land. It had a gothic chapel, an elaborate Jacobean recreation hall and a water tower. At the time the benefits to the patient of pleasant

surroundings were understood and acted upon. Many of the large Victorian asylums were in fact very 'modern' for their time; cures were effected in a sheltered environment, which was almost an independent little township in its size and variety of crafts and treatments offered. Many patients did leave, though many stayed all their lives inside its walls as carpenters, shoesmiths, tailors and cooks. The asylum was designed to be as self-supporting as possible and many also had farms in which the inmates worked. The superintendent at Claybury, Dr Robert Armstrong-Jones, was a man who was very devoted to his work and who demonstrated sympathy and understanding towards his patients. Dr Armstrong-Jones remained a friend of Helen Boyle's for many years and his work most certainly had a major effect on her career in psychiatry. Claybury Hospital — as it was later known — closed in 1997. Thanks to <www.imhl.com/history.htm>.

[4] Helen Boyle; quoted in *The Lady Chichester Hospital 1926 Appeal: Twenty One Years of Pioneer Work.*

[5] Later more would be opened, owing not a little to the necessary recognition in the First World War that even severe mental disorders could be treated without the patient being permanently institutionalised.

[6] The East Grinstead to Lewes railway line had a busy station at Horsted Keynes, which was no doubt a factor in her choice of retirement village. There was another station at West Hoathly, near the later home of Miss M. E. Verrall and her sister Miss A. S. Verrall; it is gone now but Horsted Keynes station survives on the Bluebell Line, much as Mrs Martindale would have known it, as a working museum for steam railway enthusiasts.

[7] Lady Chichester Hospital Annual Report, 1905. East Sussex Records Office HB63/1A.

[8] Possibly Dr Jones's sister Emma, a nurse living in Bexhill-on-Sea.

[9] Lady Chichester Hospital Annual Report, 1905. East Sussex Records Office HB63/1A.

5

DR LOUISA MARTINDALE

The younger Louisa Martindale was known as 'Lulu' to her immediate family, which just goes to show that she was by no means the rather terrifying personality who in later years awed the young Octavia Wilberforce. She underwent no sudden conversion to the desire to study medicine; nor indeed did she harbour any philanthropic ideas about healing the sick or carrying out the Lord's wishes with regard to the health and welfare of His less fortunate female subjects. It was her mother who had firmly decided that both her daughters should enter a profession. Originally Mrs Martindale had thought that her elder daughter might become an artist but this was an idea quickly put aside ('Lulu' does not seem to have been particularly gifted in that direction) and that she should enter the medical profession when she grew up was understood as far back as the adult Louisa could later remember. Mrs Martindale's acquaintance with Mrs Isabel Thorne, the honorary secretary of the London School of Medicine for Women, and Mayoress of Lewes in 1884/5, had probably been instrumental in her choice.

By 1882 there had been at least 30 women trained and qualified as doctors and physicians, most of them practising in England or India, and the number was growing: by 1890 there were nearly 200. There was a fully-operational medical school for women in the capital (the London School of Medicine for Women), which had opened in 1874 and had now gained access to beds at the Royal Free Hospital for clinical and ward teaching. In 1878 London University had agreed to award medical degrees to women who had originally passed the London Matriculation and for those with no university degree the examinations for the Licentiateship of Medicine and Surgery could be tackled directly at the King and Queen's College of Physicians in Dublin, shortly to be followed by the Royal faculties at Glasgow and Edinburgh.[1] But the Royal College of Physicians and the Royal College of Surgeons in London were proving obstinate and, although the British Medical Council registered qualified women (they had to), the professional body, the British Medical Association, still declined to admit more women then it had already: namely, two — Elizabeth Blackwell and Elizabeth Garrett Anderson.[2]

Louisa, who entered the LSMW in 1893 as student 404, experienced no financial concerns and was supported throughout her many years of study by her mother, presumably from her deceased father's estate.

After leaving Brighton High School for Girls in 1890, Louisa was sent to the Royal Holloway College in Egham to continue her studies (Mrs Martindale had visited all the women's colleges and this had been her choice). Still stunning today, with its amazing red brick quads and turrets in the style of a French chateau, the grounds were full of flower beds with azaleas, rhododendrons and japonica, and nearby there was a river — excellent for boating. There was a swimming pool as well as a picture gallery, a library and a museum. Louisa seems to have had a happy time here, indulging in the varied interests of student life; speaking in favour of women's suffrage at the Parliamentary Debating Society and, daringly, in the teeth of opposition from her mother's family, taking the side of the principal, Miss Bishop (the sister of Mrs Luxford the headmistress of Brighton High School), who favoured the higher rather than the lower form of religious worship.

Louisa made many friends at the Royal Holloway and in her autobiography she singles out Emily Daymond, a musician and the first woman to gain a doctorate in music, and Dr Hubert Parry, a conductor and composer who would later visit her in Brighton.

Like so many doctors, Louisa acquired in her life no deep religious feeling, although she paid homage to religious forms as a social necessity. This was of some distress to her mother, who always retained a deep faith in the tradition of the Congregational church.[3] As a young woman Louisa had even for a while been attracted to Catholicism and very impressed by Buddhism, having read *The Light of Asia* by Sir Edwin Arnold. (In later years, on holiday in Rome with her friend Ismay FitzGerald they were both received by the Pope, but this was probably due more to Ismay being a practising Catholic and Louisa being a confirmed tourist.)

In 1892 Louisa enrolled at the London School of Medicine for Women, at that time in Hunter Street. She began her adult life by living at the women students' hall of residence, College Hall, Byng Place, Gordon Square. This was run by Miss Eleanor Grove (sister of the musician Sir George Grove) and her friend Miss Rosa Morison. Miss Grove objected to her students becoming engaged to be married but, on the passing of an examination, the student was always invited to a slap-up tea party with ices and cakes. All women students were obliged to join the students' union and many attracted condemnation from the higher university authorities by joining in the rags and entertainments organised by the more boisterous male students. The atmosphere was free, open, and supported a wide range of female personalities, greatly to Louisa's delight. There were art students and law students, a fat Russian countess who was a near relation to the Czar; a Dutch baroness affectionately called 'Bones', some missionary students and an old friend — Rukhmabai from Ranjot, the Indian medical student befriended by Mrs Martindale years before in Brighton.

Louisa also became friendly with Louisa Aldrich-Blake, who had lived in College Hall since 1887, not leaving until 1896. Miss Aldrich-Blake (whose speciality was surgery) was tall, heavily built and imposing, with a silent but overwhelmingly efficient personality that would later cause the patients at the hospital in Royaumont in France to dub her 'Madame la Generale'! The daughter of a Herefordshire clergyman, Miss Aldrich-Blake had entered the London School of Medicine for Women with eight others in 1887, qualifying in 1892. She cared little for the pretty and genteel way of life, choosing to live in College Hall until she was persuaded to rent a house at 17 Nottingham Place, London W1, near the medical school, where she lived for the remainder of her too-short life. Miss Aldrich-Blake became an important friend and colleague of Louisa's. Uniquely for a woman doctor at that time, she would not enter general practice but would start her career immediately as a consulting surgeon. Later she became Dean of the London School of Medicine for Women, a post she held from 1919 until 1925, and a few months before her death she was awarded the DBE, becoming only the second woman doctor to receive this distinction.[4]

The exhilarating student life in College Hall however was sadly cut short for Louisa. In 1895 it was time for young Hilda Martindale, having followed her sister's footsteps to the brick turrets and leafy courtyards of the Royal Holloway College, to move on to Bedford College in London to study for her degree. Hilda would have to live out of college and, so that mother and daughters could all live together, Mrs Martindale took a lease on a flat in Hyde Park for two years. Reluctantly, Louisa left the exciting life of College Hall and returned to the welcoming bosoms of her family, she was no doubt pleased to see her mother and sister again, but as a young woman of 23, if given the choice, would have much preferred to remain with her friends in the hall of residence. However, the Hyde Park traffic turned out to be too noisy for Mrs Martindale's taste and at weekends the old lady frequently escaped out of London to her country cottage in Fletching Common in Sussex, leaving the girls to look after themselves. No doubt they took sober advantage of her absence.

In December 1899 Louisa successfully gained her MB (Bachelor of Medicine) and then passed the BS (Bachelor of Surgery) in January 1900, able to take this route because she had secured the

London University Matriculation — probably during her year at the Royal Holloway College. She then returned to Brighton for a short time, where her mother was living at 13 Tamworth Road, a small house just off the busy Portland Road in Hove. Mrs Martindale, never one to be inactive, had recently, amongst her other liberal and philanthropic endeavours, assumed a fresh responsibility as the president and chairman of the Lewes Road Dispensary for Women and Children. After her qualification Louisa was offered a job as a clinical assistant at the Royal Free Hospital, probably on the usual six-month contract. It was a tempting offer, but there also suddenly arrived a letter from an old friend, Dr Mary 'Murdie' Murdoch,[5] who had been Louisa's colleague (although not contemporaneously) at the London School of Medicine for Women. Murdie had built up a large and prosperous inner-city practice in Hull but suffered ill health with a gastric ulcer (which was to kill her at a too-early age) and she needed an assistant. She offered the job to Louisa at £1 a week (less 2s 6d for laundry). Sitting in a teashop in Brighton (no doubt over a nice pot of tea and assorted cakes) Louisa and Hilda solemnly discussed Murdie's offer. Their mother was not in favour; she would much have preferred Louisa to head straight back to London and, after some months as a clinical assistant, to follow in Miss Aldrich-Blake's successful footsteps, bypass general practice and set up immediately as an independent consulting physician and surgeon in a fashionable West End district. This would have been a bold step, chancy even; no doubt financial support would have been offered but, for once, Louisa put her mother's hopes to one side and decided to accept Murdie's invitation to join her in Yorkshire. Initially she stayed for only five weeks, for in June 1900 (on the occasion of Mrs Martindale's sixtieth birthday) Louisa, Hilda and their mother departed Southampton for their year's trip around the world.[6] When they returned, in June 1901, Louisa Martindale packed her personal and professional bags and went north to Hull to work for and with Murdie Murdoch.

For five years Louisa was out and about in all weathers, on a bicycle at night and a brougham or dog-cart during the day, visiting her patients. She carried out minor surgery, delivered babies, acted as nurse, dispenser and accountant and found out at nervous first hand that her employer was rightly well-known by her patients for her enthusiastic but woefully erratic performance as a car driver, although loved and admired by everyone in spite of that signal personality failure. The two women started a women's suffrage society in Hull, but on her mother's advice Louisa turned down the offer to be president of the local Liberal Association. Murdie Murdoch was to remain firm friends with both Louisa and Mrs Martindale until her death in 1916, and her relationship with Louisa was always very close and affectionate; very few other than her family — or possibly her life-long companion Ismay FitzGerald — would ever have the privilege of being allowed to speak of Dr Martindale as 'Lulu'.

In 1906 the thirty-four year old Louisa Martindale MD left Hull, not without a considerable pang and an emotional ceremony from her patients, some of whom presented her with silver gifts. The following year she returned to Brighton, purchased a good and centrally-located property at 10 Marlborough Terrace, a tall and lean, brick-built terraced house very close to the Royal Pavilion, put up her brass plate and knuckled down to starting her own general practice. Dr Martindale did not want to buy an established practice from another doctor who might be wanting to sell, since this might drive away the patients and so prove to be a poor investment. She had enough money to coast along since, like Drs Boyle and Jones, she too began her practice from scratch. (After her mother's death Louisa found that she had been secretly financed by Adam Steele, the wealthy husband of one of her half-sisters from the first Martindale family.)

While Drs Boyle and Jones's practice was in Hove, Dr Martindale was the first woman doctor in Brighton — a slight geographical distinction nowadays and possibly even then a little hair-splitting — but clearly important. She would have known that there had been two women doctors resident and practising in nearby Hove since 1898, not only through the London School of Medicine for Women but also through her mother's involvement with the Lewes Road Dispensary. Although Louisa had missed having Helen Boyle as a fellow student by twelve months, Mabel Jones had been a contemporary of hers in 1894 (albeit one of a more senior and therefore unapproachable year). That the first president and chairman of the Lewes Road Dispensary had a daughter eminently well qualified as a physician and surgeon, would have been well known to both Dr Boyle and Dr Jones.

Whether when they first arrived in Hove to set up in practice they anticipated the future arrival of Louisa Martindale MD will never be known — Mrs Martindale's ambitions for her daughter's career had not included a spell in general practice let alone one in briny Brighton — but it is surely impossible to say that a future homecoming to be close to an elderly mother might not be totally unexpected. The three women would have had much in common; not only their profession and the LSMW network, but a shared need to be friendly and supportive towards each other in an atmosphere where many pockets of distrust for women doctors would still remain. On the whole, the arrival of another woman doctor in general practice nearby might well be professionally more advantageous than of long-term concern.

Louisa did not call upon them, which indicates that this formality was not absolutely necessary, rather she wrote a polite letter asking them if they had any objection to her starting her practice nearby. The Hove ladies replied courteously to Louisa in the same vein, welcoming her arrival but indicating that they would prefer the new practice to be in Brighton and not in Hove, a not unreasonable request at a time when all patients were fee paying and poaching patients from another professional was not at all the done thing.[7] Writing in 1951 when she was over eighty, Dr Martindale revealed that at the same time they invited her to join the staff 'at the Islingword Dispensary'.*

Louisa Martindale would have known of the existence of the dispensary and would also have anticipated that, now resident in Brighton, future attendance as honorary medical officer was not to be avoided. Although by this time retired, her mother was still involved with the Lewes Road Dispensary and Louisa would also have been well acquainted with the other ladies on the Dispensary Council. However, in the years since the dispensary door had first opened to patients in 1899, there had been many changes. How the Dispensary Council and Drs Boyle and Jones had managed so successfully to cajole the public into generosity in any fashion towards what was a unique venture in a field closely associated with lunacy and the local asylum has to be wondered at — but they did. The Council would have had to emphasise to the donating public that the patients in its hospital would receive no emotional or psychiatric treatment at all, either in Brighton or elsewhere in the country, except at the Lewes Road Hospital.

The arrival of Louisa Martindale in Brighton was probably treated with open-armed enthusiasm by what was now a Joint Hospital and Dispensary Council. As an old Brightonian she would be very well placed to root out fresh local subscribers; as a one-time LSMW student she could call upon old friendships from sophisticated London which might well come in very handy in the course of time; and as a local GP she could shoulder a handsome slice of the work at the dispensary. But she was a doctor who had no interest in borderland nervous diseases; she would favour the scientific application of medicine and surgery towards the treatment of patients, and her return to Brighton with her MD firmly in her grasp could well be forecast to disturb the balance between the dispensary and the hospital.

_____

* i.e. the Lewes Road Dispensary at 145 Islingword Road.

Both Louisa Martindale and Helen Boyle were ambitious, determined and hard working. In the early years their professional paths lay very much together and there is no reason to suppose that in 1907 they saw their lives in Brighton and Hove as anything other than complementary and mutually advantageous. Miss Cock, Dean of the London School of Medicine for Women and billed as 'honorary consulting physician' at the Dispensary, may well have squeezed in some time for the occasional visit to Brighton — but with Louisa Martindale on hand these would be perhaps no longer necessary, and there is no difficulty in seeing Dr Martindale's hand when Miss Cock, no doubt with a profusion of many thanks by appropriate letter, was replaced as 'honorary visiting physician' by the elderly Dr Elizabeth Garrett Anderson. Well-known to the press as a delightful source of copy for both gossip and news, at this time she was no longer practising medicine; enjoying a vigorous retirement she had taken up local politics at her home in Suffolk.[8]

Also in 1907, the year of Dr Martindale's return to Brighton and the beginning of her association with the dispensary, the Lewes Road Hospital and Dispensary annual report shows a change in accounting procedures. The income and expenditure from both establishments had previously been calculated separately but published together; they now were both calculated and published separately. The hospital's outgoings of £476 was exceeded, if not comfortably but satisfactorily, by its income of £509. However, the dispensary was not so fortunate: its income of £130 was overshadowed by £162 of expenditure. But the routine of fundraising was now well established and, also in 1907, the local Women's Co-operative Guild held a very successful 'Pound Day' on Easter Monday: gifts of tea, sugar, cakes, bacon and many other provisions, each weighing one pound, were given to both the hospital and the dispensary. This was excellent for the hospital, helping out enormously with the food bills, but not so good for the dispensary, which did not provide hot suppers for its callers.

The dispensary at that time still charged only 3d for medication, and consultations remained free of charge. During the next few years the demand for the services provided by both the dispensary and the hospital can be seen to be steadily increasing as the flow of patients continued to rise, and the need for hard-working Joint Council members to support both establishments by keeping the funds rolling in kept up a parallel but increasingly threatening pace.

Mrs Martindale remained a generous Council member until her death in 1914. During those years Dr Louisa Martindale, herself a woman with a seemingly endless supply of energy and good health, enjoyed the love and support of her mother whilst she was busy building up her own general practice in Brighton and deepening her involvement with the medical and surgical side of the dispensary's work. Naturally she had a good appreciation of the value of fundraising and publicity and would not shrink from using mild pressure on friends or contacts should persuasion in that direction become necessary. She was also a woman who was not afraid of change; she would make careful plans and move resolutely, if with patience, towards her goals. The embrace of haste was not in Louisa Martindale's nature but it is almost as though her arrival was the proverbial breath of brisk fresh air sweeping through the dispensary; a zephyr that might even begin to whisper about the possibility of developing some medical and surgical care for local women separately from the treatment of borderland mental illness offered by Dr Boyle at Roundhill Crescent.

In 1908 the first rumble of disquiet between the two establishments appeared. It was about money, of course. A possible confusion in the minds of the donating public was put forward as a matter to be solved. The public, it seemed, was unable to tell which branch it was supporting, the women's dispensary in Islingword Road or the women's hospital in Roundhill Crescent! To solve this problem it was decided that the two establishments would acquire individual names rather than the one joint name used by both — the Lewes Road Dispensary and Hospital for Women and Children. There would be the Lewes Road Hospital for Women and Children at 101 Roundhill Crescent, (the name can just be seen in an old photograph of Roundhill Crescent) and the Lewes Road Dispensary for Women and Children at 145 Islingword Road.

On the surface this would seem to be a good idea and might well clear up a routine quandary (one which would rear its harrowing head again and again in years to come), but underneath there is a hint of concern that the apportioning of funds from the joint bank account was beginning to raise uncomfortable questions. With the dispensary running at a loss would the hospital have to lose out at some time in order to balance the books? Supposing the funds gathered for one exceeded funds gathered for the other; would any cash be diverted into the other needy pocket? The keeping of separate accounts had been a beginning and a different name for each establishment was the next step. Both would allow clarity so that everyone could see where the money was going.

Over the next few years, at one time the hospital was in deficit; at another, the dispensary, and it is clear that both were making separate bids for funds from the public, each keeping its own accounts and spending its money separately. This points to a more permanent division between the two, which might have become acrimonious unless a firm strategy to avoid this was put in place.

In 1908 the *Sussex Daily News* reported that Dr Boyle had organised a concert at a most appealing venue, the Royal Pavilion, and the Brighton Women's Co-operative Guild was still giving valuable support in ways that did not involve cash. The funds and goods would no doubt have gone directly to the hospital; nevertheless it was £22 8s 4d in deficit at the end of the year which, however, did not prohibit the installation of that most necessary of modern inventions, a telephone. At the dispensary the Martindale family were also persuaded to donate. Mrs Martindale and her brother Sir Evan Spicer gave three guineas each. But in 1910 the sour smell of impending major change was unavoidable; the lease of 145 Islingword Road was about to expire and a sharp and sensible look at the work of both the dispensary and the hospital could not be avoided.

The matter drifted inexorably to the forefront of discussion at the Joint Council meetings. It must have been transparent to all, including the clients, that the dispensary was outgrowing its function in Islingword Road and that a demand for medical and surgical hospital beds to treat more serious cases was becoming pressing. In other words, Brighton and Hove needed, and could sustain, an in-patient as well as an outpatient surgical and medical hospital for women. There was, after all, Dr Martindale — physician and surgeon — ready and available to do the job, and in 1910 another most suitable doctor also came on board: Mrs Helen Scatliff (née Collen) MB BS (Lond.) joined the Lewes Road Dispensary as an honorary medical officer for one shift a week. She had arrived in Brighton after her marriage to ear and throat surgeon Harold Harris Ellenborough Scatliff MA (Oxon) and preferred be known as 'Mrs' rather than 'doctor'. Conveniently, Mrs Scatliff's speciality was anaesthetics.

Possibly Dr Garrett Anderson gave much sound advice, but clearly something would have to be done. In 1910 definite moves were made to begin a search for suitably roomy and flexible premises for the dispensary to move to after the expiry of its lease at Islingword Road. This should preferably be in Brighton rather than Hove, and near the Lewes Road as well. Luckily, one of the four houses in the small terrace at the beginning of Ditchling Road where the sharp right turn from Lewes Road becomes Union Road and marches across the top of The Level had become vacant. It could easily provide both better accommodation for waiting patients and even a small operating room, and enough funds had been raised by Miss McClellan and her friends by way of a concert, a sale of work and a rummage sale, as well as by generous contributions from individuals (Mr Adam Steele,

Louisa Martindale's brother-in-law, was particularly kind) to finance the move and get in some more up-to-date equipment.

At the 1911 Annual Meeting Lady Chichester reported that in 1910 the Lewes Road Dispensary had managed a successful move from 145 Islingword Road into a small terraced house scarcely a stone's throw away at 4 Ditchling Road.[9]

Notes

[1] Russell Gurney's Enabling Bill of 1877 had made this possible.

[2] The Association of Medical Registered Women, founded to look after the interests of women doctors, had been formed in 1879. It became the Medical Women's Federation in 1917 and continues to this day. See <www.medicalwomensfederation.org.uk>.

[3] The families of many early medical women seem to have embraced the dissenting and evangelical faiths. See Carol Dyhouse, 'Driving ambitions: Women in Pursuit of a Medical Education 1890–1939', *Women's Historical Review* Vol. 7 No 3, 1998.

[4] The first was Dr Mary Scharlieb in 1897.

[5] Dr Murdoch during her professional life in Hull was associated with the local Victoria Hospital for Sick Children. It was at this hospital that Mabel Jones worked a short term as resident house surgeon after she qualified in 1893.

[6] They were absent when the Census was taken in 1901.

[7] After the introduction of the National Insurance Act of 1911 all eligible working men were placed on the 'panel' of a general practitioner who received an annual 'capitation fee' from the state to provide free primary general medical care. GPs could choose whether or not to participate in the 'panel' scheme: Dr Boyle and Dr Martindale did not but Dr Ross, the medical officer from the workhouse infirmary, participated in the Brighton panel, as did Mr Harold Scatliff and Dr Clifton Harris — who also took patients from the Hove panel (No. 2 Hove District). Mrs Elsie Griffith participated in the Hove panel. The scheme was nationwide, and over the years became criticised for frequently providing only perfunctory and hasty consultations, but it did provide free access to a doctor for working men and the basic structure of a good career for young GPs.

[8] The 1907 Qualification of Women (County and County Boroughs) Act finally enabled women to stand for election to county and borough councils and the seventy-year-old Elizabeth Garrett Anderson was invited to take the place of her husband Skelton, whose death in 1907 had created a vacancy on Aldeburgh Borough Council. So she began a new career as a local councillor for her home town, and a year later was unanimously chosen to be the first woman mayor in the UK. Women householders had been entitled to vote in Municipal elections since 1869 but not to stand for election to office except as a Poor Law Guardian. In 1870 the Forster Education Act allowed women to vote in elections and to stand for office on school boards. Elizabeth Garrett (she married in 1871) was invited to stand for election to the London School Board as a representative for Marylebone by the Working Men's Association that same year, and won with a majority of 34, 364.

[9] Ditchling Road begins where Union Road terminates, at Rose Hill. The first even numbers, 2, 4, 6 and 8, were once known as Ditchling Terrace. The odd numbers start further to the south at the junction with St Peter's Place.

6

MAJOR CHANGES

THE CHICHESTER HOSPITAL

It is not clear exactly when Helen Boyle ceased to attend the dispensary and carry out her shifts as honorary medical officer, since the dispensary and the hospital continued to regard themselves as one body and the reports of the Annual Meetings reflect that administrative unity. Whether or not she simply gave up because of the pressure of the work (which by no account would be unreasonable) or whether it was because of a disagreement about the way in which the dispensary was run and an idea that the Hospital for Nervous Diseases was being sidelined, can only be speculated upon. But clearly she did abandon her shifts at the dispensary in about 1908 or so and concentrated entirely upon the work of the hospital and her general practice. By the time of the move her name was no longer directly associated with the dispensary.

Number 4 Ditchling Road was, and still is, in the centre of a small terrace of four houses facing the flat and grassy expanse of The Level, at the time most pleasantly surrounded on the east, west and north sides by a thousand elm trees, the gift of the third Earl of Chichester in 1845.[1] The Salvation Army occupied a site slightly to the left and the vista from the upper windows across The Level, and above the fifty years old, but still juvenile, trees, most suitably included the delicate and stony tracery of the noble spire and taut turrets of St Peter's, the parish church of Brighton since 1873.

By 1908 there had been changes in the hospital at Roundhill Crescent as the six-monthly contracts for house doctors brought new names and faces to Brighton: Miss Rutherford MB, ChB (Lond.) arrived after the departures of Dr Gertrude Grogan and Dr Ada McLaren and Miss Pollard LSA would come along in 1910 — although Miss Read continued as the permanent matron. Helen Boyle's life had also profoundly altered. At some time, either 1907 or 1908, Dr Mabel Jones left Hove. Abandoning her partnership with Dr Boyle she shook the pebbles of Hove beach from her shoes and, leaving the green air drifting down Church Road from Devil's Dyke, travelled far away to the north to live for the remainder of her life in dim and very distant Glasgow.[2]

Until her death Helen Boyle did not take another partner into her general practice; she relied instead upon paid assistants with whom she shared consulting rooms in The Drive, Hove, and possibly her rented house at 37 Church Road (originally 3 Palmeira Terrace.) However, at about this time the house was converted into flats by the owner and Dr Boyle downsized into the first floor where she probably lived until her retirement many years later. She always retained a strong affection for Mabel Jones — and no doubt a trunkful of memories — and would remember her fondly in years to come.

There are many possible reasons for Dr Jones's departure. That she left Hove just after Louisa Martindale arrived in Brighton and only a couple of years after the Lewes Road Hospital had opened its doors in Roundhill Crescent on the other side of Brighton — with a difficult journey from the tram stop at Palmeira Square to cope with in all weathers — might or might not have been related. Coincidence seems to be too easy a word. Whether her departure was sad, angry or joyful can be only speculated, as only two scraps of evidence — and those are indirect — remain: her will, and her later career in Glasgow.

Mabel Jones's will had been drawn up on 25th May 1904, before Dr Martindale arrived in Brighton. It was short: all her estate and effects, real and personal etc she bequeathed to her sister, Emma Jones, who at the time was living in Tunbridge Wells (she later moved to Bexhill-on-Sea with their mother, Mrs Bertram Jones). There is no reason to suppose that during the remainder of her life she ever wrote another will; if she did, it was never found amongst her possessions after her death. The will contained no mention of Helen Boyle, not even the gift of a small item of remembrance. This is surely significant for it perhaps indicates that no degree of fond intimacy had arisen, at least on Dr Jones's side, while the two were practice partners and that there had been no legally-binding business agreement between them. This lack of formal agreement would have been typical of Helen Boyle who, all her life, would abhor what she called 'red tape' and positively avoid its imposition in her life. It also underlines a friendship rather than a long term commitment to each other and suggests that when both came to Hove in 1898 they came simply as professional colleagues.

The arrival of Louisa Martindale in Brighton may well have provided Mabel Jones with a welcome means of escape. Possibly she had wanted to leave for some time, but could not — out of honour, or owing to promises made on her arrival with Helen Boyle in 1898 — leave Hove until an effective substitute for her work at the dispensary had been permanently drafted in. That substitute had opportunely and possibly unexpectedly arrived, and if Mabel Jones had come to feel that her professional life did not lie with nervous disorders and that she wanted to work in a disadvantaged area amongst poor and distressed women, then this was the time to leave.

Louisa Martindale was happy with the move and content with the life she had chosen in Brighton. Well brought-up and impeccably mannered, feminine but imposing and always taking care to be supremely well-dressed, as a doctor she could claim reasonable status in liberal Brighton society; although as a unmarried woman not all fashionable doors would be immediately opened to her. But this social disadvantage could be offset by a certain distinction as a successfully returned Old Brightonian who no doubt had many schoolgirl acquaintances to look up and lean on for introductions, should they be required. And, of course, as her mother's daughter, all doors of the houses of the rich and philanthropic middle classes, not only in Brighton but also the whole of Sussex, would swing soundlessly open for her. For many years she was an active member of the long standing but traditionally managed National Union of Women's Suffrage Societies headed by Millicent (Mrs Henry) Fawcett, a younger sister of Dr Elizabeth Garrett Anderson, but she stopped short of any involvement in the radical, Pankhurst directed, Women's Social and Political Union, which sought victory by the militancy of direct and violent action, unpeaceful protest and the martyrdom of a sentence served in Holloway gaol. (Louisa would later write in her autobiography that, at the time, she felt that her mother had been mildly disappointed with her non-adventurous choice!)

Invited to dinner one evening at the house of Mr Frederic Merrifield, a local lawyer, barrister and butterfly enthusiast whose younger daughter Flora — always known as Miss F. de G. Merrifield — was the Brighton Women's Suffrage Society Secretary,[3] Louisa met on the doorstep the Honourable Ismay FitzGerald, a daughter of Lord and Lady FitzGerald of Kilmarnock,[4] and they quickly became friends. Both were daughters of a father's second marriage with no few older half-siblings; they shared many interests (including a love of lace) and soon discovered an ability to talk together happily and to enjoy each other's company. Upon the death of Lady Fitzgerald a short time later, Louisa invited her new friend to stay a while with her at her house in Brighton: Ismay came, stayed for many years, and they lived together until they were parted by Ismay's death in 1945.

In 1911 Ismay FitzGerald, as so often happens with friends and relatives, was swiftly placed on the new Joint Council, the governing body for both the dispensary and the hospital. Then, as now, it is inevitable that being associated with a companion who does a great deal of work in a field which is always ready to absorb spare cash and idle energy will swiftly lead to an assignment of responsibility. Miss FitzGerald served for many years on the Joint Council and later on the New Sussex board of management; although neither a doctor nor a local worthy she had many other good qualities: nerve, vigour and social graces, all of which she seems to have put to good use. She was also a practical person with a talent for supervising and maintaining building works, although it is impossible to say whether she learned this over the years or whether property management fell to her because no one else wanted to do it.

One aspect of the work was never in doubt: the popularity of the dispensary had not been diminished by its move from Islingword Road. In its first year, 1911, the small door into the ground floor of 4 Ditchling Road opened to over 7,000 callers from all over Sussex. However, even had each one paid 3d for medication the income generated would have been less than £100 — a quite insufficient sum to cover the cost of drugs, bills and rent, and creditors would not be satisfied with less than their due. Lewes Road Hospital up in Roundhill Crescent was doing far better and managing somehow to avoid the pitfall of debt: Helen Boyle's new treatment for cases of early nervous disorder was receiving patients living well beyond the borders of Sussex and the money to treat them was found.

The year 1911 was a flagship one that would bring along more changes. The arrival of Ismay FitzGerald on the Joint Council would give Louisa Martindale two voices in support of any change she might desire to engineer, three if Mrs Scatliff was to be included. The dispensary and the hospital were to be renamed — a change that was, on the surface, needed. Now that the dispensary had moved away from Islingword Road the name 'Lewes Road Dispensary' was clearly no longer appropriate and might even cause confusion. (The latter must never be allowed since confusion would be just the sort of thing to offend subscribers — with unfortunate fiscal consequences). The new names would have to be good ones, and so they were: the Chichester Hospital for Women and Children (101 Roundhill Crescent) and the Chichester Dispensary for Women and Children (4 Ditchling Road). The Earls of Chichester had long been associated with Brighton's charitable hospitals, the family was well known and respected in Brighton and Hove, and Ruth, Countess Chichester, had since 1905 been patron and president of the Joint Council of the dispensary and the hospital. But the prospect of yet another remove was coldly creeping along the Lewes Road; in 1912, unhappily, it was now the turn of the lease on 101 Roundhill Crescent to expire.

A new home for the hospital was sorely needed and in early 1912 the Joint Council approved a further move, fortunately aided by an anonymous gift of £200. The Roundhill Crescent premises had been very successful but now in any case the building was too small and always so full that a waiting list had had to be established — although waiting lists were the very opposite of what was needed. Prompt early treatment was, as Dr Boyle would argue, as essential as the immediate setting of a broken leg, an emergency operation or the nursing of disease. It was time for the hospital to move on to larger premises and, in Helen Boyle's mind, this was just the right time to add more beds, get more nursing staff on board and treat more patients. There was no reason at all for the hospital to stay near the dirty and crowded roads of Brighton; the new premises should perhaps be closer to the sea, in a quieter area where the thrum of horses and carriages and the roar of newfangled motor cars would be blown away by healthy salty breezes and the spray of the waves crashing on the beach. A place where the sunshine was not inhibited by smoke or tarnished by the oily rumble of industry.

The new building would also need to be reasonably near tram and motor transport, if possible, so that patients could come and go with ease for their follow-up and aftercare in the evenings. Hove, where Dr Boyle had her general practice, might just be the right place. It would also be closer to her surgery and save much of the time and energy she used up travelling across Brighton, either by cab or by a change from the horse-drawn omnibus leaving Palmeira Square onto the electric tram at the Old Steine.

A suitable building was found and in 1912 the Chichester Hospital for Nervous Diseases opened at 70 Brunswick Place, Hove. The house was much larger than 101 Roundhill Crescent and could offer thirty-five beds instead of ten. As before there was a sheltered garden, and the building was placed on a corner with neighbours on one side only. The couple of miles or so between the new hospital in Hove and the new dispensary in Ditchling Road, still labouring in the clatter and fumes of busy Lewes Road — although pleasantly near The Level and the larger houses rising to the north — cannot have made for anything other than a new distance between the individual honorary physicians; however, there is an unarguable logic for the hospital to move to healthier Hove. The treatment that Dr Boyle prescribed for borderland cases included healthy air, good food and salt water bathing as well the removal of the nervous patient away from her home and into congenial company, and it is most likely that it was always in Helen Boyle's mind that her hospital would be better placed in the wider and quieter streets of Hove.

The Joint Council took a seven year lease on 70 Brunswick Place and, rather surprisingly, the joint name was changed yet again, this time to the Lady Chichester Hospital and Dispensary, named directly after the Countess herself. This refinement does indicate some past dissent on the Joint Council. The association of Lady Chichester with a hospital for women and children, staffed from head to toe by women, seems nowadays to be so obvious that it is surprising that this name was not used from the outset. Possibly there had been a deliberate attempt at flattery towards Lord Chichester simply by using 'Chichester' and a bid for his patronage had been overthrown in the Joint Council — possibly Lord Chichester himself had disapproved of a sleight of hand to include him. Equally likely was that a clarion complaint had been launched from the big voluntary hospital just down the coast in Chichester itself — along the lines that that the name Chichester Hospital was far too close to their own for the comfortable collecting of subscriptions.[5] But for whatever reason, the name 'Chichester Hospital' was quickly dropped and the word 'Lady' neatly and very properly inserted.

At this time Dr Martindale was still living and practising in central Brighton; luckily her house and surgery at 10 Marlborough Place, though nearer to The Steine, was no more than a brisk ten minutes' walk away from what was now the Lady Chichester Dispensary at 4 Ditchling Road. Although the dispensary was — as always —struggling to find funds, it had become clear in Louisa Martindale's mind that there was an urgent need for the dispensary to be able to have medical and surgical beds readily available for the patients who were clearly too ill for outpatient treatment. A patient presenting herself at the dispensary and diagnosed as being in need of hospitalisation had, of necessity, to be sent up to the Sussex County Hospital for surgery — but into the care of a male doctor with access to his own beds. Although in London Miss Aldrich-Blake was welcomed as a gifted surgeon in many of the capital's large and wealthy voluntary and teaching hospitals, as late as 1911 the Board of the Royal Sussex County Hospital would not consider the idea of placing a woman doctor on its honorary medical staff, even though she might have been in general practice in Brighton for several years, a strange and somehow typical example of the tension between Liberal and Conservative politics of Brighton, which remains very much in evidence today. It was galling for the sensibilities of the patient as well as the pride of her woman doctor but there was no proleptic change upon the Eastern Road horizon of exclusion.

Many years later Miss M. E. Verrall would say publicly and to a wide audience that the surgical and medical hospital had started in the mind of Mrs Martindale, and it would seem very likely that this was in fact so. Mrs Martindale had wanted Louisa to follow Miss Aldrich-Blake as a consulting surgeon in the select squares and less hidebound hospitals of upmarket London rather than to stay as a plain GP in coastal and provincial Brighton, possibly a little too close to the stews of the North Laine and Edward Street. But with time ticking by it was becoming horribly clear that this was not going to happen. Lulu was not going to move and if she could not lay her hands on her own beds up at the (by then Royal) Sussex County, and if she was not going to leave her mother — now a few years away from seventy and obstinately retired to the distant and woody (but very accessible by railway) village of Horsted Keynes — then the second best would have to be done: the hospital must come to Dr Louisa Martindale in beachy Brighton. The means to raise the money (with any luck) were already in place, an abundant supply of women patients was readily available (no doubt about that); and with historical precedence to hand and advice from the London School of Medicine for Women (which was definitely available) a successful venture could be launched and a new hospital for women could be instituted in Sussex.

Dr Martindale, the consummate professional, a woman easily able to make and keep career contacts amongst her male colleagues, knew that the Royal Sussex County policy concerning women honorary physicians by no means sat universally comfortably with other doctors in Brighton. Dr Hobhouse (later Colonel Edmund Hobhouse RAMC), a physician; Dr Jowers, a surgeon; and Dr Thomas Jenner Verrall (Miss Verrall's brother) were GPs in Brighton. All held honorary posts at the Royal Sussex County and all were in favour of the inclusion of women doctors on the medical staff, honorary or otherwise. Their support could be relied upon — but they remained in a minority. In her autobiography Dr Martindale writes that she and other members of the Joint Council came to agree that a number of beds would somehow have to be provided for the medical and surgical hospital treatment of women away from Eastern Road; at no time does she declare that the idea was hers alone, although we may take this modesty with a certain measure of salt.

Whether she had elbowed Helen Boyle from her seniority, or whether Dr Boyle had willingly given up her association with the dispensary because of the pressure of work and so took no interest in any deliberations along these lines, can only be guessed at. In her autobiography Louisa Martindale awards Helen Boyle suitable credit for the work she carried out at the dispensary and the Lady Chichester Hospital, but none at all for the later opening of a small surgical and medical hospital. There is neither warmth nor animation in the few lines she gives to Dr Boyle in her pages, and it is not difficult to imagine a frosting of relations.

The callers to the dispensary at 4 Ditchling Road kept on coming and it had to be faced that the only immediate solution to relieve the frustration of both doctor and patient would be to cram in some beds and open a small hospital above the waiting room. Suddenly — almost immediately in fact — in 1912 the golden opportunity suddenly presented itself: the adjoining house, 6 Ditchling Road, became vacant and the lease was available. The Joint Council immediately snapped it up with a speed that perhaps indicates some prior knowledge of the imminent departure of the tenants; it would have been characteristic of Louisa Martindale, always thorough and practical in her approach to all ventures, to have done her homework and discovered some time beforehand that the lease on number 6 was shortly to expire. A team of letter-writers, headed up by Mrs Martindale from her home in Horsted Keynes, was organised to plead for new subscribers and more donations to furnish, equip and generally set up what would be a brand new hospital situated at number 6. One of the new subscribers, who was to stay around and become very influential, was Elizabeth Robins, a beautiful and well-known American writer and actress who lived in an attractive, rambling, eighteenth-century property, 'Backset', set in the ploughed and coppiced countryside near Henfield.

Building works were rapidly put in place to join up numbers 4 and 6. The ground floors were to be used as the dispensary and consulting rooms, while the two upper floors were to have six medical and surgical beds and a small operating theatre. Nursing staff were engaged, including Miss Clayton as theatre nurse and Miss Milborne as matron. A photograph from that time shows the two properties united by a fine shield bearing the words 'The Chichester Hospital for Women and Children' straddling the two houses. Although it has long gone the brackets which once held it in place can be seen to this day. In the photograph a nurse leans inquisitively over the iron balcony surrounding the open bay window of number 6.

By 1912 two separate women's hospitals, the smaller in busy Brighton and the larger in what was certainly more handsome Hove, were both satisfactorily up running, and awaiting patients.

Notes

[1] The trees were a mixture of *Ulmus hollandica* (Dutch Elm) and *Ulmus procera* (English Elm). Only a few remain after the terrible ravages of the Dutch Elm disease in the late 1970s and the great gale of 1987. Thanks to Peter Bourne of the mybrightonandhove egroup for this information.

[2] In Glasgow Dr Jones was associated with the Scottish branch of Mrs Pankhurst's Women's Social and Political Union, whose members suffered greatly from forcible feeding in Perth Prison. In 1914 when a royal visit to Glasgow was impending Janie Allan, the Glasgow Women's Social and Political Union organiser tried, independently, to strike a bargain with the Lord Provost of Glasgow that her members would carry out no militancy during the visit in return for ceasing the force feeding. For this, Mrs Pankhurst summarily sacked Janie Allan. Dr Jones and Helen Crawfurd visited Mrs and Christabel Pankhurst in protest, but allowed themselves to be convinced by her case: 'You are all attached to Miss Allan because she is such a fine person, so are we. Not only that but Miss Allan is a generous contributor to our funds. Do you think this action has been taken without serious thought? The position is this, that the only thing that can stop militancy is the granting of the Vote to women. We cannot bargain with the enemy. If Scottish women are prepared to bargain on any other terms then English women are not.' King, E. (1993) *The Hidden History of Glasgow's Women*, Mainstream Publishing, p130.

[3] The *Brighton & Hove Herald*, a weekly newspaper, carried a report on 18th April 1908 of a meeting at Forfar's Restaurant in Western Road that reconstituted the defunct Brighton and Hove Franchise Society, and which had a mixed (men and women) membership. The Society had suffered since the original professional organiser, Miss Watson from the National Union of Women's Suffrage Societies, had been removed to another district after an illness. The original honorary secretary, Miss F. de G. Merrifield, remained in her post and a new committee was formed, the members of which were to include Helen Boyle, Louisa Martindale, Dr Lillian Harris (recently arrived in Brighton and married to Dr Clifton Harris) and Miss Florence Pickworth, possibly a music teacher and an original member of the Council at Lewes Road Dispensary. The proposer for the committee was Dr Thomas Jenner Verrall, who made a stirring speech remarking on 'The growth of public opinion in favour of women's suffrage and welcoming the formation of the Society as a proof that in Brighton an increasing number was convinced of the justice and expediency of the claim.' The Society later became the Brighton branch of the Pioneer Club.

[4] At this time Lady FitzGerald had a house at 20 Adelaide Crescent, Hove. Lord FitzGerald of Kilmarnock was a Law Lord; his title was not hereditary but his children, unlike those of life peers today, were entitled to the 'honourable' handle.

[5] There was indeed a big voluntary hospital in Chichester at this time, known officially as the West Sussex, East Hampshire and Chichester Infirmary and Dispensary. A few years later, in 1911, the hospital was restyled the West Sussex, East Hampshire and Chichester General Infirmary and after the end of the war became the Royal and West Sussex County Hospital. These cumbersome names and name changes were blithely ignored by most ordinary folk, who naturally continued to speak of it shortly as the Chichester Hospital. It was a problem because a similarity of names between neighbouring hospitals might well warp receipts from collection boxes shaken on street corners.

7

The Two Branches

The new medical and surgical hospital at 6 Ditchling Road, with the old dispensary still going strong next door at number 4, was completed to everyone's satisfaction and was headed by Louisa Martindale in her capacity as physician and surgeon. At 70 Brunswick Place the more mature Hospital for Nervous Diseases of Women and Children was now Helen Boyle's own unique and personal arena but clearly some kind of surface reorganisation was very much in order for everyone's benefit, especially that of any prospective patient.

A busy institution on two sites does rather make for a nightmare of administration, as it also would today even with phones and emails dancing easily at our fingertips to accelerate essential communications, and it is a great credit to the ladies of the Joint Council that they faced these difficulties head on, coming up with a solution that would keep both hospitals aligned with each other — and therefore with Lady Chichester herself — but that would bestow a considerable degree of autonomy upon the physicians. Somebody, somewhere came up with the word 'branch'. Almost immediately, and no doubt with the usual satisfying notices to the local papers and circulars to the subscribers, yet another renaming saw the light. Still flying proudly under the Lady Chichester flag, 70 Brunswick Place became the Lady Chichester Hospital for Women and Children, Hove Branch, and 4–6 Ditchling Road became the Lady Chichester Hospital, Brighton Branch. The branches remained under the overall control of a Joint Council headed by her ladyship as president, although each branch now had its own individual house or executive committee (which included the doctors) for supervising day-to-day business, making practical decisions and solving small problems. Each branch had individual responsibility for spending its own money although major decisions would have to go to the Joint Council. At the time no-one thought that that eventuality would ever be a problem.

The branches would maintain their own separate bank accounts, and present separate financial records to the Joint Council and the subscribers at the annual meeting; with Miss M. E. Verrall — now an important and powerful Council member — remaining as honorary treasurer to both branches.[1]

The Dispensary, which had opened fourteen years or so before at 145 Islingword Road, was for a long while considered to be an independent, third branch of the Lady Chichester Hospital and it was re-dubbed the 'Outpatients" at the same time; however, as logic demanded, it stayed under the protective wing of the Brighton Branch.[2]

As usual, money — or rather the raising of it — was still of vital importance. Both Helen Boyle and Louisa Martindale did not hesitate to seek help for their now individual hospitals from wealthy relatives and influential friends. Dr Martindale's brother-in-law Adam Steele stepped in grandly and offered to pay the rates for the first three years on 6 Ditchling Road, and the glamorous and popular Elizabeth Robins offered her practical help and most valuable support to the Brighton Branch. Later to become chairman of the Brighton Branch executive committee Elizabeth Robins was charismatic, brilliant and popular, and knew just about everyone in artistic, theatrical and political circles.[3] Immediately she promised to launch an 'entertainment' to raise funds and donated £40 herself, while another donor, wishing to be anonymous, gallantly promised £200. Temporarily in funds, further expansion could be afforded at the Brighton Branch in Ditchling Road, a year later, in 1913, number 8, the adjoining house on the right in the small terrace, became vacant. The house was somewhat smaller than numbers 4 and 6 but was tremendously handy; the lease was quickly taken by the Joint Council, and the Lady Chichester Hospital, Brighton Branch, flowed sideways, increasing its in-patient capacity to twelve beds.

Louisa Martindale now had her own hospital. In just two years the Ditchling Road site had tripled in size and was now able to offer safe and hygienic in-patient facilities both for the treatment of illness and to perform a variety of surgical operations. The acquisition of 8 Ditchling Road was fortuitous to say the least, but perhaps not surprising, as any neighbouring tenant might well feel unhappy with a constant stream of poorly visitors passing their doors, not to mention the inevitable disturbances at night and the accumulation in the small back yard of none too sweet hospital detritus. And, of course, the constant awareness of ether and possibly death on the other side of what would be none too thick brick walls. (The inhabitants on the other side at number 2 appear to have been made of sterner stuff and never did get up and move away.)

A new consulting surgeon was now to head up and grace the hospital's honorary medical staff, and it has to be admitted the appointment was a great coup d'état. Miss Louisa Aldrich-Blake, Dr Martindale's old friend and a surgeon of great eminence from London's New Hospital for Women,[4] lent her prestigious name and offered her considerable surgical skills.

As was to be expected, raising enough cash locally and further abroad in Sussex to support two hospitals soon became a tough problem. In the early years of the twentieth century, no less then as now, the march of medical science was every year bringing new drugs, new techniques and new equipment into use for the care and treatment of the sick; more efficient, more life saving — and more expensive. Steadily increasing bills to finance the steadily improving quality of services offered by the Brighton Branch began to arrive through the letterboxes. Free medical care for poor women had characterised the opening of the Lewes Road Dispensary in Islingword Road in 1899, but perhaps it was now time to take a fresh look at this policy. Surely, if some patients were able to pay then perhaps they should? X-ray equipment was very expensive, bed care after operations was labour intensive, and nurses had to be paid, housed and fed. In-patients needed food, bed linen, dressings and a host of other supplies; the building needed heat and light and the drug companies had to be constantly canvassed for the cheapest contract to supply their wares. Upon those who had only limited means to pay the Brighton Branch imposed a charge of 7s 6d per week for in-patient treatment while for those with a fatter bank account the fees were swollen to three guineas, the fashionable currency. Despite this, there was no shortage of patients. At the Hove Branch of the Lady Chichester Hospital, Dr Boyle also struggled as long as she could to avoid imposing charges; but eventually she, too, reluctantly conceded that if a patient could afford to pay then she should do so. At the outpatients' however, the Joint Council remained firm about its charges and consultation remained free with the price of medication continuing at 3d, as it had always been.

However, the vital — not to say critical — fundraising efforts were still shared and new joint initiatives were dreamt up and put in place. New rewards for patronage were dangled: a donation of £250 would bring with it an honorary position of life governor of the Lady Chichester Hospital and a donation of £300 would name a small ward after the benefactor. A handsome £350 would bring the same gratifying title to a large ward. No doubt some of these new ventures were successful and some were not; however, what was becoming very apparent was that the success of the Lady Chichester Hospital group was being noticed, not only by the people of Sussex but also by the new generations of bright young women doctors qualifying in their profession either in London or Edinburgh and keen to go out into the world and seek work. Times were slowly changing and, as soon as they had managed to get some work experience beneath their belts, rather than going into private general practice more women had begun to look for salaried medical jobs in the public sector, with local authorities, the Civil Service or the Post Office Medical Service. They were having limited success. In Scotland a woman held the post of Medical Officer of the Highlands and Islands simply because no male doctor would consider taking the job. The big asylums would still happily take women on short contracts as medical officers but were, increasingly, not even the women's first choice. Posts in children's hospitals were opening up but the initial six-month contract for the new doctor had no long-term security and, in any case, children's hospitals were by no means thick upon the ground.

The arrival of the Ministry of Health in 1917 would open up jobs for women doctors if they had taken the Diploma of Public Health; however, the government imposed lesser scales of pay for women which the Medical Women's Federation and, to its credit, the BMA opposed. Some women, to the disdain of their colleagues, did however accept the lower pay offered. The Civil Service on the whole backed the reluctance of many male colleagues in the medical profession to employ women medical officers, although it did appoint professional women as factory inspectors, often working in the slums and inspecting the appalling conditions of the industrial towns. (Dr Martindale's sister Hilda worked for many years in this profession.) Later, when all professions became legally open to women, the public sector would dream up a new and really rigid control: the marriage bar. A woman might be employed if she were single or widowed, but not if married. If employed, she automatically had to relinquish her job should she choose to marry. The Civil Service, the teaching profession and the Post Office were particularly keen on enforcing this bar: it remained in place right up to living memory in the women's branches of the armed forces.[5]

There is no doubt that the arrival of women's hospitals across the UK[6] resulted in the creeping relaxation of stiff masculine attitudes of exclusion. The fierce opposition of the mid-nineteenth century to women doctors had become noticeably thinner: possibly by acute observation that the women's arrival had not, as was fearsomely foretold, brought about a savage erosion of male career prospects, or, even worse, a cataclysmic curtailment of earning power; or, over the years, by the sharp pangs of death. By 1913 there were more than a thousand qualified women doctors looking for useful and rewarding work, and many of them must have looked with anticipation towards the salty, yeasty air of cosmopolitan Brighton and conservative Hove that rather tolerated oddity and rewarded wholesome effort. With both Branches of the Lady Chichester Hospital up and running it was inevitable that more young women doctors, some married, some not, would get on a train, go south, and arrive in Brighton and Hove. The drift, beginning in 1898 with Dr Boyle and Dr Jones, had not stopped with them.

In about 1907 Dr Lillian Harris and her husband, Dr Henry Clifton Harris, came to Brighton and in 1908 Mrs Harris was present at the re-constitution meeting of the Brighton Suffrage Society. Mrs Scatliff would soon come on board at the dispensary in 1910, and in about 1912 Dr Florence Edmonds arrived in Hove, setting up a general practice in a graceful and roomy bow-fronted house, 5 Brunswick Place, a step away from the grassy descent of Brunswick Square down to the sea and only just across Western Road from the stony slope up to the Lady Chichester Hospital, Hove Branch. She came to Hove after some years as an assistant to Dr Murdoch in Hull and, not surprisingly, in 1913 immediately took up a place as assistant (later honorary) physician at the Brighton Branch alongside Dr Martindale and Mrs Scatliff. Dr Edmonds later employed other young women doctors as assistants, one of whom, Dr Gladys Wauchope, set up her own consulting practice in Hove.[7] In the 1920s Dr Elsie Griffith would arrive in Hove and live in Brunswick Square with her husband Dr John Richard Griffith, and Dr Octavia Wilberforce would set up her practice in Montpelier Road. Dr Gertrude Grogan and Miss Pollard came and went at the Lewes Road Hospital; Dr Alice Greaves was another assistant to Dr Edmonds; she too did not stay. Dr Christine Shearer would be an anaesthetist at the Brighton Branch; she too left Sussex but Dr Doris Odlum and Dr Cecily Lamorna Hingston did stay, and would be associated with Dr Boyle for many years.

And not only doctors were available. The Royal Sussex County employed many nurses, as did the workhouse infirmary at Race Hill. Both Branches of the Lady Chichester were fortunate: Miss Milborne as matron at Ditchling Road and her colleague Miss Clayton as the theatre sister stayed for many years. Their work was much praised by Lady Chichester in her capacity as president at the Annual Meeting in 1913. Miss Taylor became matron of Hove Branch before the war and was still there and publicly loyal to Helen Boyle in 1934.

The summer of 1914 arrived with wonderful seaside weather but earlier, in March, to Dr Martindale's great grief and distress, Mrs Martindale died at her home in Horsted Keynes. Dr Martindale would later write that her mother's death at that time had mercifully spared her the horror that would soon follow: momentous moves in Europe as well as in Brighton and Hove were afoot as a few months later, in August 1914, the Great War erupted over the old and familiar face of Europe and changed its countenance for ever.

Notes

[1] Hove Branch used Barclays Bank in Western Road and Brighton Branch used the County & Westminster in Pavilion Buildings, Brighton.

[2] In 1913 the number of callers at the outpatients' was logged at an impressive 7811 for the year.

[3] She would also bring with her the young Octavia Wilberforce, later to become a new and potential hard worker from a local wealthy and influential family, and who would also take up the study of medicine herself.

[4] The New Hospital for Women had opened with ten beds in 1872 above Elizabeth Garrett Anderson's St Mary's Dispensary (opened 1868) in Seymour Street, London. Two years later the hospital moved to fresh premises at 222 and 224 Marylebone Road. When number 220 became vacant (hardly surprisingly) later it was added to the others. In 1888 the landlord, Lord Portman, declined to renew the leases of the Marylebone houses and a new site was found at 144 Euston Road and leased for seventy years. The New Hospital, a towering red brick affirmation of late Victorian weight and volume, complete with turrets and gables, was built from scratch and opened with marvellous ceremony in 1890. After Dr Garrett Anderson's death in 1917 the New Hospital was renamed the Elizabeth Garrett Anderson Hospital. See Manton, J. (1965) *Elizabeth Garrett Anderson,* Methuen & Co.

[5] There are stories, possibly apocryphal, that a few courageous women civil servants consequently eschewed marriage altogether, living and producing families with common-law husbands, since the production of an illegitimate child constituted no grounds for dismissal.

[6] There seems to have been at least ten, all mentioned from time to time in the available literature. The New Hospital for Women and House of Recovery (opened in Barnet in 1913); The South London Hospital for Women; Canning Town Women's Settlement Hospital for Women; Clapham Maternity Hospital; Battersea District Maternity Hospital and Dispensary; the Tuberculosis Sanatorium (in Rudgwick near Horsham); the Roll of Honour Women's Hospital for Children in Harrow Road, London and the Bruntsfield Hospital for Women and Children (formerly the Edinburgh Hospital and Dispensary for Women and later the Elsie Inglis Memorial Hospital), and of course the LCH and the New Sussex.

[7] Wauchope, G.M. (1963) *A Woman Physician,* John Wright & Son, Bristol.

8

THE WAR IN EUROPE

The interruption that was supposed to be the 'war to end all wars' arrived no less theatrically in Sussex than it did in all other counties; the local newspapers took a deep and dramatic interest in all its sons from both higher and lower stations in life who went away to fight with the county's own regiment, the Royal Sussex. Concern for its daughters came later and was of a mildly curious nature but not without a certain bias in their favour. In Brighton there was a great interest in both local women's auxiliary police troupes (one uniformed and another with a designatory armband had been put together for reasons not altogether clear to anyone) and the importance of whether, as elsewhere in the country, women should be allowed the responsibility of driving the electric trams. Conducting, well yes, but driving? Certainly no major physical strength was needed, but even so was the task not outside the weaker feminine grasp? Luckily for the women who rather fancied the breeches and being behind the handle, the growing scarcity of available men took the decision away and ended a most enjoyable public speculation.

The attitude of most middle class women — professional or otherwise — towards the war is little lauded these days as it was almost wholly patriotic. In 1914 the majority agreed with much passion that active participation in the European field of battle was to be a priority until happier times should come long, and many wanted to be very involved indeed. Women in their thirties who had managed to live independent lives away from their families for many years, who had trained themselves for a demanding but caring profession — which, nevertheless, saw its fair share of blood, bones and torn limbs every day — felt strongly that their skills, without active participation in the fighting, should be put to good use behind the battlefields and as soon as possible. Were not their brothers and husbands and cousins all straining to get into khaki and depart for Europe? The medical women, with very few exceptions, yearned to serve. They had the skills and the training to be able to heal the wounded, they were readily available (being self-employed they could up and leave in a trice), as doctors they held it to be self-evident that their purpose was above the promulgation of the conflict and that they were bound by their professionalism to show no favour either to khaki, grey or blue uniforms. The realisation that they might be healing men in order to send them back into the blood, mud and burning steel of the war came later, and to most doctors, not only the women.

In the beginning, before the war had lasted a month, a group of medical women, members of the National Union of Women's Suffrage Societies (NUWSS), marched off to the War Office and briskly offered themselves and their services for the treatment and care of the wounded. They were prepared to pack their bags, leave their practices and embark, not necessarily to a war zone, but to a military hospital as medical officers. They had every reason to think that their offer might be met with open (though possibly cautious) arms, since their rivals, the members of the Women's Social and Political Union (WSPU) had abruptly and publicly ceased their destructive activities upon the outbreak of war and were now in absolute favour of total patriotism.[1] However, as was almost to be expected, the War Office peremptorily and even harshly declined the offer of their services. Whether this was because of the widespread and cheerful view of Lord Kitchener and the War Office that the war would certainly be 'over by Christmas', so there was no need for the extra administrative chaos that such an acceptance would bring, or whether because the thought of women serving alongside men was an unnatural and repugnant idea to the generals can only be speculated. Most likely it was an early application of the chronic male ability to look through the dim spectacles of the double standard. When it came to treating soldiers who might be seriously wounded in the head, belly, buttocks or private parts the War Office could not conceive of women doctors sewing them up, and yet it would have no difficulty in supplying female nurses to change embarrassing dressings and attend to overflowing bedpans. However, within a few months this official attitude was fairly easily circumnavigated by women who by now knew a thing or two about initiative and organising ability. Probably, they had already planned their next move, and the War Office was simply, and with a clear conscience, eliminated early from their plans.

The women's movement, during its many years of difficult and lengthy campaigning, had forged a matrix of interdependent, mobile and determined groups of like-minded women: the National Union of Women's Suffrage Societies, led by Millicent Fawcett. The membership of the NUWSS was of a moderate and non-aggressive persuasion, preferring the reasoned argument, the petition and the written word; theirs was known as the 'constitutional' approach. They were always known as suffragists and the number of members was far in excess of Mrs Pankhurst's independent Women's Social and Political Union, whose members were known as suffragettes.

From a multitude of small, disparate groups back in the 1880s the NUWSS had been welded together by Mrs Fawcett's awesome personality and profound organisational abilities into one vast and yet integrated organisation, so flexible that it even included the odd men's support group — as did the Brighton and Hove Women's Franchise Society, which was a branch of the NUWSS. By 1914 the NUWSS was a competent, vigorous and highly effective nationwide women's organisation, and many of its members were trained to campaign, organise and get the job — any job — done, and quickly. Either from political decision or plain patriotism, the NUWSS, like the WSPU, put aside temporarily its suffrage campaign and re-launched its efficient network into the fervent service of the country. They were already armed and poised for a battle; it was just a question of altering the sights a little.

Some women doctors chose pacifism, but not many.[2] Not long after the guns began to shake the earth and the wounded started to pile up, the setting up of independent medical missions that would travel into the combatant countries and care for the wounded became immediate, and even fashionable. The International Red Cross swiftly accepted offers of help with no caveats as to the gender of the doctor. Other governments suffering from the German and Austrian onslaughts, whose medical infrastructures had been unable to sustain the numbers of wounded returning from the killing fields, also gladly accepted help. In particular, the widely publicised sufferings and needs of 'gallant little Serbia', a small, landlocked country in the Balkans, whose social systems were scarcely out of peasantry but whose royal family was (as might be expected) descended from Queen Victoria, received much public sympathy. Alone of the invaded countries of Europe, the Serbian army had, miraculously, managed to repel the blue armies of the Austrian invader.[3]

Lady Ralph Paget — her husband Sir Ralph was a diplomat and had been a minister in Belgrade — was one of the first off the mark. Neither an NUWSS nor a WSPU member, in October 1914 she appealed in the press for gifts of bedding, pyjamas, bandages and cooking appliances. In November her medical mission, in part supported by the Serbian Relief Fund, under the official flag of the Red Cross and therefore non-combatant, left Waterloo station with nine surgeons and appropriate nurses, dressers and orderlies. They went by sea via Malta and Salonika in Greece, and came to Nish in Serbia before going on to Skopje, where they were set up in hospital buildings by the Serbian government and army.

The WSPU was energetically off the mark before the NUWSS; loudly supporting the patriotic Mrs St Clair Stobart and her Women's

National Service League who, even earlier in September 1914, speedily put together a mixed medical mission composed of doctors, nurses, and all other staff needed, and headed to Belgium to set up a field hospital.[4] The WSPU then plumped its support totally behind a new organisation entirely comprised of women doctors, nurses and orderlies: the Women's Hospital Corps. It was organised and headed by Dr Louisa Garrett Anderson (Elizabeth Garrett Anderson's daughter)[5] and her lifelong companion Dr Flora Murray, who had both been WSPU supporters for many years and embraced patriotism with the fervour adopted by Mrs Pankhurst's orders (in the WSPU pacifism was not an option). They, too, started by tackling the War Office, but not surprisingly, their potential services were rejected and so the medical duo swung about and offered their help to the Red Cross.[6]

As 1914 became 1915, many independently funded missions would be put together by medical men and women and placed at the service of the Red Cross. They gave their help voluntarily or received a nominal salary; not only doctors but nurses and orderlies, the latter often students and young, public-school men who wanted to serve abroad but chose not to enlist in the armed forces. Funds to buy tents, beds, blankets, dressings, cooking equipment and medical instruments were raised by public subscription.

The NUWSS weighed in with panache in late 1914 and deposited its wholehearted and wide ranging support behind Dr Elsie Inglis, a Scottish doctor and contemporary of Helen Boyle, who had studied at the London School of Medicine for Women and qualified in 1892. Dr Inglis, a lady of supreme energy and talent, though somewhat ruthless and with her own individual sense of discipline and purpose, had also independently offered her services to the War Office and had been flatly and patronisingly turned down: 'My good lady, go home and sit still!' was the response she received. But Dr Inglis was made of sterner stuff; undeterred, she would not be swayed from her determination and she persuaded the NUWSS to support the idea of not only one but a whole series of hospitals, all to be officered solely by women doctors. Boldly, the NUWSS agreed and the Scottish Women's Hospitals came into existence.

The Scottish Women's Hospitals (SWH) would become the best organised and most well-known of all the medical units staffed by women doctors in the First World War. The NUWSS had a vast network of organised and experienced women's societies. It was bigger than the WSPU and had considerably more popular support than its smaller and, at the time, none too highly regarded sister organisation, whose breaking of windows, bashing of policemen and firing of post-boxes were far less humorous to the public at that time than they seem ninety years later. Its financial resources were much greater; its political clout heavier. It was well versed in administrative expertise and funding accountability, had greater influence and power to fundraise and it had a democratic, grass roots structure rather than, as was the case with the WSPU, a charismatic and powerful leader who would tolerate criticism neither of herself nor her daughter, or their joint policies.

The Red Cross was enthusiastic about the SWH and proved to have no qualms about sending them into some of the nearer theatres of war as well as the more distant. The first SWH was opened at the abandoned Cistercian Abbey of Royaumont, twenty-five miles north of Paris, just before Christmas in 1914. The hospital, when it was cleaned up and had running water, lighting and heating installed, was attached to the French Army and received its home and colonial wounded. In 1915 Dr Inglis herself took a second SWH unit across the Mediterranean to mountainous Serbia, arriving at Kragujevatz in May.

Dr Helen Boyle left Hove for Europe in April 1915. She travelled to Serbia, not with the SWH, but to join another fully equipped medical unit officered and supported by the Royal Free Hospital under the leadership of Dr (later Sir) James Berry and his first wife F. May Dickinson Berry MD. Dr Boyle travelled to Dr Berry's unit in charge of a Ford motor car which had been donated for use in Serbia by Miss Reckitt.[7] Dr Boyle did not drive (although she had no antipathy to cars and owned several herself during her lifetime) and so Ethel Thackeray, who did service with the unit as a masseuse (physiotherapist) and Voluntary Aid Detachment (VAD) orderly, was the driver.[8]

At the time of Helen Boyle's arrival at the spa town of Vrnjatchka Banja in May 1915 (via the usual and not unpleasant route of Malta and Salonika, courtesy of the Royal Navy) there had been a lull in the fighting on the Balkan Front after the Serbian Army had sent the Austrian Army packing at the end of 1914. But the fighting had been heavy and, with its lack of hospitals and medical officers, Serbia slipped perilously into the grip of a severe typhus epidemic. British medical units, responding to the pleas for help from the Crown Prince, managed to fight the typhus with all means at their disposal; they engineered a considerable degree of success and by May 1915 the epidemic had been thankfully contained.

With no actual fighting in either field or mountain, there were no freshly wounded to attend to and during her time in Vrnjatchka Banja, and so Dr Boyle managed an outpatients' surgery for the local

Serbs — who were not immune from typhus, accident or the ravages of war upon their farmlands. Luckily Dr Berry and Mrs Gordon, the VAD nurse, could speak some Serbian. Helen Boyle recalls her experiences in chapter ten — 'The Out Patients' — of Dr Berry's book *A Red Cross Unit in Serbia* with the gaiety, wit and humour which characterises even the most solid of her medical treatises. All her life Dr Boyle retained lively memories of her time in Serbia and existing photographs of her show the long string of pearl-like beads around her neck and shoulders that she bought during her time there. Helen Boyle left Serbia on 25th August, 1915 and, at the end of the war, the Serbian government awarded her the Order of St Sava, 2nd Class.

Dr Berry's Royal Free Hospital mission remained in Serbia and eventually saw the service of some fifty volunteers: doctors (senior and junior), anaesthetists and radiographers, nurses and orderlies. It was a mixed mission of men and women surgeons and, although the nurses — all termed 'sisters'— were women, there were both men and women orderlies. The orderlies were volunteers from middle-class families; of the gentlemen orderlies one was a medical student, one a country squire who had judged the Royal Horse Show, one a professional singer and one a sculptor.

The Scottish Women's Hospitals however were entirely staffed by women as a matter of principle; no male doctors, nurses or orderlies were accepted, even to lift heavy, bedridden patients. At Royaumont Abbey an exception was made once: a former patient returned gratefully to act as a gifted but temperamental cook. Cicely Hamilton (1872–1952), a well-known actress and writer and friend of Elizabeth Robins, although a pacifist by inclination, had not been able to resist volunteering and she approached Elsie Inglis, quoting her qualifications as 'An ability to keep accounts, speak tolerable French and write adequately in that [language].' Dr Inglis, like all forceful women of her time, was well aware of Cicely Hamilton's popular if somewhat risqué reputation, and was no doubt fully conscious that her presence might well attract more donations and even volunteers. She immediately offered Miss Hamilton a job as clerk at a salary of 10s a week, and a few weeks later Miss Hamilton found herself with the advance party at the stony, dirty, freezing, ruined but spectacular medieval Royaumont Abbey in December 1914, unexpectedly elevated to the job of hospital secretary.[9]

Miss Hamilton was still there when, in August 1915, Louisa Martindale did her duty and volunteered for war service with the Scottish Women's Hospitals. Dr Martindale wrote later that she was 'divided into choosing' where her duty lay: her practice was growing and needed her presence and the LCH Brighton Branch was continually busy, so leaving for a lengthy period would mean closing hospital beds. She finally came to a happy choice, which was to volunteer for a month's locum work at the nearest SWH, which happened to be Royaumont Abbey, instead of taking her annual holiday. This would mean that a regular volunteer surgeon from Royaumont could go back to Blighty[10] for a well earned month's rest whilst Louisa could 'do her bit'.

The women who arrived at Royaumont Abbey in the winter of 1914 and early 1915 had found a damp, cold and gloomily cavernous building. There had been only straw mattresses to sleep on, only one cold water tap to be shared between everyone, and that in a distant kitchen. There had been no coal, only wood for the fires and it was arranged in true female co-operative style that each occupant of the Abbey — whether doctor, nurse or orderly — who had to ascend one of the great staircases should always carry up a log with her. The many rooms, thick with the dust and grime of ages, had to be scrubbed with brushes and pails of lukewarm water and, for months, a bath was a chilly experience to be avoided rather than welcomed. By the time Dr Martindale arrived in September 1915 however, the hospital was up and running with five wards accommodating two hundred wounded French *poilus*[11] and with operating theatres and X-ray machines on the first floor. Her autobiography includes a chapter on her time at Royaumont, which was still caring for French soldiers wounded at the Battle of the Marne earlier in 1915. The wounded came from the casualty clearing stations behind the front-line trenches via the local railway station at Creil and thence by ambulance to Royaumont Abbey. All the ambulance drivers were women.[12]

Both at Vrnjatchka Banja and Royaumont, when a job needed doing all hands were put to work and there were no divisions of labour applied by the status that would apply back home in Britain. In Serbia, Dr Berry himself was observed to sweep the courtyard and give practical help with building drains, and his wife Dr F. May Berry was admired as a superb washer-up of dishes. In Royaumont Abbey during the early days of 1915 everyone scrubbed floors and carried water, though it is difficult to see Dr Martindale taking these duties upon herself. Indeed it is not likely that at Vrnjatchka Banja Dr Boyle would have been offered any task, other than possibly supervisory, away from her out-patients' surgery.

Neither Dr Boyle nor Dr Martindale returned to active war service, although the experience was by no means lost from their lives. It had been a practical application of their medical experience and, on their return, both gave captivating lectures about their time abroad to invited and ticket purchasing audiences in order to raise funds for the Lady Chichester Hospital. Proud of their doctors' participation in the war effort, the audience rummaged deep into their pockets in gratitude for what must have been a very fine evening's entertainment, not without poignancy for those mothers and fathers whose sons — and, indeed, daughters — were still serving abroad. From the sons would come little description of their time in Europe; the conspiracy of silence which would not allow them to describe to their women the horrors of their experiences was equally binding upon the women who went alongside them.

Many women who served in Europe with the Scottish Women's Hospitals later published their wartime experiences, describing from their diaries what was frequently a mud soaked, cold and often dangerous landscape. Some of the SWH functioned under wet and dripping canvas; for months only cold and soapless water was available for bathing; inadequate and cheerless food was not unlike queasily remembered boarding school fare and clothing was continually patched and reused until the fabric made its unavoidable descent into dishrag and duster. All these are described with wry humour, unquenchable cheerfulness and an amazing energy and determination to overcome hardship which fairly zips out of the thick and tufty pages. Nowadays these war books are nearly forgotten; but if located they make wonderful, if somewhat dated, reading.

Notes

[1] Even before the war started in 1914 the WSPU's militant campaign was faltering. Christabel Pankhurst was in exile in France and Mrs Pankhurst was suffering serious political paralysis under a three year prison sentence imposed in April 1913. She was fettered by the Prisoners' (Temporary Discharge for Ill Health) Act of 1913, also known as the Cat and Mouse Act, which tackled the problem of the notorious force-feeding of women prisoners on hunger strike by releasing them from prison under licence, usually to return in a week. The offenders had to register their addresses with the police and obtain permission to be away from home for more than twelve hours. Failure to do so would result in immediate re-arrest.

[2] Some women associated with the suffrage movement were not so ready to serve their country. The International Women's Suffrage Alliance and its journal *Jus Suffragi* experienced some considerable pressure from many suffragist members of the NUWSS to embrace pacifism. On the whole it resisted. The Socialist Women's Congress of April 1915 held in Berne in neutral Switzerland, also came across division in its ranks of delegates: Margaret Bondfield MP, the old friend and protégée of Mrs Martindale, attended but was strongly criticised for her public assertion that Britain had gone to war only to defend Belgium. The Russian women socialists present also condemned the war. Later in April 1915 the International

Congress of Women held in The Hague, Holland (also a neutral country) provided a major attempt by women pacifists to meet and to discuss how women could make a real effort to find solutions to the war. It was, however, deemed a failure: the British women, dubbed 'Cranquettes' and 'Peacettes' by the press, never got there because the British Government placed an embargo upon ferries leaving Tilbury. Mrs Pankhurst, witheringly scornful, said: 'What we criticise is the holding of the Conference at all. We are perfectly satisfied and have information which supports the belief that the whole thing has been engineered by agents of Germany. I am very glad that the cancellation of the service has made it impossible for Englishwomen to attend [and am] glad to say that no one officially connected with the Women's Social and Political Union or prominent in it has had anything to do with the Congress.'

[3] It was actually a Serbian nationalist who had assassinated Archduke Ferdinand and his wife Sophia in Sarajevo in August 1914, and so started the dreadful slide into Europe-wide hostilities. Living not in free Serbia, but under Austrian rule in Slovenia, nevertheless he was a Serb and his action was the excuse for Austria's invasion of Serbia in July 1914. This fact was frequently pointed out in grumbling letters to newspapers in Britain during early calls for support for 'gallant little Serbia'.

[4] Mrs St Clair Stobart was a patriot who founded the Women's Sick and Wounded Convoy Corps to help soldiers on the battlefield who had seen action in the Balkans War in 1912. The WSWCC became the National Service League and in September 1914 under the Red Cross went to Belgium and set up a hospital. It was overrun by advancing German troops and retreated to Brussels setting up a hospital there.

> 'Mrs St Clair Stobart was arrested as a British spy in Brussels, where she had established a British Red Cross hospital. She was thrust into prison, being led forth on the third day, expecting to be shot or imprisoned. A kindly German officer, however, allowed her to cross the Dutch frontier. She next established a base hospital at Antwerp and quitted the city on top of a munitions wagon, the last vehicle to leave during the German bombardment'. (*The Times*, 6th March 1915)

Undaunted, Mrs St Clair Stobart then set up a hospital for the French Army and having done that crossed the Mediterranean and went on to establish a field hospital in Serbia. Riding a black horse at the head of one of the columns she accompanied the Serbian Army during the bitter retreat over 800 miles of mountains in the winter of 1915. It seems very likely that the 'kindly' officer who back in Belgium 'allowed' her to escape, was probably very relieved to see such a formidable woman leave. Mrs St Clair Stobart survived the war and became a well-known writer and spiritualist.

[5] Louisa Garrett Anderson was also the niece of Mrs Henry Fawcett (née Millicent Garrett) of the NUWSS.

[6] The Women's Hospital Corps with Dr Louisa Garrett Anderson and Dr Flora Murray was housed at Claridge's Hotel in Paris from 16th September 1914. This occupation lasted until January 1915, dealing mostly with Belgian refugees. It then moved to a hotel in Wimereaux. The Corps later returned to London and at the invitation of the army set up as a general military hospital in an old workhouse building in Endell Street, where it remained for the duration of the war. All staff

of the hospital were women, but they were under the not always happy command of the Royal Army Medical Corps. Initially denied commissions in the army and given no tax relief under the Service Acts, such as was given to the serving officers and men of the RAMC, a campaign for equal recognition began. After the war they were each awarded the CBE. By 1918 commissions were granted to the women doctors for the duration, and the tax relief given. Women doctors were not officially recognised as officers in the Royal Army Medical Corps until 1939.

[7] There is no record of any wealthy Reckitt family in Sussex at that time. It is most likely that the donor of the car was Miss Juliet Reckitt (1870–1955), a daughter of the wealthy Quaker family of Hull who made their fortune from the starch and blue factory before becoming the Reckitt-Colman industrial manufacturer. Mr Isaac Reckitt, aged 93 in the year 2003, who had been acquainted with Miss Reckitt, suggested when asked: 'Yes, that would have been just like Juliet!' Miss Reckitt was a generous benefactor and today there are almshouses which bear her name. Thanks to the Reckitt-Colman family archivist and Mr Isaac Reckitt.

[8] Miss Ethel Thackeray may have been a daughter of Colonel T. M. G. Thackeray and his wife Louisa who lived in St Aubyn's in Hove at the end of the nineteenth century. The colonel seems to have died and Mrs Thackeray moved to 27 Church Road, not too far from Dr Boyle at number 37. No more is known about Ethel Thackeray, but she is mentioned as attending a lecture titled *Three Months in Serbia*, given at Hove Town Hall by Dr Boyle in November 1915. (Details from 1901 Census, directories at Brighton and Hove Libraries and the *Sussex Daily News*.)

[9] Cicely Hamilton's plays, *How the Vote was Won* and *The Pageant of Great Women*, were very popular, and her book *Marriage as a Trade* (1909) became a feminist landmark. She was a member of the Women's Freedom League, a new women's suffrage society formed after the great secession from Mrs Pankhurst's WSPU by the 'moderates' led by Mrs Charlotte Despard (a sister of Sir John French) in 1907. See Whitelaw, L. (1990) *The Life and Rebellious Times of Cicely Hamilton,* The Women's Press.

[10] An affectionate, slang term for Britain, current during the First and Second World Wars.

[11] French slang for a private soldier: the British soldiers were called Tommies after Tommy Atkins who was a mythical but archetypal soldier invented by the Duke of Wellington in the Napoleonic wars.

[12] The ambulance drivers were mostly members of the First Aid Nursing Yeomanry (FANY).

9

THE WAR AT HOME

In March 1914, at the age of seventy-five, Mrs Louisa Martindale died at her home, Cheeleys, in the village of Horsted Keynes in West Sussex. Denying the seriousness of her illness, she was not at all anxious about herself and seemed to be more interested in the latest deeds of Mrs Pankhurst, whom she had from time to time invited to speak at garden parties at her house. Nevertheless, her daughter was alarmed and installed two nurses in the house, insisting (although her mother did not heed her words) that she organise a male consultant to be driven over from Brighton. It was to no avail. With the miracle of antibiotics still to be discovered Dr Martindale was powerless to save her mother and, in spite of the arrival of an oxygen cylinder, nothing could be done.

A 'Service for the Living' was held in the village hall and part of that service was taken by a woman since Mrs Martindale, typically, had believed in the ordination of women into the church (that momentous change being further away even than the discovery of penicillin). She was buried in the churchyard of St Giles in Horsted Keynes, where her grave can easily be found beneath a striking blue granite Celtic cross beside a tree and hedge near the church. Her house does not survive but there is a new housing estate called 'Cheeleys' in the village, which must surely be where the house once stood. There is a pleasant building named the Martindale Centre set back from the road leading into the village, which in still in good use. In her will Mrs Martindale left £500 to the Lady Chichester Hospital, Brighton Branch, to pay off some pressing debts.

Writing in her autobiography thirty years later, Dr Martindale cannot hide the desolation and grief which she felt after her mother's death. Her friends were deeply concerned. Towards the end of April 1914, Murdie Murdoch and Ismay FitzGerald took her to Italy to participate at the International Council of Women conference in Rome where both Louisa and Murdie were scheduled to speak. It was being held in Rome and they drove down through Basle, Lucerne and Lugarno with a stop at Lake Como. Although she managed the road trip through Switzerland and Italy, Louisa found herself unable to face the conference. She returned home alone leaving Ismay and Murdie in Rome.

The love between mother and daughter had always risen above the occasional tensions. She describes her mother as always being 'divinely dissatisfied with my progress' and, indeed, in 1914 Louisa Martindale was forty-one years old and progress, although good, was not spectacular. Now well established in Brighton with her own town property, a fine circle of personal and professional acquaintances and the lease on 'Colin Godman's' (a handsome but remote cottage in the wilds of Sussex with no conveniences but very popular with friends from London for weekends), she had made no steps to further her career in the manner which her mother had continually urged: to start up a consulting practice in London. That she had reached her fifth decade and was still in general practice in Brighton with honorary work only at the Lady Chichester Hospital, Brighton Branch, seems not to have weighed upon her — although her interest in the use of X-rays to combat cancer was certainly slowly maturing — and it is quite in keeping with Mrs Martindale's character that it was the mother who had been the more dissatisfied of the two.

A little older than Louisa, at age forty-five, Helen Boyle's career was not dissimilar. She too was reaching the age when a physician and surgeon should begin to enjoy a certain acknowledgement of seniority in the profession, when good money and prestige should begin to accumulate hopefully alongside a bundle of gratifying honours. By 1914 Dr Boyle did, however, have a unique advantage: her own hospital, although, counter-productively, it was in a field with less of the spotlight attracted by medicine and surgery.

It was time for Louisa Martindale to catch up. The progression of medical science had accelerated at a phenomenal rate during the war years as the X-ray machine leapt into mass production. Marie Curie had toured the battlefields with a mobile unit of her own design that she had built inside a truck and in the operating theatre the latest aseptic techniques, with rubber gloves and sterile steel instruments, had replaced the older and more clumsy antiseptic methodology of the lavish application of carbolic acid spray (except in the prevention of gangrene). The administration of ether or chloroform to induce anaesthesia was used alongside muscle relaxants, such as curare, and surgical operations were now performed within the deepest recesses of the body. Post-operative care, as well as the care of the patient during its effects, had become considerably more skilled and many patients were undergoing complex operations that had not even been heard of only ten years before.

Psychiatry then, as often now, was a branch of medicine not always popular either with doctors or the public; but in this field, too, a change was coming. As the war years ground past a new class of patient arrived home from the trenches: men suffering from all kinds of acute nervous disorders; sleeplessness and screaming nightmares, loss of speech, uncontrollable shaking limbs, inability to eat, fear of noise, fear of silence, and a new malady — shell shock. The important realisation that with early and appropriate treatment these men could be cured put them squarely into the class of recoverable mental breakdown which, however reluctantly and to the disbelieving huffing and puffing of some generals, would have to be treated by the army. The importance of getting the mentally wounded soldiers well as soon as possible was recognised and an Act of Parliament, the Mental Treatment Act of 1915, made it possible for serving men to be able to receive psychiatric treatment before they had become certifiable.

This was exactly what Helen Boyle had been saying for years: that borderland mental illness caused by stress, worry, exposure to unbearable accidents and terrifying sights and sounds, could cause breakdown and ought to be remedied by early treatment before certifiable insanity set in. However, civilian women were not protected by the new law and it did not help that filling the short-term post of house physician at the Lady Chichester, Hove Branch, became difficult. In 1914 Miss Woodcock is listed as consulting physician but there is no house physician and when Dr Boyle enjoyed her adventure in Serbia, Dr Lillian Harris took over the reins at the Hove Branch.

The increase in number of distressed women patients treated by Hove Branch did not decline and a steady stream of women victims of the war were admitted to Brunswick Place. Many women whose husbands had been sucked into the conflict engulfing all of Europe from the Atlantic to the Caspian Sea faced news of death or serious wounding with a despair that they could not bear and broke down. The hardships and difficulties of having to cope with the loss of a husband, and yet still having to house, feed and clothe her children with little or no income could often shatter a woman's mental health if she were left to bear her losses unaided. In addition, shell shock could also strike children who had been the victims of civilian bombing: in one case a child of five who had been in a tram that was struck by a bomb was seriously affected. There were also cases of mental breakdown in adult women engaged in war work in factories, the land army and the uniformed services such as the railways, the police and the postal services. There were nurses, too, who had become unwell, women of the VAD and ambulance drivers who had been the victims of shell-fire whilst working near the front line or who had faced and survived a watery death by torpedo on a troop or hospital ship. Sir Robert Armstrong-Jones praised the Lady

Chichester Hospital publicly for its work with the forgotten women left at home or invalided out of war work to cope as best they could.

By 1915 the Hove Branch of the Lady Chichester Hospital at Brunswick Place was full, there was a waiting list for beds, and Dr Christine Shearer arrived in Hove to take up the position of assistant physician. It was seriously short of funds and, in a move which would have been very contrary to Dr Boyle's wishes, the situation was deemed to have become so serious that patients could not be admitted at all unless they could pay something, however small, towards their stay. Those who really were too poor to pay anything were encouraged to apply for relief from charitable bodies, or rather the referring doctors could do so on their behalf before suggesting admission.[1]

A year previously at Ditchling Road the Brighton Branch had admitted 216 patients and carried out 146 surgical operations in spite of the patriotic but early departure of Miss Clayton, the theatre sister, who served at the 2nd Eastern General Military Hospital at 30 Dyke Road for the duration. But on the ground floor of number 6 the cost of medication to callers at the outpatients' rose from 3d to 6d, the first rise since 1899 and, at a hundred per cent, a steep and disturbing increase.

Shortages of materials and supplies followed by the inevitable price rises underlined the financial concern. A hospital already struggling to pay its way would encounter in no small way the same difficulties as the civilian population in wartime; the War Office always took a major slice of any available supplies, whether comestible or medical. Feeding and clothing the forces took priority and both Branches of the little Lady Chichester Hospital down at the bottom of the heap would always struggle as the price of meat, eggs, milk and butter all shot up but had to be met if patients were to be fed. New linen for bandages and sheets became more expensive; towards the end 'launder, match and mend' would be routine for dressings, and everyone, including former patients, would buckle down and help out. The ready availability of drugs diminished and even the larger civilian hospitals with more funds at their disposal experienced difficulties as prices escalated. One jarring note: at Hove Branch the house physician was H. Maurice, Esquire, a dentist practising at 47 Church Road. He was a neighbour and no doubt a friend of Dr Boyle and his appointment may have been attributable to the exigencies of the war, but for the first time an officer of the Lady Chichester Hospital was not a woman.

At the Brighton Branch Miss Louisa Aldrich-Blake lent a hand as the consulting surgeon. Now promoted to the high-status job of Dean of the LSMW after the death of Dr Julia Cock, she remained a friend of Louisa Martindale until her own early death in 1924 soon after being awarded the DBE. The medical officer was Dr Edmonds and Dr Christine Shearer came over from the Hove Branch as assistant anaesthetist, helping out Mrs Scatliff.

It was Hove Branch which felt the pinch most acutely. The 1915 account shows an income of £1,290 against an expenditure of £1,732, a shortfall of just under £450. It is possible that some regular subscribers had withdrawn their support; reporting the news of the overdraft at the 1915 Annual Meeting Lady Chichester called for more subscribers and for more efforts to find new ones, and a document was circulated which enabled a bequest (hopefully, a handsome one) to be made to the hospital in the event of death.

The finances at the Brighton Branch were in better order: the income for 1915 was £1,220 compared with £1,247 the previous year, a decrease of £27, by no means as gloomy as the deficit suffered by the Hove Branch. Nevertheless, the writing was on the wall and the increase in hospital charges, as well as the doubling of the cost of medicines for the outpatients at Ditchling Road, was there to stay. Fundraising continued, enhanced by the lectures on war service by Dr Martindale and Dr Boyle, and Miss Elizabeth Robins turned her experienced writer's hand to a new appeal for the Brighton Branch picturing on the front page a handsome Pre-Raphaelite figure of a woman embracing all three houses: 4, 6 and 8 Ditchling Road. The appeal, which refers obliquely to the death of Mrs Martindale and directly to the war, is headed in clarion tones 'What Can I Do?' and describes the hospital:

> Bright sunny rooms, pleasantly furnished; Lawson Tait[2] beds, enamel and glass lockers, electric bells to every bed, and, to every bed, electric light switches. The little operating theatre is perfect of its kind, and all surgical cases have up to this time healed by first attention. There is no atmosphere of grim institution; the waiting room is 'a kind of cheerful club' to those who wait, and 'several in-patients have volunteered the information that their stay in The Lady Chichester has been the happiest time of their life'.

Miss Robins added some history of women in medicine, and underlined the joy women felt to be treated by members of their own sex. The appeal is a delight to read: it bowls along merrily with a delicate turn of phrase and would make a great deal of sense to local dignitaries and their wives. However, it focuses entirely on the Brighton Branch and a fresh reader would be hard put to recognise that the Lady Chichester Hospital cared for the mind as well as the body, and offered another hospital for women where the officers were as highly trained, qualified and caring as any at Ditchling Road.[3]

Fundraising, even in wartime, had to go on. On 15th April 1915 the *Sussex Daily News* chirped cheerfully that Elizabeth Robins had organised a splendid evening entertainment and performance at Henfield Assembly Rooms, near her Sussex home, 'assisted ably by her young friend Octavia Wilberforce'. The entertainment boasted a brisk piano recital by Miss Jean Campion (which included the rendition of some ragtime to get the feet tapping) and there was a musical sketch by Mr Norman Richards. Miss Fannie Wood played, no doubt sweetly, on the violin and Mr Stacey Aumonier gave character sketches of artistic merit. Miss Robins herself entertained with a reading from *Uncle Remus*, featuring Brer Fox and Brer Rabbit. The whole merry event was rounded off with Mr H. W. Nevison's description of The Fighting Life.

Following this dazzling event, a more sedate, two day sale of work was held at Ditchling Road, opened on the first day by Lady Chichester and on the second by that other great lady of Brighton, Mrs Thomas-Stanford of Preston Manor. The speakers at the opening ceremony paid tribute to Mrs Martindale; in particular Mrs Corbett, who made a cash donation on behalf of her old friend and who in doing so declared that she owed to Mrs Martindale 'the satisfaction of doing any public work'. She then proposed the vote of thanks to Lady Chichester. Louisa Martindale seconded the vote, no doubt pleased with the £62 that was raised on the first day.[4]

Sales of work were popular with everyone and like most fundraising events chimed nicely with a good afternoon out. They were not dissimilar to church hall jumble sales, except that almost all items sold would have been new, but handmade at home. For a small fee, stalls were hired by the many women's organisations to display their work which visitors were expected to buy. These would include knitted or embroidered items such as handkerchiefs, collars and tablecloths as well as other useful articles such as egg cosies, painted picture frames and hand-woven baskets and rugs. A few unwanted items — books and old lampshades — might also sneak their way onto the stall top. Afternoon refreshments were served at a tea stall, and there would have been much rivalry over which lady had donated the most delicious cake. It was mandatory for the celebrity who opened the sale to be most complimentary about the high quality of the work, to buy a few choice items, and praise 'the delicious spread'. This particular sale of work was held at and raised money for the Brighton Branch, and is a clear pointer that the funds raised would stay there and not be shared with the Hove Branch.

As 1915 turned into 1916 Sir Douglas Haig was putting together his plans for the summer campaign in France (an assault which would be called the Battle of the Somme) and the Hove Branch again had difficulty in finding physicians. Both consulting and house posts were unfilled and Dr Boyle and Mrs Harris were no doubt very overworked at 70 Brunswick Place. In Brighton and Hove other hospitals had sprung up to take care of the wounded; the town's closeness to London and its good rail links, along with the sea, fresh air and sunshine had made it a good choice for the repair of battle-torn and wounded men. The workhouse infirmary on Race Hill had been taken over by the War Office in 1914 for use first by Indian and later by regular army wounded (the Indians were later moved into the Royal Pavilion), and the 2nd Eastern General Hospital spilled over from Dyke Road into Portland Road. There was a small hospital for wounded officers in The Drive and the many convalescent homes for other officers were doing very good business. All attracted charitable support and alongside this activity the Lady Chichester Hospital experienced the usual efforts to keep the money rolling in. In her speech at the 1917 annual meeting for subscribers Lady Chichester emphasised the uniqueness of the Hove Branch, which — she candidly admitted — had been somewhat of an experiment when it had first opened, but could amply justify its existence by continuing to treat women who were equally suffering, but rather from the wounds of deprivation and grief. The Brighton Branch, she added, had provided valuable training for women doctors in surgery and medicine now so badly needed.[5] But, as usual, funds were disturbingly absent with £468 still owed to the bank.

At the Brighton Branch in Ditchling Road Dr Alice Ley Greaves took up a post as house physician (she later worked behind the scenes as a pathologist at the Royal Sussex County), living with and possibly assistant to Dr Edmonds at 5 Brunswick Place. There was no drying up of the stream of patients — 150 operations had been carried out — but the finances were unsteady and nearly £303 in deficit. The Hove Branch was beginning to face an even more serious problem: the lease of 70 Brunswick Place was due to expire in 1918 and there was no chance of a renewal. Another move would inevitably have to be made, and soon, not a prospect to be viewed with equanimity.

As the noise of the guns in Western Europe began to diminish and the possibility of the war ending became reality, a different clatter of gunfire would make itself heard at the Lady Chichester Hospital. The 1918 Annual Meeting would be an historic one and its echoes reverberate coldly down the years even now. On 24th October 1918, at the Sussex Pioneer Club in New Road,[6] Lady Chichester addressed the subscribers, medical staff and other interested bodies all gathered and present. She stated that because of 'confusion in the minds of the public between the two Branches in Hove and Brighton, and also between the medical and surgical branch and the hospital at Chichester [7] the Joint Council had resolved that the two Branches become separate, independent, and working as two hospitals.[8]

Notes

[1] Helen Boyle was not averse to taking immediate advantage of any sudden opportunity to collect funds on behalf of the hospital. In 1918 Miss Beatrice Gordon Holmes (1884–1951) arrived in Brighton to convalesce after an appendectomy in London and her woman surgeon — sadly, she does not name her — had recommended Dr Boyle to supervise the convalescence. Miss Holmes was well on her way to becoming the first woman stockbroker; later she would have her own financial house in the City of London and become a successful financier enjoying a wealthy international lifestyle with high fashion and a litter of celebrities at her handsomely-gloved fingertips. Upon arrival at the bedside and after a crisp examination, Dr Boyle engaged her patient in the obligatory few words of social chat during which Miss Holmes happened to drop the word 'finance'. She was then immediately introduced to a long description of the Lady Chichester Hospital and its continual need for money. Miss Holmes was captivated by this 'little dark woman in glasses' and even from her convalescent bed immediately came up with an idea: 'get someone to promise you £25 provided that you get another nine to promise you the same.' After the convalescence Dr Boyle promptly asked Miss Holmes to stay a while with her in Hove to try to raise more money for the hospital. Miss Holmes did so and her ideas and energy eventually raised several thousand pounds for the Hove Branch. Dr Boyle later appointed her 'honorary financial organiser' to the hospital, a title which she enthusiastically enjoyed, and they remained friends for many years. Miss Holmes's autobiography *In Love With Life* is warmly dedicated to Dr Helen Boyle. She founded the Business and Professional Women's Association <www.bpwuk.co.uk> which is still in successful existence. Holmes, B. G. (1944) *In Love With Life — A Pioneer Career Woman's Story.* Hollis and Carter, London. Chapter XVIII.
[2] Dr Robert Lawson-Tait (1845–1899) was a well-known gynaecologist and a pioneer in abdominal surgery who could also clearly turn his hand to a spot of designing. He was an anti-vivisectionist and a great believer in asepsis — the liberal use of soap and water and iodine before operating, rather than antisepsis — the application of carbolic acid when the operation was over. He was a supporter of women doctors and frequently employed them as his assistants.
[3] In January 1915 the local Dr Barnado's Home, the Brighton and Hove Habitation, held a sale of work at Hove Town Hall. Helen Boyle attended and was placed third in precedence by the *Sussex Daily News* reporter, after the Mayor and Mayoress of Hove. *Sussex Daily News* 28 January 1915.
[4] *Sussex Daily News* 29 May 1915.
[5] In fact the need for trained doctors and dentists to treat the soaring number of war-wounded had become so great that some of the London teaching hospitals — St Mary's, Charing Cross, St George's, Westminster, St Bartholomew's, the London,

King's College and University Hospital — all opened their doors to women. However, most did so with the proviso that this was 'for the duration only' and at the end of hostilities the doors started to slam shut.

[6] The Pioneer Club was a women's club in London. By 1918 the aims and objectives of its members included the acquisition of the parliamentary vote for all women. Founded about 1876 by Mrs Massingberd, the Pioneer Club was part of a thriving network of women's clubs which had sprung up in London to offer comfortable reading, dining and drawing-rooms to middle-class women, as White's and Boodle's offered them to men. There were bedrooms for overnight accommodation, educational classes, and a dress code which included short hair, upright posture and tailored frocks. Nicknames were used and alcohol was very absent. Men could be invited to 'At Homes' on Wednesday afternoons. The Pioneer Club in Brighton seems to have been founded by Mrs Martindale and was situated in rooms at 4 New Road. No doubt it was less grand than its London namesake, probably being simply a set of rooms to which women could retire privately if required. There was a meeting room which could be hired by members. 'Home and away: the Feminist Remapping of Public and Private Space in Victorian London' by Lynne Walker in Rosa Ainley, ed. (1998) *New Frontiers of Space, Bodies and Gender*, Routledge.

[7] This 'hospital at Chichester' so disingenuously pitched into the plot by her ladyship, was officially known in 1918 as the Royal West Sussex County Hospital, and was situated at Broyle Road in Chichester. The 'Royal' garnish was gained during the war. At the turn of the nineteenth century the hospital had been known as the West Sussex, East Hampshire and Chichester Infirmary and Dispensary, but by 1911 had become re-styled as the West Sussex, East Hampshire and Chichester General Infirmary. These changes of title and name were blithely ignored by both ordinary and not so ordinary folk, who naturally continued to speak of it as the Chichester Infirmary, which just goes to show that Lady Chichester might, or might not, have had a point.

[8] East Sussex Records Office HB 63/1A.

10

SEPARATION

The formal announcement of an impending separation between the Brighton and Hove Branches of the Lady Chichester Hospital must have come as no surprise to most of the subscribers present that evening, and can by no means have been the bombshell that it appears. The ostensible reason — that having two hospitals with the same name in Brighton and Hove caused confusion in the minds of the public — although not without a certain element of truth, was clearly a whitewash intended for public consumption. Lady Chichester went on to say that the hospital at Ditchling Road would be renamed the New Sussex (it seems to have been given this name as a temporary measure for public consumption since no permanent decision had yet been made) leaving the name 'the Lady Chichester' for the Hove Branch.

With the war winding down, 1918 might not have been a good time to impose such a change upon the people of Brighton and Hove, as the downside was that — inevitably — more not less money would be needed. Two independent establishments within a few miles of each other would result in an even fiercer scramble for subscribers and donations and, of course, supplies of ready and willing volunteers to help out when required. In 1918 Brighton and Hove were already awash with war charities, and not only those seeking to aid wounded men and officers, whose nursing and convalescent homes were always eager for help and support. The RSPCA and its Fund for Sick and Wounded Horses also looked for donations, as did other hospitals and sanitary societies, and organisations catering for poor girls, orphaned boys, distressed gentlewomen, Belgian and Serbian refugees and lost cats and dogs. The list of local needy causes was always growing. The two branches had for some time carried out their own fundraising; would it be so different now with the change of names? Probably the lines had already been drawn.

The circumstances surrounding the break-up of the two branches have a bitter taste about them even in the small amount of documentation that has survived. It manifests itself more by an absence of goodwill than outright hostility; an outline rather than a mass of solid evidence. The enormous scientific advances in the treatment of the sick and wounded would have been well known to Louisa Martindale. Her experience of work at Royaumont Abbey, with its opportunities for bigger, better and more successful surgery, could well have caused her to look again at the three cramped houses in Ditchling Road. Maybe her ambitions at last sprang into action and the prospect of moving an independent Brighton Branch out of the confines of Ditchling Road and into premises more keenly resembling the New Hospital in North London[1] and the South London Hospital for Women in Clapham,[2] fired up her vision. Brighton, too, would have a modern and indeed prestigious women's hospital. However, things were not as simple as they appear on the surface

In reality a newly built women's hospital had been in the planning stages for a whole year before the separation was formally announced. As far back into the war years as December 1917, a Site and Buildings sub-committee, separate from the Brighton Branch Executive Committee,[3] (which was itself separate from the Lady Chichester Hospital Joint Council) had already been put together and was meeting regularly at Dr Martindale's house, 10 Marlborough Place. Dr Boyle and the Hove Branch were not involved.

Mr C. E. Clayton, a local architect,[4] along with Sir William Gentle, a magistrate and one time Chief Constable of Brighton,[5] had already made an investigative visit to Clapham, on behalf of the sub-committee, to look at the South London Hospital for Women. They were 'favourably impressed', and by mid 1918 a tentative plan for building a brand new women's hospital in Brighton had been already drawn up. Both the New Hospital and the South London Hospital had been purpose built from an architect's design. Was this the way to go? If so, where would the money come from?

Momentous disagreements are often caused by subjects such as religion, sex or money. Religion was never a talking point amongst medical women, generally there was an agreed policy that these matters would not be brought to the workplace. Sex was not talked about — at least not in public. This leaves money, and back in 1917 in Brighton there had suddenly been a good chance that a great deal of it was about to wash about when Sir John Howard, a very rich man who was genuinely loved for his compassion and generosity and who had lived for many years in Preston, just north of Brighton, died at his home on 20th April 1917. A successful businessman and philanthropist, in his will he left £40,000 — then a very large sum of money — to be invested in a legacy fund for the benefit of local medical institutions.[6] The fund was to be administered by several trustees and a part of it was, by the terms of the will, to benefit local hospitals, both for men and women, and to be used 'for one purpose'. A sudden and unlooked-for opportunity to acquire a generous amount of cash had fortuitously arrived; and it was money that could well be used to build a new hospital. All that was needed was to meet the terms of the will and to submit, without delay, an application to the legacy fund trustees. Someone at the Brighton Branch of the Lady Chichester Hospital was very quick off the mark and did just that.

It cannot be without significance that Mr Clayton, the architect chosen to design the proposed new hospital, had also been the designer for Sir John Howard's Nurses' Home in Kemp Town. He would have known Sir John personally and probably knew the provisions of his will. So it is not improbable that it was Mr Clayton who told Louisa Martindale about the legacy fund soon after Sir John's death, enabling the Brighton Branch to get in an early bid.

An appeal called 'What Can I Do?',[7] written by Elizabeth Robins and published in the early years of the war, referred to the death of Mrs Martindale — 'One of the most generous friends of this Institution has just died' — as well as to the war, but it included only scant mention of the work of the Hove Branch as an 'allied establishment', although Miss Robins did follow up with a footnote 'for Treatment of Nervous Diseases under the direction of Dr Helen Boyle'. But during the later years of the war the Lady Chichester Hospital Joint Council was most likely to have been primarily concerned with the consequences of the expiry of the lease of 70 Brunswick Place and the house committee for the Hove Branch would surely with a single mind address itself to this thorny situation. Regrettably, no notes of any meeting have survived. Whatever actually happened, even if by then it was well understood that each Branch would address itself strictly to its own internal and funding problems and so not necessarily have any responsibility for those of the other, at this time it was the Hove Branch that would have been experiencing the more savagely pressing need for funds. When the Brighton Branch, with no apparent qualms about the looming homelessness of its sister Branch, slipped in first with its own independent bid for a slice of the Sir John Howard cash in order to build a new hospital — which cash after probate and any other legalities to be settled would be available most satisfactorily in about a year's time in 1918 — it must have been a very vinegary pill indeed for Dr Boyle and the house committee of the Hove Branch to have to swallow.

The minutes of the Site and Buildings sub-Committee of the Brighton Branch, most of which have survived,[8] indicate that a final separation of the Lady Chichester Hospital into two establishments was not originally of its seeking. The sub-committee did indeed want to build a new hospital for surgical and medical cases along the same lines as the South London Hospital for Women, but there seems to have been no original intent that the two Branches should change from being complementary, albeit independent, parts of one Lady Chichester Hospital for Women and Children. However as 1917 swung into 1918, it became obvious that the acceptance of money from the legacy fund would also mean the acceptance of any conditions that the trustees were minded to impose when carrying out the terms of Sir John Howard's will. One of these, it appeared, was that only one Branch of the Lady Chichester Hospital should benefit, and by August 1918, when the money was about to become available, the trustees were hinting strongly that they would prefer a complete separation of the Brighton from the Hove Branch. If the Site and Buildings sub-Committee wanted its new hospital it would have to abandon the Hove Branch and become totally independent. The problems that this would cause might well be unpleasant and come to divide not only old friends but colleagues and even subscribers. Yet it seems most likely that a complete separation had been looming for some considerable time and that this eventuality was already widely accepted.

The minutes of the annual meetings indicate that Helen Boyle did not ever work at the Ditchling Road Outpatients': after 1908 she ceases to be mentioned as an honorary medical officer at the former Dispensary in Lewes Road, although she can hardly be blamed for that. Dr Jones left in about 1908, leaving her to carry on her general practice by herself. It is a long haul to Ditchling Road from Hove and she was very busy with her work at Roundhill Crescent and then later in Brunswick Place. The responsibility for the shifts at the Dispensary would have fallen heavily upon Dr Martindale and although the arrival of Mrs Scatliff in 1910 alleviated this it may well be that Dr Boyle, after leaving the Dispensary and re-organising the Hospital's move to Brunswick Place in Hove, was also deemed to have relinquished her interests in the Brighton Branch's future. Possibly Mrs Martindale (still alive at that time and very much involved with the dispensary) had not been pleased and may even have felt hurt by Dr Boyle's absence. The one thing that Louisa Martindale would never have pardoned was treachery of some kind towards her mother. Was this slipping away of Dr Boyle in some way the cause of a tangible but unfocussed rift between them, a warmth missing, a lack of acknowledgement, an invisibility towards each other's presence? All kinds of disagreements and grudges, either personal or professional, could be forgiven and forgotten over the years, but never a wound, either real or imagined, to her mother.

The decision to lay hands on the Sir John Howard legacy money and start up independently would be a mighty one and if left to the ladies of the site and buildings sub-committee to deal with, without the injection of firm leadership, they may well have wavered. But Louisa Martindale was convinced, and it is at this point in the story of the two women's hospitals that she steps into centre stage.

Dr Martindale herself kept the notes of the early sub-committee meetings; they are written in her own hand, a large and bold writing which makes all efforts to take down precisely what other members were saying but, being human, does sometimes disintegrate into illegibility. Granted, meetings at Marlborough Place would have been best for everyone, being most conveniently situated in central Brighton but, nevertheless, on her own turf she was in a good position to sway the possibly more timid minds of other sub-committee members. She emerges very much as the prime mover, organiser and power behind the sub-committee's programme and seems to have developed a talent for interesting herself not only in the medical aspects of the hospital, but also the structure. Bricks and mortar, plumbing, painting, provisions and the employment of nursing staff all came under her gaze; not by nature ever excitable or impulsive, at this time in her life she was able to lift herself into a position of leadership and find the ability to weather difficult decisions and to carry the committee with her. Reserves of energy, patience and vision would be called upon in the months to come and were found. The notes of the meetings show that she was in favour of the final separation, as was her friend Ismay FitzGerald, who could be counted upon to give Louisa the public support and loyalty that might be required.

A milestone was reached on 26th August 1918, when the site and building sub-committee met with the Brighton Branch executive committee, at 10 Marlborough Place. They took a collective deep breath and tackled the thorny and distressing problem of the future of the entire Lady Chichester Hospital complex. Those present were Elizabeth Robins — always managing to get to a meeting if dramatic happenings were anticipated — as Chairman of the Brighton Branch executive committee, Mr and Mrs F. E. Cobb, Mrs Godfree, the Hon. Ismay FitzGerald, Mrs Catherine Ryle, Miss F. de Gaudrion Merrifield, Mr Clayton, Miss Turner (the Ditchling Road voluntary secretary), Dr Martindale, Mrs Scatliff and Dr Florence Edmonds.

From the beginning the new hospital leaned towards Liberal politics and selected for its women leaders those active in pursuit of independence for women, their demands for entry into all professions and the parliamentary vote. Miss F. de Gaudrion Merrifield was the secretary of the Brighton and Hove Women's Franchise Society and involved with the Ladies' National Sanitary Society; Miss M. E. Verrall was honorary secretary of both the Brighton Ladies' Association for the care of Friendless Girls and the Girls' Friendly Society;[9] Mrs Catherine Ryle was married to a local doctor (the Ryle family, along with the Verralls, and later the Eggars, produced solid solicitors as well as dedicated doctors); and Mr F. E. Cobb was a businessman and one-time mayor of Brighton. The great news was that the bid for the Sir John Howard legacy had been successful and an advance offer of £5,000 had been received from the trustees. Their delicate suggestion that they would prefer a complete separation of the Hove and Brighton Branches was presented to the meeting by Mr Cobb and supported by Mr Clayton, the architect. The minutes reveal that Mr Cobb added:

> In view of what had happened during the last few months, it was plainly impossible that we should continue our building scheme unless we completely severed ourselves from the Hove Branch.[10]

The details of 'what had happened' have — tantalisingly — not survived; but whatever it was everyone deplored it and, clearly, a nasty taste had been left in the mouth. It is not difficult to speculate that an exchange of unpleasantness over the award of the Howard legacy to the Brighton Branch had occurred. The possibility and advisability of separation was discussed, and all were aware of the grave importance of their deliberations and that this meeting would be a momentous occasion. Mr and Mrs Cobb and Mrs Ryle were openly in favour of the separation; others were unsure. After a somewhat feeble suggestion by Dr Edmonds that the whole matter should be placed on the agenda of a meeting of the Lady Chichester Joint Hospital Council, Miss Turner added rather unhelpfully that in fact separation of the two Branches was a constitutional matter and as such could only be decided at an annual meeting of subscribers.

Dr Martindale, having done her homework since she had not been in Brighton either in 1899 or in 1905 when the first hospital opened in Roundhill Crescent, swiftly despatched this argument by replying that in fact no constitution existed. Sadly, one must feel, this was another — and this time deadly — example of someone's lack of interest in administrative procedures. If there was no constitution there would be no distressing and legal formalities: a separation could not be halted by a technicality. It was a stormy meeting and, not surprisingly, no decision was reached, although a step forward was taken. With Louisa Martindale's interesting intelligence that no constitution existed, swiftly backed up by Ismay's prompt urging that a decision should be made immediately, most ditherers became convinced, although Miss Merrifield, ever the committee animal, stepped in and won the day by proposing that the awesome decision to separate should be carried forward to an emergency meeting of the Branch executive committee.

Mrs Ryle agreed with this, and, pounding the nail firmly into the coffin so that there might be no doubt, proposed (seconded Miss Merrifield) that a resolution reading 'that the site and building sub-committee consider it advisable that the two branches of the Hospital should become completely independent and work as separate hospitals' should be presented to a Brighton Branch executive committee meeting on 25th September 1918.[11]

After this suitable interval for everyone to draw breath and for the news to fly quickly — as it always does — to Dr Boyle and Lady Chichester at the Hove Branch, the sub-committee met again with the Brighton Branch executive on 25th September to formalise the separation and declare independence. Mrs Ryle was in the chair, and Miss Merrifield, Mrs Cobb, Mr Clayton, Mrs Godfree and Ismay FitzGerald were present along with Drs Martindale, Scatliff and Edmonds. It was again at Dr Martindale's house and she had not been idle during the previous month: she had visited Mr Yates Lee (a Howard trustee) and obtained from him an assurance that the new hospital could have the £5,000 'any time now' and that he did not anticipate that any further conditions would be attached. The proposal was passed and the meeting peacefully closed. It now remained for the newly independent hospital — albeit still sited for the time being at 4–8 Ditchling Road — to start getting its act together. To set up administrative committees and financial structures; to think about the constant problem of fundraising and the employment of nursing staff; and to address that perennial but absorbing problem that had always plagued the dispensary and hospitals: its name. It was decided that all current executive committee members of the Brighton Branch, prospective trustees for the new hospital, vice presidents and — most importantly — subscribers, should be invited to a grand public meeting. There would be a full and frank public discussion and the agenda would include this time the presentation of a nice new constitution (no doubt thanks to Dr Martindale's urging) to be drawn up by the solicitors, the selection of a bank for the new accounts was to be made, the election of the trustees, and the drawing up of a new appeal for subscriptions. The structure of the board of management was to be decided, and the prickly problem of the new name tackled.

This momentous grand public meeting of the subscribers and donors to the building scheme of the Lady Chichester Hospital,

Brighton Branch took place on 18th October 1918 at the Pioneer Club in New Road, with Elizabeth Robins this time able to be in the chair. Much business was attended to. The pristine constitution, put together by the solicitors Messrs Baines & Wooley, was accepted and a Board of Management formally put together which was composed of familiar names most of whom had served on the old Site and Buildings sub-Committee — Mr and Mrs Cobb, the Hon. Ismay FitzGerald, Mrs Godfree, Miss Merrifield, Mrs Ryle, Mr Clayton. They were joined by Miss Maule, the head of St Michael's Hall, a local girls' school; Mrs Eggar and Mrs Herbert Jones, the wife of the Bishop of Lewes (her name was Madeleine but she was always known formally as Mrs Herbert Jones). Mrs Godfree, married to another local solicitor conveniently practising in Marlborough Place, who could be relied upon, via her husband, to give the Board sound and helpful advice on practical matters, such as buying property and dealing with builders, was also welcomed, as was Miss Millicent Lawrence, the middle sister from the Roedean School family business. She was a sensible and intelligent woman and, of the many Lawrence sisters, the one most interested in matters outside the school. A member of the NUWSS, she was firmly committed to the struggle for the parliamentary franchise, and was an active member of the Brighton branch of the Pioneer Club. Mr Clayton, a magistrate as well as an architect, was welcomed on board as were Sir Berry and Lady Cusack-Smith.

Trustees of the new hospital were also appointed; Miss Elizabeth Robins, Miss M. E. Verrall, Mrs Cobb and Mrs A. O. Jennings being amongst the familiar faces. Miss Merrifield and Miss Verrall were also asked to be joint treasurers and it was also settled that the medical officers — Dr Martindale, Mrs Scatliff and Dr Edmonds — would be members of the Board of Management. The meeting managed to get through a great deal of very important business, indicating that all those present were either very well behaved or, most likely, all pulling together and generally of one mind. Dr Martindale is reported as having 'alluded to the recent separation' but, sadly, the note does not indicate what she said. The only dissension appears to have been the naming of the new hospital; it is almost as though, after such a busy and momentous meeting, all present allowed themselves a relaxation from seriousness, but as might be expected no agreement could be reached.

Various names of varying sensibilities had been suggested: the Princess Royal Hospital, the New Sussex Hospital, the Gundrada Hospital,[12] the 20th Century Hospital, the Peace Hospital — 'any further suggestions to be sent to Dr Martindale'! A date, 31st

October 1918, was set for the first meeting of the reshuffled Board of Management of the new hospital (still sited at Ditchling Road.)

It would be at the full Annual Meeting of Subscribers to the Lady Chichester Hospital on 24th October 1918, that the announcement of formal separation, suitably disguised but by now no secret to anyone, would be made smoothly, but no doubt horribly painfully, by Lady Chichester herself. Troubles, however, might be only just beginning.

Notes

[1] See note 4, chapter 7.

[2] The South London Hospital for Women was unusual since it did not begin its life as a dispensary. It was founded in 1912 by Dr Maud Chadburn. The story goes that, having found a most suitable site in Clapham, Dr Chadburn appealed for funds to help with the building. She launched her appeal with a letter to *The Times* which, along with a small amount of money, brought forth an offensive and scornful letter from a male doctor, that the editor saw fit to publish. However, an anonymous supporter of hospitals for women became so enraged by this letter that, after receiving an assurance from Dr Chadburn that indeed the hospital would treat only women and children, he donated £100,000, which enabled the hospital to be built. The hospital was opened in 1912 by Queen Mary. It closed in 1984 although, scandalously, the building remained empty, locked, barred and neglected for twenty years. Moberly Bell, E. (1953) *Storming the Citadel.* Constable and Co.

[3] Its equivalent at the Hove Branch was the House Committee.

[4] Charles E. Clayton was a well-known architect in Brighton and partner in the firm Clayton and Black of 10 Prince Albert Street. His best known building standing today is the Duke of York's cinema, opened in 1910, but he was also responsible for the concert halls on the Palace and West Piers, the Nurses' Convalescent Home at Black Rock (now modern flats), the Sir John Howard Homes in Kemp Town and several bank buildings in Brighton. After his death his firm Clayton and Black designed the King and Queen public house opposite Victoria Gardens.

[5] Sir William Gentle caused much excitement in October 1918 when he lent a collection of criminal tools, revolvers and jemmies to an exhibition in the Chapel Royal, Brighton, on behalf of the Imperial Club for Nurses (Chairman: Lady Otter). *Sussex Daily News* 29 October 1918.

[6] To this day there exists a nurses' home charity maintained by an endowment from Sir John's will.

[7] Brighton & Hove Local Studies Library.

[8] East Sussex Records Office HB 12/1–16.

[9] Miss Flora de Gaudrion Merrifield and Miss M. E. Verrall were sisters-in-law. Miss Flora had an elder sister, Margaret, who was a lecturer at Newnham College, Cambridge, and a noted medium, active in the Society for Psychical Research. Margaret de Gaudrion Merrifield married Professor Arthur Woollgar Verrall, also

- 89 -

a Cambridge man, and they had a daughter, Helen, who also became a notable medium. Professor Verrall was a brother of Miss Verrall and Dr (later Sir) Thomas Jenner Verrall, the Brighton physician.

[10] The members of the site and building committee were also members of the Brighton Branch executive committee, the meeting on September 24th 1918 was a rubber stamp exercise.

[11] East Sussex Records Office HB 12.

[12] Gundrada was the wife of William de Warenne, the Norman baron who founded Lewes Priory in the eleventh century.

THE OLD VICARAGE

Exactly when the Brighton Branch Site and Buildings sub-committee came to the reluctant conclusion that to build a new hospital from scratch was not feasible and that it would be better to look for an existing building and to modify it to the required standards, has not been recorded. However, the minutes of the meetings show that, by December 1917, soon after Mr Clayton and Sir William Gentle had made their visit to the South London Hospital for Women, the sub-committee had begun to look around seriously for suitable premises for a relocation of the Brighton Branch rather than a potential building site. Originally, some thought had been given to staying put in Ditchling Road and to this end the owner of number 2 — the only house in the small terrace not occupied by the hospital and reasonably sized — was approached and asked if she would sell the lease. Had she agreed, this would have been a cheaper option for expansion; but the owner, although willing in principle, had wanted to retain use of the garden and laundry to the rear of the house, and this was not acceptable. In any case, the houses were small, having been originally built as dwelling places, and they were in a noisy location, and suffered from the din and fumes of both horse-drawn and motorised traffic continually passing to and fro in front of The Level. Something bigger and better was needed; a more suitable building that might easily be altered, and one that was perhaps situated in a more agreeable area of Brighton. Detached, and with its own surrounding land, suitable either as gardens or for future development, would be ideal.

After the fact-finding visit to the South London Hospital by Mr Clayton and Sir William Gentle, a business plan had been submitted to the Howard legacy fund, and one of the trustees, Mr Yates Lee, had personally poised himself to take a great interest in the new hospital. In April 1918 he told Dr Martindale and Mr Clayton that the two chief competitors for the first award from the legacy were the Royal Sussex County Hospital and the Lady Chichester, Brighton Branch, and in May 1918 he imparted even more joyful news: a sum of £30,000 was now available from the legacy fund and the Lady Chichester Hospital, Brighton Branch, could happily anticipate the use of £5,000. The hunt could now begin in earnest for that suitable property and during the summer of 1918, and some months before the actual separation of the two Branches took place, what might be a satisfactory (though not inexpensive) property on the borders of Brighton had been found. Windlesham House was built in a style neither Regency nor Victorian and was bordered on three sides by residential roads. Built as Windlesham School, it had been for sale for some considerable time; since before the war in fact, when the boys had moved out to their new school in Portslade.[1] The building was roomy, and naturally had extensive plumbing, was quite near the sea but within easy distance of shops, banks and public transport, and was available. There was also a garden which might be useful and a swimming pool which possibly was not. But would it do? It was certainly expensive, but it was spacious. Should they wait for something cheaper and risk losing the legacy money, or buy now? Mindful that a decision had to be made and conscious that a prolonged wait for the ideal property to materialise was not perhaps wise, by mid 1918 the site and building sub-committee was much in favour of buying Windlesham house — although Mr Clayton had grave misgivings about its suitability. Windlesham House may even have been eyed up by Dr Boyle as a possible home for the Hove Branch: the minutes give a tantalising but baffling reference to a letter received at 10 Marlborough Place from the estate agents Wilkinson, Son and Welch, addressed to Mr Clayton, Miss Merrifield and Dr Martindale, although it had been originally addressed to Dr Boyle. The letter delicately indicated that the owner of Windlesham House, Mrs Scott Malden, the mother of the headmaster of Windlesham School, had received another offer to buy from another party and consequently was pressing for a decision on her price to the sub-committee of £4,000 for the house and a further £6,000 for the adjoining ground, a situation by no means unknown today and accompanied, then as now, by severe nervous tension.

However within a stone's throw of Windlesham House, almost like a miracle from heaven, another very tempting property appeared unexpectedly on the market in June 1918, giving the committee cause to think again. This was the Brighton vicarage, a detached and roomy early Victorian building, grandiose to look at but very discreetly shielded from the public and the traffic of Montpelier and Victoria Roads[2] by an acre or so of garden dotted with flower beds and mature trees. It was undoubtedly overwhelmingly superior and immediately thrust portly Windlesham House into the shade. Once highly suitable to accommodate the large Victorian family expected from the incumbent of a wealthy parish such as Brighton, it was the home of Canon Dormer Pierce, Vicar of Brighton at St Peter's Church, but far too large for him as his family then consisted of only his wife and himself.[3] The Diocese of Chichester had recently decided to sell the property and to re-house Canon Dormer Pierce elsewhere and, provided that he could find alternative accommodation suitable to his liking and his needs, the diocese was even willing to pay for any small alterations he might find necessary. However, since the object of selling the vicarage would be financial prudence, then naturally such alterations would have to be within reason.

Mr Clayton and Dr Martindale had viewed the vicarage and its grounds and pronounced them most satisfactory to the eager ears of the Site and Buildings sub-committee meeting in June 1918. Elizabeth Robins, again not missing out on drama, chaired the meeting and asked Mr Clayton to describe the property. Obediently but enthusiastically Mr Clayton circulated a rough plan of the house, and added measurements of the principal rooms. Warming to his theme, he cheerfully gave his considered opinion that the diocese might even reduce the asking price to £7,500 (from the initial demand of £8,000), a great improvement on the £10,000 being asked by Mrs Malden for Windlesham House.[4]

In the light of this fortuitous arrival of more suitable premises at a price that would generate a huge saving of funds, the balance of opinion swayed sharply in favour of the vicarage and the committee, swiftly making up its mind, rapped out an order that Messrs Wilkinson, Son and Welch should be informed straight away that their interest in Windlesham House should be withdrawn, and that the latest offer from Mrs Malden was to be declined. Dr Martindale was also instructed to communicate with Mr Yates Lee of the Howard legacy trust to put forward the new plan to purchase the vicarage rather than the school, and to try to wring from him a definitive date for the arrival of the money.

It was the beginning of a drama that would last for nearly two trying years, stretch everyone's patience to near breaking point and even bring about a question in parliament. But, with the money nearly in the bag and a most suitable property located, it was time for matters of management and administration to be organised. The first independent Board of Management meeting (as opposed to the old site and building sub-committee meetings) after the momentous Annual Meeting of Subscribers to the Lady Chichester Hospital on 18th October, when the separation had been formally (but with little acknowledgement of the truth) announced by Lady Chichester, first met at 10 Marlborough Place on 31st October 1918, this time with Miss Merrifield rather than Miss Robins in charge from the chair.

Clearly no drama was anticipated, but this would turn out to be wrong. The nucleus of the Board of Management was now formed: Dr

Martindale and Ismay FitzGerald, Sir Berry and Lady Cusack-Smith, Miss Maule, Dr Helen Scatliff, Miss M. E. Verrall, Mrs Godfree, Mrs Ryle, Mr and Mrs Cobb, Mr and Mrs A. O. Jennings, Mrs Eggar and Mrs Herbert Jones. Technically, the chairman was Elizabeth Robins but with her health always frail her appearances at routine meetings became fewer as time passed, but no doubt she followed events with deep interest. Miss Millicent Lawrence attended the first meeting and Mr Clayton was also present, although he said for the record that as the architect he felt it inappropriate to serve on the Board. This was no doubt wise, but his presence was both weighty and persuasive.

The first Board of Management meeting took a firm grasp of its new responsibilities and the members launched into interesting discussions about whether the constitution should receive some further fine tuning and, having done that, set about forming a dedicated finance committee to keep a strict eye on expenditure. Sir Berry Cusack-Smith could be relied upon to take care of what might well turn out to be tricky financial negotiations in the future and would be the ideal chairman. On fiscal matters a small disagreement arose. It had been proposed at the general meeting that the new hospital should have two treasurers acting jointly, and Miss Merrifield had been suggested along with Miss M. E. Verrall (both were elected as trustees and both had long been associated with the Lady Chichester Hospital). Miss Verrall however, at this first Board of Management meeting, rather stiffly declined to continue as Joint Treasurer, giving as her reason that she 'had always objected to Joint Treasurers in principle'. This was a blow, and a new treasurer would have to be found (although Miss Verrall would remain as a trustee) and it was Dr Martindale who suggested that Margaret Haig Thomas, Viscountess Rhondda, be asked if she would kindly consent to take on the job.

Importing titled women into the running and well-being of the new hospital was a feature essential for good publicity then as now; today we draft in 'celebrities' to raise the public profile, add a little glamour and glitz and to come up with the odd hefty donation. Titled women, particularly today's life peers, do particularly well and in 1918 Margaret Haig Thomas, Viscountess Rhondda, was a fine catch now that the Brighton Branch had cut away from the benison of Lady Chichester's powerful influence.[5] She was prominent in the women's movements, published her own magazine *Time and Tide* and was an active NUWSS member as, of course, was Louisa Martindale. Living in London, however, and a very busy lady indeed, it must have been understood that Lady Rhondda would have no time to do any actual figure work nor to be closely involved in the day-to-day organisation of the hospital. But lending her name, writing the odd cajoling or complaining letter to the newspapers and making the occasional appearance at an annual meeting or fête in Brighton, would be most satisfactory.

At the next Board of Management meeting a month later the Bishop of Lewes, Dr Herbert Jones, was present. Prudently, he had been asked to serve on the newly formed finance committee. This was a great idea by someone, since not only did his association with the new hospital carry spiritual weight and authority, but he could also, as a brother cleric, perhaps help out with the growing problem of Canon Dormer Pierce and his continued (and rather irritating) occupancy of The Old Vicarage. It was now several months since the vicarage had been put up for sale and the vicar had not yet located himself any alternative accommodation. He had found a much smaller property in Hanover Crescent which he quite liked, nearer to St Peter's Church and in a pleasant and graceful terrace, but fussily remarked that it would need some structural alterations before he would consider moving in. That was his position and obstinately he stuck to it.

Hanover Crescent today is a desirable place to live. Near the trees and grass of The Level (sadly many of the elm trees which survived Dutch Elm disease fell to the winds of the hurricane in 1987) it is pleasant, handsome and architecturally distinguished. No doubt it was no different then and Mr Clayton was much put out by Canon Dormer Pierce's reluctance to move there. It may well be that he had been instrumental in shipping the bishop onto the finance committee to help to lever the canon away from the vicarage, aware that any tardiness in locating adequate premises for the new hospital might have a detrimental effect on the delivery of the grant from the Sir John Howard legacy fund. Mr Clayton was probably acquainted with Mr Yates Lee and Mr Pape, two of the legacy trustees who would soon have to hand over the cash to someone else if progress were not made, and with the lease of 70 Brunswick Place critically about to expire and Helen Boyle and the Hove Branch also looking for new premises in Hove, it would be unbearable if the opposition were to suddenly step in and snatch the prize at the last moment if negotiations to buy the vicarage should become mired.

Louisa Martindale knew this, too, and since the vicarage was a very suitable house indeed, at the November 1918 Board of Management meeting she and Mr Clayton opted to continue the pressure to push the vicar to remove himself, deflecting arguments that the other site should continue to be considered. The costs of making the necessary alterations to the vicarage would be moderate, Mr Clayton argued, adding that, as the war had terminated (a few days previously, on

11th November) the price of rebuilding works at Hanover Crescent might at some time in the near future become just too expensive for the church to agree to, so haste was sorely needed before this happened.

This may not have been a good ploy, since the Bishop of Lewes replied rather sourly that he thought the ecclesiastical commissioners (who had first agreed that the vicarage should be sold) would not, in that case, approve the purchase of the Hanover Crescent property anyway. This was not helpful and pressure was mounting; defeated, and only able to respond feebly with the faint suggestion that the vicar might like Clifton Lodge as a home (even though it had not yet come onto the market), Mr Clayton had to back down. He suggested that a letter go to the church commissioners, no doubt very strongly worded, asking for clarification and a definite date for the vicar's removal. His troubles, however, were not yet over. Someone — Dr Martindale, who was busily writing the minutes as well as eagerly participating, unfortunately managed not to say who — did not agree with Mr Clayton's insistence that the vicarage was the only possible site. That person reminded the Board of Management that the original option, Windlesham House (by now known intermittently as Sussex House) was still available, causing Mr Clayton to reply sharply that in his view the house was not suitable! Tempers were clearly becoming frayed and were not helped by Ismay FitzGerald's attempt at pacification: she suggested that, instead of moving, perhaps new building could take place on the Ditchling Road site?

Scenting serious discord Miss Merrifield, in the chair, instantly proposed a diversion and carefully steered the meeting into that perennially interesting discussion, a permanent name for the new hospital: would it be the Women's South Coast Hospital; the Women's Hospital for Women; Thanks Offering Hospital; the New Hospital; the New Brighton Hospital? Capitalising on her manoeuvring skills, and possibly anticipating the arrival of yet more tedious dissension, Miss Merrifield hopefully suggested that a postal vote might be organised but, yet again, Dr Martindale had done her homework: with great aplomb she promptly suggested 'The New Sussex', the name temporarily in use at Ditchling Road after the separation, and was instantly seconded by Miss Maule. The proposal was, unsurprisingly, carried unanimously. The great sigh of relief can almost be heard today, but the vicarage problem was not done yet — like a rabbit leaping from a conjurer's hat, Canon Dormer Pierce himself walked into the room and joined the meeting.

What he said would nail the coffin lid on Mr Clayton's fervent wish to get his hands on The Old Vicarage, and one wonders whether or not he had known that the vicar might appear; possibly the Bishop of Lewes had a hand in this. Speaking of his difficulties in finding a new home and adding that he did not care for the Hanover Crescent house, he plaintively added that, if the commissioners approved his alterations, he would of course live there but that he would prefer Clifton Lodge, which in a year or so would become available. It was clear to all that the vicar did not want to move and would do all he could to prevent it; and it was equally clear that the Bishop of Lewes could not influence him to do so.[6] Almost apologetically the Bishop suggested that a new site sub-committee be set up to reopen the search for premises and nobly offered his own services. With no alternative ready to hand the Board of Management rapidly agreed and Mr Cobb and Mrs Ryle were selected for the new committee with Dr Martindale, Dr Edmonds and Miss Merrifield to serve ex officio. The plan to buy the vicarage as a home for the new hospital was abandoned.

The meeting had been long and exhausting, everyone was no doubt eager for it to draw to an end, and so the remaining business was conducted swiftly. The amendments to the constitution were passed without dissent; the appointment of a paid secretary was gladly postponed (although Elizabeth Robins, well informed of events, had suggested Miss Green for the post); the reports from the matron and the almoner at Ditchling Road were referred onwards to the House committee (the remains of the old Brighton Branch executive committee) and it was decided that the almoner should be allowed to keep her notice in the outpatients' department which instructed that all outpatients should firstly be seen by herself. Everyone also agreed that this was a good time for the late Brighton Branch of the Lady Chichester Hospital in Ditchling Road to publicise its new (though possibly by no means permanent) name, the 'New Sussex Hospital', and arrangements were made for all authorities to be notified as well as the governors, trustees and subscribers.

After the meeting the Board of Management must have wondered what it had let itself in for, whether it had taken on just too much, and whether a New Sussex Hospital would ever open its doors.

Notes

[1] Windlesham House was built by Lt. Charles Robert Malden, the headmaster of a preparatory school for boys that had been founded on the Isle of Wight in 1832 by the Rev. Henry Worsley. In 1837 Lt. Malden removed the school to Brighton and when the new building was opened in 1844 renamed it Windlesham School after a village in Sussex for which his wife had a great liking. Windlesham Road was

named after the school. The school was very successful but in the early years of the twentieth century the Malden family became increasingly dissatisfied with the site, because the surrounding area was built up after the development of the Goldsmid estate. The school moved to Portslade in 1913 and then to Highden in West Sussex, where it remains to this day. The school is nowadays co-educational and the fifth generation of the Malden family continue as head teachers.

[2] The top end of Victoria Road is now Temple Gardens.

[3] The Old Vicarage, an imposing tudor style mansion with concrete cladding spreading beneath three towering gables, had been built in 1835 by Henry Michell Wagner, the Vicar of Brighton. At the time it fronted directly onto the wooded hill of Montpelier Road, inside two acres of land and lawn. He built the house at his own expense, so naturally designed it to his own high taste; from the garden the building looked grandly imposing, but in reality it was uncomfortably large, rambling, and stuffed with oversized rooms that were glacially difficult to heat.

[4] He based this opinion on his perception that the diocese would prefer to sell to the Brighton Branch of the Lady Chichester Hospital rather than to the other interested party, the proprietor of a Jewish boarding house. An attitude of this slant seeping from the diocese at Chichester, would today be unacceptable; nevertheless, there is a ring of truth about it, although whether Mr Clayton had received this intelligence officially or by a whisper from a professional friend cannot be ascertained.

[5] Viscountess Rhondda inherited her title from her father.

[6] In December 1922 the vicarage was let on a long lease to the Girls' Public Day School Trust, where it remains as the sixth form annexe at Brighton and Hove High School for Girls. The Canon and his wife did in fact move to Clifton Lodge — re-named Vicarage Lodge — in Dyke Road. From a later report in the *Sussex Daily News* 3 December 1923.

12

ALDRINGTON HOUSE

The separation of the two Branches of the Lady Chichester Hospital was final and no one doubted that the two would not get back together. Dr Boyle's reactions remain unknown, but they cannot be difficult to guess when the news of the award from the Sir John Howard legacy trust became known. The success of the bid from the Brighton Branch in 1918 effectively robbed the Hove Branch of an opportunity to do the same since the single hospital, the Lady Chichester, could not have benefited twice. It is not impossible that Dr Boyle saw this acquisition of funds from the legacy as an aggressive action for which she never quite forgave Dr Martindale. Her professional work, by now widely acclaimed, would always depend upon the availability of roomy hospital premises to accommodate the steady arrival and subsequent treatment of patients. Throughout her long life Dr Boyle would maintain that the treatment of nervous disease was 'part and parcel of the treatment of the body' and that diagnosis and treatment for nervous disorders should be as easily available as that for physiological and anatomical malfunction. Once diagnosed, both types of patient should be treated in the same hospital.[1]

The Lady Chichester Hospital for Nervous Diseases of Women and Children, Hove Branch, had been built upon the success of the Lewes Road Dispensary, and it came as close as was possible to the fulfilment of this ideal. The expansion of the small Ditchling Road premises into a large medical, surgical and outpatients' hospital, functioning totally independently, meant that this ideal was now bitterly unobtainable. That alone would have been disappointingly dreadful, but coming at the time when the Hove Branch itself was so urgently in need of new premises to move to and of new money to spend when it got there would have been doubly, and indeed ferociously, harrowing.

The surviving reports of the Lady Chichester Hospital Annual Meetings are far removed from the daily arguments and decisions that made up the thoughts of the women and men of the Hove Branch at the time, and only speculation remains. Although in the hot seat, Helen Boyle has not left us a description of her feelings; never a woman to broadcast any aspect of her private life, she would not have brandished any distress in public, though her Irish inheritance may well have been one which did not easily brush aside a slight or forgive a wrong. In her old age she was still said to have a piercing gaze through her pebble spectacles; 'You couldn't lie to her', Mr Reg Boyce remembers most emphatically, rendering due reverence to the force of her personality.[2]

Helen Boyle and Louisa Martindale should have been close and supportive friends. Both were forceful and highly educated women, accustomed to public speaking and aware of the need to persuade and impress listeners with their hortatory skills as well as their medical expertise. As doctors they also understood the assumption of responsibility; human lives were frequently in their hands, whether under the knife or in the delicate piecing back together of the torn fragments of the mind. They should have been able to work closely together with mutual advantage a high priority for both; yet, sadly, no evidence remains that this was ever so, although in the early days after Louisa came back to Brighton, with so much in common they must have made efforts to get to know each other better. Although their backgrounds were not similar, they were much the same age and were from well-to-do families. Louisa Martindale's family money came from the paper trade, with a nonconformist and low church loyalty which she did not follow. Helen Boyle's English grandfather was an industrialist, her Irish father was a professional man and a Protestant rather than Catholic, while she retained a deep Christian faith throughout her life. Not much the same, but not too much different either. Neither married, and both chose to live for many years with a woman companion. Miss FitzGerald became a personal friend to Louisa Martindale in about 1910, and was quickly drafted onto the old joint branch council and the Brighton Branch executive committee, the Brighton Branch site and building committee, and then the New Sussex Board of Management. Cecily Lamorna Hingston was secretary and driver to Dr Boyle before she qualified as a doctor; her place was taken in about 1929 by Miss Rita Gore-Lindsay who took no part in the work or administrative functions of the Lady Chichester, although she seems to have escorted Dr Boyle to official functions as both driver and dinner partner. It is most likely that she was in fact a paid companion.

They even shared some leisure pursuits: each had a wide and diverse circle of close friends, artistic, scientific and local; both were dog lovers and both enjoyed living in the countryside, where modern conveniences of all varieties were missing — Dr Boyle in her cottage 'Rock Rose' and surrounding pastures above Pyecombe; Dr Martindale in the more remote (but equally starved of modern conveniences) property 'Colin Godman's'.[3] The *Sussex Daily News* in the early years of the twentieth century frequently carried reports of meetings of societies set up to further the advancement of women, and both Dr Boyle and Dr Martindale are often mentioned as attending. In the small confines of Brighton and Hove where, even today, if you walk out you will meet at least one or two friends or acquaintances in the street, there was no way in which they could have avoided each other's company.

Most of all they shared one peculiar status in Edwardian England: that oddity — a woman doctor. Both had undergone the frequently comfortless — but probably exhilarating — experience of the London School of Medicine for Women, with its classes and ceremonies, grinding studies, hostility from the major teaching hospitals and the necessity of keeping back from relatives the student tales of the gruesome proximity of disease, death and the cadavers which made up the daily lives of the medical student. Both served abroad, however briefly, during the Great War. They were talented medical women devoted to their calling; both were ambitious and independent; both had powerful characters that could sway management councils and committees; both knew how to get their own way.

Helen Boyle and Mabel Jones must have come to know Mrs Martindale well in the early years of the Lewes Road Dispensary, before 1905. As a woman of warm and generous heart, deeply interested in the careers and well-being of young professional women living away from their families, Mrs Martindale would have immediately taken Dr Boyle and Dr Jones into her heart; and a sure way to Louisa's affections would have been through her mother.

Years later, writing in her autobiography in 1951 Louisa Martindale paid a long tribute to her mother and to Dr Mary Murdoch as well as to Ismay FitzGerald, after whose death in 1946 she seems to have remained living alone; but of Helen Boyle there is hardly any mention. In its pages she pays no tribute to Dr Boyle as a colleague, either to her early work for women in Hove or to her long and prestigious career — a strange and rather sad omission since their professional and private lives would have so much overlapped. There is a swift and jaunty gallop through the birth of the dispensary in 1899 and a glancing acknowledgement of the first hospital for nervous diseases in Roundhill Crescent, but there is no hint of warmth in the paragraphs, and of the latter years of Dr Boyle's distinguished career and the title Lady Chichester Hospital, she is silent.[4] She does however describe a startling occasion when, in unusual anger, she called her maid to 'show the door' to a visitor, whom she describes as 'one of the local women doctors'. At the time the Brighton Branch was making plans for a new women's medical and surgical hospital, and the visitor had come to point out, in angry tones, 'the futility of our daring to found a new hospital; officered by women doctors only, and talked of the conceit of imagining that we had anything to offer.'

Dr Martindale added that, a few days later, the same woman called a meeting of all the women doctors in the district — except herself — to try to halt one of the appeals. Unfortunately, no names are mentioned in this rather intriguing passage. At the time of writing she was in her eighties, and so perhaps allowances need to be made for the drift of memory over the years; yet, clearly there was an incident and ill-feeling and resentment was swilling around. It is hard to believe that Dr Boyle would have acted in that manner or even approved of such an approach, though she may well have known that something was afoot. Mrs Scatliff and Dr Edmonds were both loyal members of the Brighton Branch executive committee, and it does not seem likely that any of the younger women newly coming to Hove and Brighton as temporary medical officers at the start of their careers would have summoned up enough courage to criticise Louisa Martindale face to face in her own home. The visitor is most likely to have been Dr Lillian Harris, who worked with Dr Boyle only at the Hove Branch and acted as her deputy in 1915. Dr Harris appears to have had an interest in psychiatric disorders and homeopathic medicine; she was not a former student of the LSMW and so not part of its wide-ranging and very effective network.

Emotions had to be put to one side, however, and continued efforts made to find a new home for the Hove Branch, no doubt to the amusement and scepticism of many people, both interested and uninterested. It must have been widely known that both Branches had been looking for suitable new premises, one in Brighton, the other in Hove, and Windlesham House was in Brighton — by a whisker! Aldrington House, the future home of the Lady Chichester Hospital was most definitely in Hove.[5]

Aldrington House, then situated at 47 New Church Road, was passably suitable for Dr Boyle's hospital. Built by Councillor and Mrs William Hammand in about 1891[6] it was — and is — a detached, chunkily solid and imposingly gabled house in fine knapped flint, with a sweeping gravel driveway leading up to an imposing porch and front door. It was not too far along the quiet and leafy stretch of New Church Road heading west out of the scramble of urban Hove and Brighton down towards the village of Portslade-on-Sea, and was prettily surrounded by a pleasant garden with maturing trees. Large windows stared sunnily south and opened easily to let in the bright Hovean sunshine and crisp, salty air. The property, although very suitable in position, was rather smaller than would have been liked, and had not been modernised up to 1917 standards; but it would do.

William Hammand had died in 1894 and is buried in St Leonard's churchyard; his widow died in 1912, although a Mr Carlton-Piercy seems to have either bought the house — or most likely rented it — for a short time. Bought from the executors, the purchase money of £4,900 was raised with the help of a massive overdraft. A further £900 had to be added to the loan to make the necessary alterations: rooms had to be turned into wards since the hospital would need to accommodate sixty beds. Treatment and consulting rooms, as well as occupational therapy rooms and storerooms, were also needed. Aldrington House was probably the best that could be found, as neither Hove nor Brighton were awash with detached houses large enough to metamorphose into hospitals at a price which could be afforded, and the garden could always provide space for future expansion. Indeed, before the opening in June 1920 permission was obtained from Hove Council to place a temporary hut beside the house and a corrugated iron building was subsequently erected with an agreement that it could be used for up to ten years. The overdraft was massive and, although there is evidence in the annual report that the purchase of Aldrington House was made with the help of an independent legacy from an anonymous source,[7] the move appears to have been carried out in a hurry, either before all the funding needed had been raised or, possibly, after a budgeting miscalculation had not been rooted out.

Only a short while after the move in June 1920, the now fully independent Lady Chichester Hospital found itself in serious need of £350, which it could not raise as the property was already financially burdened. The money was required urgently to install baths and hot water boilers. Treatment for patients had always included a great deal of hydrotherapy, which involved a long immersion in warm, or even hot, water and the provision of enough baths and boilers would have been crucial. Opening the new hospital with too few would have been either incompetent or, far more likely, accelerated by events, and Lady Chichester found herself in a position of having to make an urgent public appeal for funds. She wrote to the *Brighton and Hove Herald*:

> SIR, At a time when hospital appeals are both numerous and urgent, one hesitates to add to them. If I do so it is because the cause for which I plead is one of special urgency. The Lady Chichester Hospital, which has recently moved into a new home, finds it necessary to install baths and boilers at an estimated cost of £350. At a meeting of the Executive Committee [sic] held last week the work could not be authorised, as the hospital is already in debt some £1500, and the committee did not feel able to authorise further expenditure, however urgent, unless the money could be found independently. A member of the committee very generously

offered £50 in the hope that it might be met by six other like amounts, and it is in the hope of receiving such offers that I venture to appeal to the generosity of the public. And meanwhile there are no baths available!

Yours etc.
Ruth Chichester, President,
Stanmer, Lewes.[8]

Sadly, no details are known about the circumstances of the purchase of Aldrington House, but the move does seem to have been rushed and ill-funded. Eventually the Lady Chichester Hospital (with its own outpatients' department and Dr Boyle steadfastly at the helm) opened inside the grey walls of Aldrington House in June 1920. The name of the house was not used at the time although the engraved stone tablets on the posts of the driveway were never removed, just painted over.[9] An exhaustive search of the local papers of the time has failed to uncover any details of a grand opening ceremony. Sadly, it appears that there was none, either through lack of funds or lack of time.

For many years Helen Boyle rented consulting rooms at 9 The Drive, a grand, yellow brick, barn of a detached house belonging to Dr Parry, a well-known medical man and one-time president of the Brighton & Sussex Medico-Chirurgical Society. She may even have lived there in later years. Street directories and electoral registers reveal that Dr Parry's house also accommodated several other women doctors from time to time; for example, Dr Christine Shearer and Dr Cecily Lamorna Hingston[10] and it is unlikely that Dr Boyle at this stage of her life would have shared rooms with junior and employed younger doctors. It was customary for doctors to use working addresses rather than private addresses for purposes of business, which makes it difficult for latter-day researchers to be quite sure where they lived.

Following the move by the former Hove Branch of the Lady Chichester Hospital to Aldrington House in 1920, gaps in relations between itself and the former Brighton Branch seem to have yawned more widely at management level. Official communication between the two hospitals appears to have dwindled to such a point that it almost vanished, except when trouble loomed. Any ill-feeling seems to have been at the top, however, and did not necessarily affect individuals. For example, Miss Verrall seems to have retained her association with both hospitals. At one time treasurer and vice-president of the dispensary at Islingword Road from 1899, and a trustee and member of the Board of Management the New Sussex, she retained her vice-presidency of the Lady Chichester Hospital for many years.

Lady Chichester in 1951
Reproduced by kind permission of Lord Chichester

Dr Helen Boyle in 1939
Photograph reproduced by kind permission of the Royal College of Psychiatrists

Dr Mabel Jones

Family photo of Helen Boyle
as a young woman, c1890
By kind permission of Richard Boyle

Dr Thomas King Chambers
Reproduced by kind permission of the Royal College of Physicians

Dr Louisa Martindale in the 1920s
Photograph by Lafayette, reproduced by kind permission of the Wellcome Trust

Mrs Martindale
From a drawing in From One Generation to Another by Hilda Martindale

The Hon. Ismay Fitzgerald
Photograph reproduced by kind permission of Mrs Pamela Brotherton

Memorial to Sophie Boyle
in St Nicolas's Church, Portslade

Mrs Martindale's grave
in Horsted Keynes churchyard

THIS THEATRE HAS BEEN EQUIPPED IN MEMORY OF M^{RS} MARTINDALE WHO ORIGINATED THE IDEA OF A SUSSEX WOMEN'S HOSPITAL OFFICERED BY WOMEN DOCTORS

A brass plaque in Mrs Martindale's honour
at Millview Hospital, Sussex Partnership NHS Trust

The Lady Chichester Hospital, Brighton Branch, 4–6 Ditchling Road, c1912
Reproduced by kind permission of the Wellcome Trust

145 Islingword Road in 2005

70 Brunswick Place in 2005

4–6 Ditchling Road in 2005

Lewes Road Hospital for Women and Children, 101 Roundhill Crescent, about 1906
Thanks to Step Back in Time Photograph Library, Brighton

101 Roundhill Crescent in 2006

The Lady Chichester Hospital, Aldrington House, 1922

Thanks to Step Back in Time Photograph Library, Brighton

Aldrington House, 2006

The New Sussex Hospital, Sussex House, Windlesham Road
Thanks to Step Back in Time Photograph Library, Brighton

'Temple Heights', 2006

The Old Vicarage, now Brighton & Hove High School Sixth Form Centre

The medical team at the Lady Chichester Hospital at Aldrington House included Dr Lilian Harris from 30 Dyke Road and, in 1921, Helen Boyle's old friend Sir Maurice Craig, the distinguished psychiatrist, was roped in as a patron. From Claybury Asylum and days newly qualified came her former mentor Sir Robert Armstrong-Jones offering his long years of experience as a consultant. An increasingly active participation by the masculine portion of the medical profession began during the war years when two men (an honorary dentist and an honorary oculist) were appointed to the hospital; this did render mildly inaccurate the original boast that the hospitals were 'officered by medical women' and Dr Martindale's unpleasant interview with the unknown woman doctor comes readily to mind. The Lady Chichester Hospital remained, however, a hospital for women, and men were not admitted as patients; however, a sceptic might hazard a sour guess that only the right push might be needed for this to change.

Helen Boyle has not left us her thoughts on this subject, although early on she had maintained that the treatment of women by women was essential. In her autobiography Louisa Martindale asseverated her belief that there would be a continuing need for women's hospitals to be officered by women doctors until they were allowed to work alongside men on the wards — the emphasis is on the professional needs of the doctors rather than the women patients. It is possible that Dr Boyle, by importing male colleagues onto the medical staff, struck an early blow for equal opportunities, although this may well have been out of necessity rather than by choice.

There is a charisma and a grace, a charm and a lightness about Helen Boyle which can be found in abundance in her written works. She was, it would appear, no great organiser or planner; she took no heed of paperwork and administration was possibly not practical. But she was a devout Christian who could inspire loyalty and seems to have worked by intuition, flashes of genius and obstinacy. She was a lover of poetry and, always suffering from poor eyesight, she did not drive her own car and would always engage a chauffeur. Should the sudden necessity to change a wheel come about most likely she would have absolute faith that someone would certainly turn up to help out — and they probably did.

It is to Dr Boyle's credit and fine skills as a doctor that her patients greatly improved and even thrived with what must have been very spartan and crowded conditions in the early days at Aldrington House. Her design and plan for the alleviation of early mental disorder by a raft of treatments — which included individual emotional and psychological curative therapy as well as a fine and relaxing environment with good food, gentle occupational therapy and exercise — could be extended in the new house, which was much roomier than Brunswick Place and had ample lawn and garden to hand. Her wide-ranging treatments continued to be designed on an individual basis for each patient; for physical well being there was cricket, tennis and croquet in the garden with swimming from the nearby quiet beach. Less energetic contentment was taken care of by picnics and visits to concerts, theatres and cinemas with other patients. There were communal evening activities such as a monthly fancy dress party (where relatives were allowed to participate) and the regular compilation and production of a hospital magazine, written and produced entirely by the patients. Patients still helped with cooking and cleaning, collective tasks less enjoyable perhaps, but equally effective in conserving their *esprit de corps* when coping with none-too-comfortable beds and wards. Re-education and retraining for work was much favoured. Jobs were often found for a patient leaving the hospital so that she could support herself without falling into the poverty 'trap' which Dr Boyle had early recognised as a frequent root cause of nervous collapse. She considered religion to be an important influence and felt strongly that a non-sectarian chapel should be provided for the use of patients.

The hospital achieved a high rate of success, and as the 1920s progressed it became well-known for its high standard of care. There was always a waiting list for admission and patients came not only from Sussex but from far and wide outside the county. Dr Boyle's staff were immensely loyal. The matron of Lady Chichester Hospital, Miss A. Taylor, stayed for over twenty years. At a fancy dress Coronation Dance held at Aldrington House in 1934, Miss Taylor ceremoniously presented Dr Boyle with an illuminated address, a gift from the staff, who had all signed their names. A report in the *Brighton and Hove Herald* shows Dr Boyle, clearly in her later years, as a small but very upright figure, formal in her academic gown and with her long pearly Serbian necklace gracing the folds of its bosom. She is smiling through her rimless spectacles at the portly figure of Miss Taylor.[11]

Dr Boyle had lived for over twenty years in Sussex and by the time she entered her fiftieth year she had become a well-known and respected inhabitant of Brighton and Hove society. She had long been a friend and colleague of Grace Eyre Woodhead, founder of the Brighton Guardianship Society, which cared for poor children classed as 'defective' under the Lunacy Acts, and she served on the Guardianship Society's committee along with Dr Lillian Harris, always a dependable colleague.

Dr Boyle had found that some children who had been classed as 'defectives' were not in fact so, and could benefit from treatment at the Lady Chichester rather than suffer under a misdiagnosis for all of their lives. As might be expected, she always interested herself in the welfare of the children who were (in her terms) borderland defective, holding strong views on their care. Helen Boyle believed in the desirability of training for the kind of work which they could carry out effectively when grown up, and in their being able to lead as normal and fulfilled a life as possible. Unlike views current in the later years of the century, she believed that children who would respond to education and training were in fact better off in the early stages of their lives living in institutions designed for their care; possibly she was thinking of the benefits of companionship and friendship as well as the learning of social skills. However, she was very much in favour of uneducable 'high grade defectives', who could not respond to the teaching of moral sense or critical faculty, being boarded out in private homes. Here, she maintained, they would lead as near a normal everyday life as far as was possible, occupied by daily household tasks and offered love and security by their foster families. She also felt that it was good for society in general that such children should not be hidden away.[12]

Dr Boyle's avoidance of paperwork all her life was luckily taken care of by her colleagues and very soon after moving to Aldrington House the now fully independent Lady Chichester Hospital began preparations to register as a charity. It was also incorporated as a limited company with an open mandate for investment on the stock exchange with a very accepted target of making money as quickly as possible. There is a distinctly masculine feel about this sudden — and what proved to be very successful — enterprise. Investments were made in war stock, the Great Indian Peninsular Railway and Woodworkers Inc., inter alia; and, after a few years, enough money was made not only to pay off the debts but to realise a modest profit.

There was a new LCH Council of Management at Aldrington House with men who were not doctors (although Dr Nethersole Fletcher, President of the Brighton & Sussex Medico-Chirurgical Society in 1930 attended for a while as honorary physician); Mr A. Graves (the secretary) was a solicitor; Mr F. B. Stevens and Colonel Langmuir Watt were business and professional men. Clearly, they knew how to handle Dr Boyle, who happily accepted that it was their job to amass the money, and the Boyle family continued to lend valuable assistance (her younger sister Olive had joined the old joint council in 1917 before the separation) and the Reverend Vicars A. Boyle joined the LCH Council of Management three years later in 1920. Colonel and Mrs Campion, well known in Sussex society, as well as Lady Ruth Pelham also joined the Council bringing both prestige and, hopefully, generous subscriptions.[13]

Traditional fundraising activities such as tombolas, workmen's collecting boxes and 'At Home' entertainments continued and brought in steady, if small, amounts. However, a problem suddenly arose: in 1920 the government dealt a nasty blow which would strike heavily upon fundraising, and both the Lady Chichester and the New Sussex would be affected. No doubt for very good moral reasons, known only to themselves, the men of Whitehall saw fit to impose restrictions upon the sale of refreshments, tobacco, and alcohol at licensed places of entertainment during all charity performances and after 8.00 p.m. The immediate consequence of this stern judgement was that local impresarios, such as the hotel owner Sir Harry Preston and other businessmen in the entertainment industry, ceased to give free use of their premises for fundraising concerts, which had been their usual contribution. No longer able to count on bar and snack receipts to meet their expenses, offers of free accommodation for performances were withdrawn. However, there was no immediate problem with the usual small 'At Home' concerts and performances in local and unlicensed halls, although as the 1920s drifted away such small fundraising activities tended to fade as an important source of filling the financial gaps.

By the late 1920s the Lady Chichester Hospital would come to make its own indelible mark on the treatment of early nervous disorder amongst women and children. It would achieve wide and respected acclaim for its treatments and Dr Helen Boyle would go on to become a leading authority in the field she had taken up so many years before and made almost her own. With Sir Maurice Craig she co-founded the National Council for Mental Hygiene, where she was vice-chairman, and also served on the Feversham Committee, whose recommendations in 1939 led to the establishment of the National Association for Mental Health (MIND). She was the first woman President of the Brighton & Sussex Medico-Chirurgical Society, and a Fellow of the Royal Society of Medicine. She was also a member of Council for the Royal Medico-Psychological Association, the Central Association for Mental Welfare, the People's League of Health, the Medical Committee of the Child Guidance Council, the Standing Committee of the Psychological Group of the Medical Women's Federation, and vice-president of the Sussex Federation of the Council of the League of Nations.

Notes

[1] Westwood, L. (2003) *A Quiet Revolution in Brighton: Dr Helen Boyle's Pioneering Approach to Mental Health Care, 1899–1939*. Society for the Social History of Medicine. Boyle, H. (1922) 'The Ideal Clinic for the Treatment of Nervous and Borderland Cases', in *Proceedings of The Royal Society of Medicine, Section of Psychiatry*, 15 (1922) pp 39–48.

[2] As a young man Mr Boyce worked and cared for Dr Boyle and her secretary Miss Lindsay at her house 'Rock Rose' in Clayton. Personal reminiscence to the writer.

[3] 'Rock Rose' is now the Three Greys Riding School; 'Colin Godman's' remains a private house.

[4] Unlike Dr Wauchope who included a warm and generous appreciation of Dr Boyle in her semi-autobiography *The Story of A Woman Physician* pp 83—84.

[5] The Parish of Aldrington was absorbed into Hove in 1893.

[6] Middleton, Judy (n.d., unpublished) *Encyclopaedia of Hove and Portslade*. Brighton and Hove Reference and Local Studies Libraries.

[7] In the book *Octavia Wilberforce, the Autobiography of a Pioneer Woman Doctor*, edited by Pat Jalland, Dr Wilberforce's (previously unpublished) narrative states that it was Mrs Yates Thompson (Dolly) who anonymously gave the money to buy Windlesham House. No entry in the New Sussex Hospital records indicates an anonymous donor coming forward, and the grant from the Sir John Howard legacy seems to have been adequate. However, the bound copies of the reports of the Annual Meetings of the Lady Chichester Hospital state that money was received from an anonymous source to buy Aldrington House. It seems most likely that Dr Wilberforce, writing in the late 1950s, misremembered, either owing to the confusion caused by the hospitals' various name changes or the passage of time. At that time (1918–19) Dr Wilberforce was not yet qualified or active at the New Sussex, which did not open until 1921. Interestingly, Dolly Yates Thompson helped Dr Wilberforce buy a house in Brighton to set up her practice, and was a close friend of Elizabeth Robins.

[8] *Brighton & Hove Herald* 23 June 1920.

[9] The original name plates from Aldrington house are now uncovered and can be seen on the gate posts.

[10] Cecily Lamorna Hingston MBE 1896–1989 became senior psychiatrist at the hospital in 1948, after Helen Boyle's retirement, and was also consultant psychiatrist at the Royal Sussex County. Dr Hingston retired in 1970 and lived to the age of 92. *Brighton & Hove Herald* 27 February 1960 inter alia.

[11] *Brighton & Hove Herald* 15 April 1934.

[12] Report of a speech made by Helen Boyle. *Sussex Daily News* 18 May 1920.

[13] Lady Ruth Pelham, a sister of the Earl of Chichester, left Sussex in 1923 and joined the Order of the Sisters of St Elizabeth in London. *Sussex Daily News* 2 October 1923.

13

WINDLESHAM HOUSE

In late 1918, with Christmas on the horizon and heavy demands from family and relatives for most of the newly minted and not quite permanently named New Sussex Hospital Board of Management, Dr Martindale probably found herself very busy. Any remaining hopes about snapping up the vicarage were dashed when letters were received (no doubt with regret from the former and with some smug satisfaction from the latter) from the Bishop of Lewes and Canon Dormer Pierce confirming that the sale would not go ahead. Time was running out and there was little choice left; if the hospital was ever to leap off the drawing board and into reality it was going to have to be in Windlesham House (later to be called Sussex House). The freeholder, Mrs Scott Malden, was getting edgy, decisive action was needed, and soon. Acting on behalf of the probably rather dazed Board, Louisa Martindale asked Mr Eggar the solicitor to oversee the purchase of Windlesham House and he was drafted onto the Site and Buildings sub-committee, along with his wife Katherine, who was also involved with the Linen Guild at the Royal Sussex County Hospital,* which might well come in useful. Mr Eggar was aware that Dr Martindale needed sensible help; however his investigations began to unearth unpleasant facts about Windlesham House.

At the beginning of the war the army had commandeered the Brighton workhouse at Race Hill, with a view to using its wards and infirmary as a military hospital; in particular for the care of sick and wounded Indian troops fighting in Europe alongside the British Expeditionary Force, and later for those from Lord Kitchener's army. High in the hills above Brighton, beside the springy, fashionable turf of the racecourse, the workhouse — officially titled the Poor Law Institution but never called anything other than the workhouse — was a sprawling mass of dour but solid buildings that spread frigidly across a whole seven acres of cheerless hillside. Every workhouse had its infirmary which served not only the destitute, long-term inhabitants and casual itinerant callers but also the poorer people of the local parish who needed hospital treatment but who could not pay the fees charged by local doctors or the nearby voluntary hospitals.

---

* King George V granted the Sussex County the privilege of prefixing itself 'Royal' in 1911.

The Poor Law Board in London was the central government committee responsible for nationwide control of the Poor Laws, but at local and parish level it was the town and city corporations and the vestry who funded and managed the workhouses out of local rates and taxes though an elected local committee or board. The committee, responsible to the town council for ensuring that the workhouse was run efficiently, that expenditure was adequate rather than generous and that no waste was incurred, was known as the Board of the Guardians of the Poor. The Brighton Guardians, both gentlemen and ladies,[1] were elected at regular intervals and gave their services freely, although a salaried clerk (with sundry other salaried or waged lesser staff) was always available to take care of administrative details. The Guardians were directly responsible for the management of their workhouse and amongst other interesting duties carried out the necessary hiring and firing of the full-time and part-time paid workhouse staff: a master and matron (usually a mature married couple and often their grown up daughters and sons), a full-time medical officer, nurses for the infirmary, a chaplain, a woman superintendent for the laundry, an engineer, a porter and any other staff that might be required. The master was responsible for the male inhabitants and for contracting out services to local shopkeepers and businessmen to supply food, coal, water and gas to the workhouse; the matron acted as his deputy and was responsible for the female inhabitants. Staff were usually given accommodation on site and had generous food allowances along the lines of a certain amount of bread, meat and drink per day. Naturally the Brighton Guardians were anxious that funds were not spent unnecessarily, a view in which the master usually concurred.[2]

The Brighton workhouse was unusual. The 1834 Poor Law Amendment Act had enabled all country parishes, for the purposes of saving money and increasing efficiency, to unite together and build a workhouse large enough to accept inmates from more than one surrounding parish: the 'Union' workhouse. The Brighton workhouse did not belong to a union of parishes; somehow the town had obtained exemption from the 1834 Act because, in 1822, the Corporation and vestry officials had already built themselves a very nice new workhouse on a good site just above St Nicholas's Church (for the none-too-small a sum of £11,400) and they were, understandably, reluctant to fill these handsome premises with inmates from surrounding areas, for whom the ratepayers of Brighton had no responsibility. If a man or woman born in the parish of Hove for example fell upon hard times, then it was the Steyning Union workhouse to which he or she had to apply for entry.

However, only thirty years later the St Nicholas's workhouse building had not only become inadequate but was also much too near the new residential houses, large and small, slowly creeping up Clifton Hill, and which were taking over the Laines after the arrival of the railway in the 1840s.[3] Quite clearly a new workhouse, satisfactorily well away from Brighton town, had to be found. And in 1865 a new workhouse was opened at a fine and far away location on Race Hill, solid, distant, and very functional. It was as good — if not better — than any other workhouse in rural Sussex, with a particularly effective infirmary and dedicated medical officer.

In 1918 the Clerk to the Guardians, a post always filled by an educated and professional man, was Mr Horace Burfield and the master and matron of Brighton workhouse were Mr Wilfred John Daking and his wife Ethel Mary. The medical officer, who held the post for over thirty years, was Dr Douglas Ross. By 1914 his infirmary had a fully functional operating theatre with a visiting part-time consulting and operating surgeon; he also had an assistant medical officer, working on a six month contract, and a full-time dispenser. The infirmary nurses were qualified, having benefited from both Louisa Twining[4] and Florence Nightingale's interest in training and status for their profession: the infirmary itself had been recognised as a training establishment for men and women wishing to take up nursing. There were ten charge nurses, a night sister, eight staff nurses, a non-resident male nurse and thirty nursing probationers. It was a large hospital, well equipped and up-to-date and, by 1911, it had general male and female wards, a lock ward for venereal diseases, fever wards, smallpox wards and a maternity ward. In 1914 the name 'workhouse' was delicately changed by the distant Poor Law Board to 'institution'. This was hardly an improvement and the word 'workhouse' has never to this day been abandoned either by the English language or the British people although, at the time, in official correspondence, 'institution' was the preferred word.

In 2006, now functioning as Brighton General Hospital, the main building still bears a plaque commemorating the opening of the workhouse in 1865. Its isolation and heavy buildings remain forbidding, but in 1914 they attracted the roving eye of the War Office as being very suitable indeed. Brighton workhouse and its excellent infirmary was wonderfully placed to become a military hospital for the expected sick and wounded. An approach was made by the War Office to the Brighton Guardians, and probably through gritted and ungrateful teeth the Guardians had obligingly responded by offering use of the workhouse and its infirmary to the War Office 'for the duration'. No doubt they were made an offer which they could not refuse.[5] The casual intake of itinerant or destitute men and women who came to Brighton looking for seasonal or short-term work but who could find none was halted. The permanent elderly, sick and lunatic inhabitants were removed and scattered all over Brighton and Hove into a multitude of houses; some even went as far as the union workhouse at Steyning. The elderly men had been accommodated in vacant Windlesham House and, in January 1919, they were still in residence. There was no sign at all of them moving out but, at the time, no-one was particularly worried.

The silencing of the guns in Europe in November 1918 had coincided almost precisely with the failure of the purchase of The Old Vicarage, and it is tempting to wonder whether Canon Dormer Pierce's reluctance and eventual refusal to move had something to do with the Armistice and the cessation of hostilities. That was water under the bridge now: the war was over, everything was getting back to normal, allowances had to be made in the name of patriotism and obviously the Brighton workhouse Guardians would soon have no choice but to arrange for the master to move the elderly men from Windlesham House and return them to their old quarters on Race Hill. (No doubt that would be to their deep disappointment; the softer air at Windlesham Road must have been greatly preferable to the briskly chilly winds which continually sweep the wintery workhouse buildings up on the hills.) Dr Martindale, when informing the Board of Management that Windlesham House was not yet vacant, envisaged no problem. The purchase would take some time: a mortgage would have to be raised to buy the property and carry out the building works, a limited company would have to be formed so that the loan could be serviced, and Mr Eggar had kindly volunteered to do all the paperwork. There was even a small income coming in from the Guardians: they were paying £8 a quarter to Mrs Scott Malden for use of the house.

No-one was worried either that Mr Horace Burfield, clerk to the guardians, had agreed with Mrs Scott Malden and her son back in 1914 that the elderly men could continue to occupy Windlesham House until their own accommodation on Race Hill could be returned to them, and that could not happen until all the Race Hill buildings were both empty and in an acceptable condition. The army had been in residence for four years, during which time many alterations had been carried out, and who knew what cleaning and repairs would be necessary! The soldiers had been used to luxuries which would not do at all for a workhouse; new fangled inventions such gas ovens and electric light had been installed as well as warm wards, comfortable mess rooms and cheerful fireplaces. Some, if not all, would have to come out again.

A long look was taken at the layout of the whole Windlesham site, for it was not only the house that was on offer. In the hopes of maximising profits Mrs Scott Malden and her son had divided the property into two parts. The house and the land surrounding its walls, some 400 feet fronting more or less onto York Road was to be sold as Lot 1. The area directly behind and north of the house, much larger and running alongside Windlesham Road, was to be sold separately, as Lot 2. As well as paying a rent of £8 a quarter for the house Brighton workhouse Guardians were paying £30 per year for the use of Lot 2. A third lot — a narrow strip of land some 100 feet wide and with a garage running alongside Lots 1 and 2 — had been used by Windlesham House School but had not been owned by it; it was rented, at £123 per year, from the D'Avigdor Goldsmid Estate. The Guardians had use of the narrow strip but, mindful of his patriotic duty, Mr Scott Malden (the headmaster and son of Mrs Scott Malden) had gallantly continued to pay the rent to the D'Avigdor Goldsmid Estate himself. The apparent complication caused by having three lots with two different owners caused no initial worry; after all, the D'Avigdor Goldsmid Estate had agreed to sell Lot 3. The reserve asking price for Lot 1 was £3,500 and for Lot 2 £5,500, should the Board wish to go ahead and secure both sites. This amounted to a great deal of money, far more than the vicarage would have cost. Questions arose as to whether all the land was needed. If they also bought Lot 3, at a price of £4,770 from the D'Avigdor Goldsmid Estate, that would total £13,770, clearly an impossible sum to raise.

The Eggars had done their homework and it was Mrs Eggar who had been deputed to give the bad news to the Board. The D'Avigdor Goldsmid Estate (at the time in the process of dismantling itself) was prepared to sell Lot 3 in two halves but the price would be very high. According to the Eggars, the Estate as a business concern was notoriously difficult to deal with. To make matters even worse, Mr Eggar had found out that Lots 1 and 2 were inside the Brighton border, whereas Lot 3 was just inside Hove. This information had not been offered by Mrs and Mr Scott Malden, no doubt with good reason — possibly this was why they had continued to rent the land rather than buying it. At the time Brighton and Hove were separate authorities and parishes, each with its own mayor, council, councillors and aldermen, town halls, magistrates and police, and all with accompanying inter-town rivalries.[6] The very thought of the complications of having to deal with the two town councils was almost too awful to contemplate. What is more, the Sir John Howard legacy fund specified 'Brighton' for the receipt of money; the question was: would the trustees turn a blind eye?

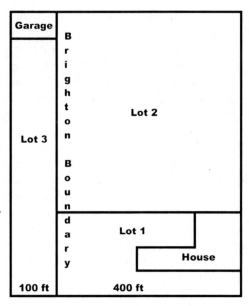

Plan of site — not to scale

Mrs Eggar was still not finished with the grim news: there was a significant difference geologically between the two sites; the Brighton site (Lots 1 and 2) were on gravel, and the Hove site (Lot 3) was on clay.[7] Mr Cobb, chairman of the Site and Buildings sub-committee, mentioned ominously the householder's nightmare: subsidence. A decision had to be made. It was a grave choice, which would have consequences that would be irrevocable. Elizabeth Robins, a rich woman and artist of much breadth of vision who would never allow her ill-health to cause her to miss out on a drama, was in the chair at this third Board of Management meeting and very much in favour of purchasing all three lots and worrying about money, border details and the state of the subsoil later. Mrs Ryle was in favour of buying Lot 1 only; Mrs Herbert Jones preferred Lot 1 and half of Lot 2; Mrs Eggar fancied Lot 1 and Lot 2, but preferred to leave out the subsoil and inter-town problems of Lot 3. The debate must have been desperate but, one hopes, polite. Money, position, space, responsibility; all these matters must have bounced hotly around the room with some degree of despair settling like fallout; but one thing was sure, they were not going to give up having their new hospital.

Dr Martindale took notes of the meeting, although she seems to have taken little part in the discussion. However, it cannot be coincidence that at the appropriate time Ismay FitzGerald came up with the proposal that the recommendation of the sub-committee should be adopted: the purchase of the house and Lot 1 at the asking price of £3,500, and a corresponding part of the Hove site fronting onto York Avenue (some 185 square feet) at an offer of £8 per square foot. The total probably amounting to just under £5,000. Hastily, Mr Cobb seconded and, no doubt with a collective sigh of deliverance, Ismay's proposal was unanimously carried. Lot 1 was inside Brighton and therefore technically qualified for a grant from the Sir John Howard legacy fund. Windlesham House would just have to do as the hospital and no doubt Mr Clayton, the architect, would knuckle under and come up with some nice new plans. The corresponding slice of Lot 3, in Hove, might well be unsuitable for building and, now that it was definite that Windlesham House was to become the hospital, there was no money over for further building in any case, so it wouldn't matter about the clay soil. Lot 3 could become a garden and, being sited in Hove, with its separate mayor and corporation, might even open up fresh opportunities for patronage and fundraising. New fields to be explored; new friends to be made. The fact that they were coming rather close to the Lady Chichester Hospital, still in Brunswick Place, could not be helped: Dr Martindale makes no reference to any possible repercussions from that prickly direction.

The Board turned to more pleasant matters now that a decision had been made. A joint treasurer for the new hospital still had to be found to fill Miss M. E. Verrall's shoes (although she remained as treasurer for the Ditchling Road Branch, which would stay up and running until the new hospital opened). Dr Martindale had suggested Lady Rhondda way back in October 1918 when Miss Verrall had first declined to stay on and the Board was delighted to learn that the Viscountess had accepted the position.[8] She would however assume the mantle of 'honorary' rather than 'joint' treasurer, the former title being more appropriate since she no doubt made it very clear that she would not do any actual number-work but was happy to boost publicity efforts and pen persuasive letters as required.

Lady Rhondda visited in April 1919, most successfully. Upon arrival she was taken to see the proposed new hospital building and showed a lively interest in arrangements for the employment and housing of nurses. She then promptly handed over a very gratifying cheque for £500, although she stipulated that she did not want her private address to be made available on the new appeal, which was in the process of being written. Lady Rhondda was only ever connected with the New Sussex Hospital in Windlesham Road, and that by very little other than her presence; and yet that was very useful, for during the run-up to the closure of the hospital at the old Brighton Branch (4, 6 and 8 Ditchling Road) and its re-opening as in Windlesham House — now known intermittently as Sussex House — fundraising was still a priority. *The Times* carried a stirring letter appealing for funds to raise an endowment of £50,000 for the New Sussex to ensure its future, which was signed by Lady Rhondda and the Bishop of Lewes, asking for donations to be sent to Viscountess Rhondda at 4–8 Ditchling Road. Sadly, the money received did not ever reach that amount.[9] During the continuing work and struggle the Brighton Branch at Ditchling Road, finally known as the 'Hospital' in joyful anticipation of moving to Windlesham House, and to prepare the public to get used to yet another name change, was still fully operational. Patients were seen and admitted, supplies maintained and nursing staff paid. Honorary staff, doctors and the volunteer secretary and almoner had to be kept both busy and happy.

The purchase of Windlesham House went according to plan. The money came in from the Howard trustees, the New Sussex Hospital became a limited company and a mortgage was obtained from the bank. The finance committee looked after funds coming in and going out, and Mr Clayton swallowed his architectural indifference to Windlesham House as a suitable vehicle for the hospital and produced some workable plans.

The finance committee soon assumed the length of stride that was needed for the job and became very powerful, charging itself with a strict control of the slender purse strings, and so the Board of Management could turn its attention to locating suitable builders — not too expensive, but of good quality — and began to pour a good deal more energy into stretching the boundaries of fundraising into fresh pastures. The new appeal, still not written, would have to be completed and exquisitely poised, poignant phrases would hopefully burrow deep into generous hearts and thence towards capacious pockets. A delicate balance was needed: with the Ditchling Road premises still up and running but with the future move to Sussex House nearly in the bag, much time was spent on whether or not to engage paid administrative assistance in the form of a permanent hospital secretary. A part-time honorary secretary, Miss Turner, did the honours at Ditchling Road, but after the move was made (and also beforehand, when everything was in the planning stage) she surely could not be asked to do more. There would be much extra work to be done, whoever was appointed might well have to put in full-time hours. Miss Millicent Lawrence from Roedean, a recent arrival on the Board of Management, argued that a salaried post should be created, at £250 a year, not a bad wage at that time. She added, shrewdly, that whoever was appointed could then be used in other ways, in particular with drafting and circulating the appeal. As might be expected, Dr Martindale had already made her choice; having put an advertisement in *The Times* she had, with Miss Merrifield in support, interviewed Miss Ruth Green, who seemed to be very suitable.

In spite of rather weak opposition from Mr Cobb and Mrs Ryle, who were in favour of one of the other applicants, and a classic Ismay FitzGerald murmur (faithfully recorded by Dr Martindale) that surely this was unfair to Miss Turner, Miss Green was appointed.[10] A bright and enthusiastic woman, she brimmed with good ideas for fundraising and was endowed with the energy to carry them out. Successfully negotiating with the Board for what would certainly have been only a third class season ticket to cover her fares to Brighton (she lived in London), amongst her other duties she took over the responsibility of writing the minutes of the Board of Management meetings. Dr Martindale's vigorous hand sadly leaves its pages at this point and her ease of control of events is observed rather than injected into the narrative.

Time passed, but nearly a year later, in the summer of 1919 the elderly men of the workhouse were still in residence at Sussex House and showed no signs of leaving.

AUTHORS' HELP FOR SUSSEX HOSPITAL.

In aid of the building fund for the much-needed extension of the New Sussex Hospital for Women and Children, the Roedean, St. Michael's Hall, and other schools are holding a bazaar at the Grand Hotel, Brighton, on December 16 and 17. For the bookstall autographed books, pictures, letters, have been received from the following among many others :—Sir James Barrie, John Galsworthy, Joseph Conrad, Rudyard Kipling, General Sir Ian Hamilton, John Masefield, G. K. Chesterton, Hilaire Belloc, Sir Owen Seaman, Mrs. Meynell, Mrs. W. K. Clifford, and Sir Arthur Pinero. Mr. Sutro has sent his autograph in the form of a cheque. Other gifts include an original *Punch* cartoon from Bernard Partridge, a characteristic letter of Robert Louis Stevenson's, a letter of Henry James's, and autographs of Coquelin, Verlaine, &c. Books, &c., will be gratefully received at c/o Dr. Edmonds, 5, Brunswick-place, Brighton, by Miss Elizabeth Robins and Miss Beatrice Harraden.

The Times, 10 December 1919

Notes

[1] Mrs Jessie Blatch, the first woman town councillor in Brighton or Hove, was one of the guardians. She was elected on 3rd October 1918 and was a member of the Mental Deficiency Committee.

[2] The workhouses have gone down ill in history as halls of misery and starvation ruled over cruelly by vicious and heartless masters. No doubt this was often the case but workhouses also provided reasonably well paid and secure work for women — sometimes there was no master, only a matron — and daughters were frequently given work. The infirmary at Brighton under the long-term care of Dr Ross not only employed many nurses but also served as a training establishment for young women seeking a career in the hospital service.

[3] The London, Brighton & Croydon Railway started up its popular and successful services from London in 1846.

[4] Louisa Twining (1820–1912) was a social reformer and writer concerned with conditions in workhouses: she established the Workhouse Visiting Society in 1858, and formed the Workhouse Infirmary Nursing Association in 1879 to ensure that workhouse infirmary nurses were trained and qualified. She wrote in *Suggestions for Women Guardians* (1885) 'I would ask [the] Guardians to remember that their duties and their guardianship are not limited to the poor alone, but are equally required for the officers, for whose welfare they are also responsible.'

[5] Gooch, J. (1980) *A History of Brighton General Hospital.* Phillimore.

[6] In 1892 Hove had been created an urban district within the administrative county of East Sussex; in 1898 it became a municipal borough.

[7] The terraces around Palmeira Avenue and Holland Road where the houses are below the road level are the remains of the brick industry, which removed much clay in the nineteenth century.

[8] Miss Merrifield agreed to stay on as co-treasurer and would most certainly have done all the hard work.

[9] *The Times* 16 May 1919.

[10] Miss Turner was later offered a part-time position at £25 a year as registrar of the new hospital if she would help out with the accounts, no doubt thanks to Miss FitzGerald's concern.

14

THE STRUGGLE CONTINUES

The events leading up to what nearly became a crisis, when it seemed that the Guardians would never see fit to remove the old men from Windlesham House, were recorded alongside plentiful — and at times inspired — manoeuvrings to raise money. It was by no means an easy ride. The ladies of the Board of Management, although experienced, were not professional fundraisers and from time to time were both alarmed and flummoxed by the market forces they had to deal with. But they learned, and quickly. Louisa Martindale, forty-six years old in 1919, was both leader and inspirer, yet even she was sometimes moved to exasperation.

Uneasiness around the permanent name of the new hospital continued to crop up. In February 1919 Miss Green, now employed as secretary on a starting contract of six months at £250 p.a. and with her season ticket allowed initially for three months, was given responsibility for arranging a very important detail, ordering the official notepaper, tastefully headed with the new name of the hospital. But what was that name to be? At this early stage did the notepaper need to specify the doctors or, indeed, the non-medical staff? Amazingly, there was still dissension over the name, but having no mind for further aggravation Dr Martindale, who had probably been warned that this wearisome topic would yet again rear its tiresome head, sensibly asked the Board to come to a swift and binding decision between the two latest suggestions, the 'New Sussex Hospital' or 'New Sussex House'. Put to the vote, even after all this time there was no agreement, with six votes cast each way. It would seem most likely that Dr Martindale had primed Miss Millicent Lawrence, who was chairing the meeting, what to do in this event and, on a casting vote, Miss Lawrence agreed on the 'New Sussex Hospital', no doubt to Dr Martindale's intense relief.

But a month later, yet again the subject came up for discussion. Mrs Eggar, in her capacity as Linen Guild organiser up at the Royal Sussex County Hospital (which seems to have carried much influence and a seat on its Board) had been the target of complaints from her colleagues along the lines that the name New Sussex was too similar to theirs for comfort. She had managed to escape the onslaught only by promising that she would bring the complaints to the New Sussex Board. This time the Board of Management stood fast and refused to change the name, sending a pert message back to the Royal Sussex to that effect.

It may appear difficult for us to understand what all the fuss was about but, in their defence, there was no doubt in the minds of the Board of Management that confusion in the minds of the public might interfere not only with the generosity of cheque-books, but also with the destination of spare change when passers-by were faced in the street with pointedly shaken Workman's Collecting Boxes. The copper and (hopefully) the silver might well end up in the wrong box by mistake if the names were too similar. There had been an ominous precedent: only a few years previously the Chichester Hospital in the city of Chichester, just down the coast in West Sussex, had complained that the Lady Chichester Hospital had wrongly received funds which had been intended for itself because of confusion between the names. How problematic this really was for the New Sussex and the Royal Sussex County cannot easily be estimated, but in the cut-throat world of fundraising and the fragility of a steady cash flow, the possibility of such confusion could not be ignored. The problem would crop up again and again; although it could have been argued that any possible misdirection of funds could, in practice, work either way, and what was 'lost on the swings' could be 'gained on the roundabouts'. Nevertheless, since 1899 there had perhaps been too many name changes for comfort.

High profile help would be needed. The Bishop of Lewes (whose wife Madeleine was a member of the Board of Management) was asked if he could suggest any local luminaries whose help might be solicited. Mr (later, Sir) Harry Preston, the local entrepreneur and owner of the York Hotel (and who would in 2002 have a Brighton & Hove bus named for him) was approached. He was already engaged in arranging a grand charity entertainment in aid of the Royal Sussex County Hospital, at which he anticipated raising £2,000, and promised to help the New Sussex after Easter 1920. Getting into her stride, Miss Green suggested canvassing shops and banks for contributions; she was given permission to do this herself and recommended Mr J. Edward Stafford as a potential supporter. He was a local businessman and one time Mayor of Brighton (1900–1901) whose name is borne by a block of flats in Upper Rock Gardens to this day. It was a shrewd move: Mr Stafford and his wife would later join the New Sussex Board of Management.

Elizabeth Robins was detailed to write supportive and introductory letters to *The Times* and *The Observer* since any letter from her would automatically be published. Might she also write an article for *The Common Cause*, the magazine of the National Union of Women's Suffrage Societies? A colourful poster was being designed by a Mr Mark Milbanke, carefully excluding the colours green and purple, which were associated with Mrs Pankhurst's Women's Social and Political Union — now thankfully defunct.

By May 1919 Miss Green could report to the Board of Management that she had successfully contacted a whole host of local ladies, amongst them Mrs Stephen Ralli,[1] Lady Cunliffe and Lady Cayger, all of whom would be willing to lend their large and fashionable drawing rooms for the staging of money-raising entertainments. She added that various hotels had offered their help but she had not followed this up as, she hinted rather heavily, an entertainments committee had still not been formed. Lady Cunliffe had scooped up the local branches of the Women's Institute and well-known amateur organisers of pageants and tableaux were tapped for use of their expertise; after all, fundraisers might be needed but a source of potential patients should also not be neglected. Miss Dobson, an acquaintance of Lady Cunliffe, promised to organise a garden fête, while other female worthies were suggested as possible sources of help: Lady Bagot, Lady Cusack-Smith (and her husband Sir Berry, who was on the finance committee), Mrs Brownley Davenport, Mrs Arthur Wagg and Miss Octavia Wilberforce, the protégée of Elizabeth Robins, who would later qualify as a doctor, set up her practice in Montpelier Villas and join the medical staff at the New Sussex. Madame Sterling would give a recital on 11th October and Drs May Thorne and Mary Scharlieb would be invited to speak. Husbands were by no means to be left out. The resourceful and energetic Miss Green arranged a meeting of sympathetic Brighton businessmen to help with fundraising, and succeeded in volunteering Alderman Colborne to be its chairman. Other businessmen, from as far afield as Horsham, would hopefully also form what would become a supportive committee composed entirely of men rather than women. This might well form a point of magnetism to attract regular subscribers of the masculine sex, as well as their wives. The vicar of Hayward's Heath promised his support. Plump and prosperous mayors of both Brighton and Hove were not to be neglected and Sir Ernest Cassel's name as a contributor was to be included in the appeal. The new appeal, probably composed by the writer Miss Hope Malleson, writer of a biography of Dr Mary Murdoch and a work on Italian paintings,[2] was eventually put together and by July 1919 it was ready to be printed. Now that the New Sussex Hospital was a limited company the constitution would have to be reinspected and any other current and irksome problems ironed out by the Board of Management.

There was the question of what use should be made of the rent being paid by the Guardians in respect of the elderly men who were still living at Sussex House? Should the income from ongoing fundraising events go straight into the building fund account for Sussex House or be used to run the old hospital, still functioning, back in Ditchling Road? A 'Grand Sale of Work' — always a popular money-spinner — had been planned for 13th December but that date unfortunately clashed with a similar sale of work to be held by Brighton High School, which would not do at all. The problem of what day to choose caused no little anxiety — there are just not enough weekends before Christmas — but the revered senior citizeness Mrs Henry (Millicent Garrett) Fawcett of the National Union of Women's Suffrage Societies cheered everyone up at a distance by having heartily agreed that a nice article about the New Sussex written by Elizabeth Robins would be warmly appreciated by the editors of *The Common Cause.* In July 1919 Alderman Colborne, who had been so very welcome when he volunteered to chair the businessmen's committee had, however, unpalatably suggested that special terms might be given to those patients who were employed by subscribers — no doubt as a businessman he had an eye to his own employees. It was hard to know what should be done about this because, while he would have to be appeased, if his request were granted all other subscribers might, not unnaturally, expect the same privileges.

Dr Martindale, either prepared beforehand or by now accustomed to thinking on her feet, suggested deferment of discussion and that a letter be sent to Alderman Colborne telling him that the matter was 'under consideration'.[3] Miss Turner, the Ditchling Road voluntary secretary, was also the subject of uneasy discussion during the summer months of 1919. No doubt there had been some lobbying out of office hours since it was Ismay FitzGerald who had first spoken up for Miss Turner a few months previously when the appointment of a paid secretary was discussed (possibly Miss Turner had applied for the job but was unsuccessful). In July, during talks about the new appeal, Dr Martindale suggested gently to the Board members that, since Miss Turner did such responsible work at Ditchling Road, her name should appear on the list of officers. This, however, was too much for the other ladies to digest. Rather meanly they did not agree since, they said, Miss Turner had not been involved with its production; however, they would graciously allow Miss Turner to feature on the next annual report as registrar of the outpatients' and accountant of the Ditchling Road site. The attitude of the ladies of the Board of Management towards their paid and unpaid staff may seem harsh these days and it is to Miss FitzGerald's credit that she had been prepared to bring Miss Turner's devoted duties to their notice and, presumably, to Louisa Martindale out of office hours.

Otherwise, everything might just be going well. Mr Clayton, the architect, had managed to produce sketches of designs for the building, and the surgeon Mr Harold Scatliff (Dr Helen Scatliff's husband) had scored a real coup by purchasing a quantity of surplus army medical materials from the closure of the 2nd Eastern General (Medical) Hospital, late of 20 Dyke Road, as the War Office started the ponderous task of closing down its war machine. Miss Merrifield, wearing her treasurer's hat, constructively suggested that payment should come out of the building fund but, rather uneasily, everyone was reminded that the workhouse at Race Hill had still not been released by the Royal Army Medical Corps, and that meant that Sussex House was still a home from home to the elderly men from Race Hill. During the hectic and busy months of the summer of 1919 this sticky problem had rather slipped out of consideration, but it could not be ignored for ever, since looming grimly nearer were those shrinking leases of the three houses 4, 6 and 8 Ditchling Road. A fearsome dilemma might well be more close than comfort would accommodate. The move out of Ditchling Road into Sussex House must, surely, be made soon.

With the closure of the 2nd Eastern General Hospital by the army and the disposal of its equipment, hopes were allowed to soar, however, and at long last, in November 1919, the Royal Army Medical Corps finally indicated that it planned to move out of the gaunt workhouse buildings at Race Hill and release them back to the Guardians. At Sussex House the committees that made up the structure of the Board of Management were already in place; the finance committee was poised with the money and the new appeal fund was primed to be set up at the bank in warm anticipation that the final version of the appeal was nearly ready for a massive mail-shot. The building committee had the rising fund under control and the medical committee was functioning happily.

Only the house committee had a small problem, having concluded that it needed paid clerical assistance to help Miss Green, who was rapidly becoming indispensable. A part-time assistant for her was needed, but one with appropriate qualifications. An advertisement had been placed in the local papers and responding applicants interviewed, but the house committee had been unable to make up its mind and brought the ticklish problem to the Board. The choice was between Miss Jones, currently working for Sir Berry Cusack-Smith, who was qualified but who really wanted a full time position and a salary of 36s 6d a week, and Miss Box, currently employed by Miss Rendell. Miss Box would happily work mornings only but, unfortunately, lacked the necessary qualifications. It is interesting that the middle-class, volunteer ladies of the Board, skilled in hiring and firing servants, were still sufficiently unsure of themselves to be unable to solve this basic management problem and Miss Ruth Green, always the professional, helpfully suggested that Miss Box could be tested on her skills by her current employer. However this neat solution seems not to have been satisfactory and agreement was not forthcoming. Mr Cobb put an end to the discussion by asserting that, since it was Miss Green who would have to work with whosoever was to be employed, then she should decide, but with the restriction that no more than £1 per week could be offered. The Board agreed and Miss Green chose the unqualified Miss Box.

In blithe anticipation of an imminent move to Sussex House an agreement was made in October 1919 with the Pioneer Club at 4 New Road in Brighton (near the Theatre Royal) for the rental of a room, complete with telephone, for the Board of Management to use as an office and for meetings. With economy in mind it was agreed that the Pioneer Club should also have access to the telephone, for a fee of £3 a year. Gearing up for the move, and brushing aside more bleating from the Royal Sussex County Hospital about the name, the Board gave instructions that a painted board announcing the arrival of the New Sussex Hospital should be erected above the railings outside Sussex House at an estimated cost of £4 10s, but it later transpired that this estimate did not include the cost of the posts needed to raise it above the surrounding railings. The members of the Board were learning the hard way and this time they took decisive action: Miss Merrifield was instructed to use her own judgement, get an estimate, order the board and get it fixed 'at a suitable elevation'.

Otherwise, things really were looking up: in November 1919, £300 had been joyfully received into funds by a gala performance on the pier, helping the overdraft considerably, and the Army Medical Corps finally vacated the workhouse, so that with any luck the elderly men could move out of Sussex House before Christmas. However, no promises were forthcoming. By December Mr Burfield, a not unkindly man who had been clerk to the Guardians since 1902 (having followed his father into the job) made it clear that, as yet, he could give no date for the men's removal and that it was at that time impossible for them to be removed. He quoted the agreement that he and the Guardians had hammered out with the War Office: 'that they should only return their home on Race Hill when the old buildings had been returned to a state acceptable to themselves.'

In practice, this meant they had to be acceptable to the workhouse master, Mr Daking, and he was not an easy man. Before the war he had been stiffly known to decline to turn a blind eye to the male inhabitants smoking the odd pipe of tobacco in the evenings, if they could get one and, sternly watchful of his duty to the ratepayers of Brighton, he was not minded to allow the returning workhouse inmates to benefit from the improvements that the War Office had made for the comfort of its wounded and sick soldiers.

By this time added pressure was also coming from the owners of the three houses in Ditchling Road who, not unreasonably, wanted to know what was happening so that they too could make long-term arrangements. The old Brighton Branch (now functioning under the name the New Sussex Hospital) when it eventually left Ditchling Road would also have to make repairs and replacements in all three buildings where alterations to rooms had been made and new plumbing and drains introduced. Walls that had been demolished would have to be rebuilt, fittings suitable only for hospital use would have to be removed. Wear and tear — or what was called, rather neatly, 'dilapidations' — would have to be seen to. The crucial question was: when should the Board give notice to leave to the owners of the Ditchling Road sites? With no date for the vacating of Sussex House on the horizon and with the necessary building and repair works still having to be made at both sites, who could make an accurate assessment? A wrong decision could be ruinous, and the finance committee had to give the grim news that the overdraft had now climbed to £1,000, although the Christmas bazaar planned for the 13th and 14th December would, hopefully, raise some much-needed cash.

By January 1920 it seemed as if all sides were mired in a helpless inability to move. The owners of 6 Ditchling Road (where the lease ended earliest) tried to be helpful and, after diplomatic negotiations, offered a monthly tenancy. The tenancies of 4 and 8 were due to end in June 1920, which gave a little time, but not much. As forecast, this was by no means a good time to find a builder; it was not too long after the end of the war and builders were so busy that they could pick and choose their clients at will and charge what they liked. A suitable, that is to say not expensive, building firm would not easily be found. With the elderly men still not moving out, and with the Sir John Howard legacy trustees inviting the Board of Management to make further applications for another, smaller, grant (an offer not to be refused) it was, to say the least, a nervous and tense time. Wanting at least a toe in the door the Board, rather sensibly, approached Mr Burfield for permission to open an office at Sussex House. After all, they owned the building and the occupancy of one room should not cause the Guardians and their temporary 'Officers in Charge', Mr and Mrs F. S. Gander, any inconvenience. The Board would then be able to find out exactly what was going on. Luckily, the Pioneer Club agreed to be sympathetic about the rent of the room on their premises, which had already been agreed.

At the same time, plans to draft in more noble ladies as non-working hospital patrons and, indeed, as president were started. The Duchess of Norfolk, being both local and very noble indeed, was approached with an offer that she become president, but sadly, she declined the offer 'on account of her many duties'. Lady Denman of the Land Army was asked to join up but was also reluctant to become involved. This was a pity since high profile help might well be needed if nothing happened soon at Sussex House. It was Elizabeth Robins who came up trumps. She promised to ask her friend Nancy, Lady Astor of Cliveden, the wealthy and dazzling American socialite whose husband was a viscount, and who was herself a recently elected MP, (indeed, the first woman MP to take up her parliamentary seat) if she would hold a drawing room meeting to put the plight of the Board of Management to a sympathetic audience.

Despite these achievements, by February 1920 the situation was still gloomy. The War Office, who had promised a date of the 16th to hand back the workhouse buildings to the Guardians (with the dilapidations put right) had signally failed to do so since it still had a few patients in its hospital wards there. The approaches to the owners of 4, 6 and 8 Ditchling Road regarding the possibility of a monthly tenure were in some part under way: although number 6 was still available on a monthly let the owners of number 4 wanted a 10% increase in rent if the agreement was to be monthly, while the owners of number 8 had not yet replied to enquiries.

Discussion as to which typewriter to buy for the office must have been a happy diversion; in a rare moment of choosing quality over cost a reconditioned Remington at £30 was eventually picked over a second hand Empire at £12 10s and a rebuilt Monarch at £24 10s. No doubt Miss Green had a great deal to do with that decision. With this fine instrument to show for their endeavours and the appointment of Mrs Holmes Siedle as dentist at Ditchling Road[4] the Board faced the first Annual Meeting of subscribers to the New Sussex Hospital in March 1920, with Elizabeth Robins confidently in the chair and all went reasonably well. Both Miss M. E. Verrall[5] and Miss F. de G. Merrifield stepped down as treasurers: Miss Verrall, as everyone knew, had not approved of joint treasurers and retained only her care for the finances of the Ditchling Road Hospital since the separation. She now relinquished this remaining responsibility to Mr E. F. Gribble, a most suitable person as he was a banker at the London County & Westminster Bank and also a local councillor. At the same time Mr Gribble also took over Miss Merrifield's side of the joint treasurership; in one sweep becoming the working half of the New Sussex Hospital joint treasurership, whilst Lady Rhondda — gracefully but with little effort — securely remained in her supporting and honorary capacity. Messrs Edmonds, Clover and Jones of Pavilion Buildings, Brighton, were appointed as auditors. (Dr Boyle also retained this firm, presumably since they had been auditors to the Lady Chichester Hospital for years; neither saw any reason for change.) As a banker Mr Gribble seems to have shared none of Miss Verrall's qualms: as treasurer he joined the Board of Management, along with Mrs Herbert Jones, Mr Stafford, Mrs Cuthbert Radcliffe, Mrs Godfree and Dr Helen Webb, a new arrival in Brighton.

Elizabeth Robins remained as chairwoman of the Board of Management, in spite of her poor health, with Miss Millicent Lawrence as vice chairwoman and Dr Martindale as second vice chairwoman. The sub-committees were set up: the finance committee was to be chaired by Sir Berry Cusack-Smith, and included Mr F. E. Cobb, Miss Millicent Lawrence, Dr Martindale, Mrs Eggar and Mrs Ryle, with Lady Rhondda and Mr Gribble as ex officio members. The house committee comprised Mrs Herbert Jones, Miss Maule, Mrs Cobb, Mrs Montague Williams, Mrs Godfree and the Hon. Ismay FitzGerald. The building committee consisted of Sir Berry and Lady Cusack-Smith, Miss Maule, Millicent Lawrence, Dr Martindale, Mrs Scatliff, Dr Florence Edmonds and the writer and art critic Miss Hope Malleson. Miss Malleson appears to have been an acquaintance of Dr Martindale, possibly through the women's suffrage network. An entertainments committee was also set up, presumably the membership was either rather fluid or not deemed worthy of explanation since the members were not listed.

After the interruption of the AGM the Board of Management members got down to work. There was good, mixed and bad news. The bad news was that the Board still had to tackle the distressing problem of the elderly men who still occupied Sussex House, but the good news was that Sister Clayton, who had left the Brighton Branch in 1914 to serve as a nurse for the Royal Army Medical Corps, had returned to her job at Ditchling Road after the closure of the 2nd Eastern General Hospital, with a (no doubt increased) salary of £45 a year. The mixed news was that Mrs Scott Malden and her son were making a cut price offer of the remaining land around Sussex House at considerably less than the original price of £4,000. Mr Scott Malden hopefully suggested that the Board locate a rich patron to buy the land and, in a generous gesture, simply hand it over to the New Sussex. It is not clear from remaining records exactly when this extra land was added to the lots already bought, but bought it certainly was. Most likely the purchase was made at this time, possibly with the aid of a further grant from the Sir John Howard Legacy fund, which had helpfully indicated that there was still some cash left over and the Board may well have jumped upon this to buy the remainder of the

Sussex House property. However, seemingly very good news indeed was the information that the army had — finally — got around to moving out the last of its patients from Race Hill and the hunt for suitable builders to begin work at Sussex House could start.

The more prudent members of the Board probably did not hold their breath for too long. Two months later, in May 1920 — at a time when Ditchling Road was still taking in patients (although the tenancies of the buildings were in serious debate), when taxes were having to be paid on Sussex House and when the finance committee was becoming very fretful because the results of their 'Buy-a-Brick Campaign' by no means met the shortfall — the Guardians still had not moved the elderly men back to Race Hill. Not surprisingly tempers were beginning to fray: would they ever leave? Could anything be done? Now that the army had gone, the fear of appearing unpatriotic by launching thunderous complaints to any authority that would listen could be disregarded. The efficient Miss Green took it upon herself to find out exactly what was going on. As suspected, it was the master of the workhouse who was causing the delay, by clinging tightly to the clause in the Guardians' agreement with the War Office, which stipulated that upon vacating the buildings the army should put right 'to his satisfaction' the dilapidations which they had made. And a major dilapidation, in his eyes, was the state of the old coal and coke-fired kitchen range.

The workhouse had used gas as a mean of lighting since 1865 (at the time it had been a modern and no doubt welcome innovation and there was nothing the master could do about that) but had retained the use of solid fuel in its kitchen range and bread-making ovens. The army, not unnaturally, had abandoned the coal and coke-fired range and installed new gas ovens and hobs, utilising the gas supply which was already in place, and the old kitchen range had subsequently fallen into disrepair. The army had now removed their gas cookers and Mr Daking had every intention of going back to using the old range when his workhouse was up and running again, but he was not satisfied with its condition and would not budge until the army had put it right.

Thinking on her feet, Miss Green suggested that, since a gas supply was now readily available in the kitchens, could a temporary gas appliance be installed? Mr Daking, replied Mr Burfield by letter, declined this suggestion. The Board then suggested that, since the bakery ovens were still in use, and coal and coke fired, could they not also be used for cooking meat? Mr Burfield said he had already put this to Mr Daking who had, somewhat imperiously, not agreed; he was adamant that the coal-fired range must be used. This would take time: the army engineers would have to come back, examine the range, make their report, and (if the army agreed) arrange for the works to be carried out and, if this involved looking for a local firm to do the work, a long delay was expected. The work would then have to be re-inspected by the army engineers and by Mr Daking.[6] It was a real and serious problem. Only a rich and plentiful supply of money could keep Ditchling Road going and at the same time pay the mortgage on an unproductive Sussex House; it didn't help that a fundraising matinée featuring Mr Seymour Hicks had had to be postponed because of the tiff between the government and the music hall owners on the vexed question of the sale of refreshments, tobacco and alcohol in their theatres.

At the New Sussex, it was becoming hard to avoid the shortening of tempers with frustration. Ismay FitzGerald, trying to help, suggested that the town council might be persuaded to put pressure on the Guardians to hurry up and move out, using the argument that it was clearly a waste of public money for the elderly men to live in Sussex House if it was not absolutely necessary. She probably had not checked this question with Louisa Martindale first, for Mrs Cobb (a former Mayoress of Brighton) replied, crushingly, that perhaps Miss FitzGerald herself would like to find out whether or not anything could be managed in that direction? Rather disloyally, Dr Martindale seconded Mrs Cobb's remark, and no doubt words were exchanged at 10 Marlborough Place afterwards. Daily business ground on. Happily, Dr Martindale's friends Lady Denman and Lady Cowdray, having been invited again, this time agreed to become vice-presidents, although the Duchess of Norfolk declined for a second time. Plans were made however to hold a drawing-room meeting, followed by a garden fête, at the home of Lady Sybil Smith (a sister-in-law of Lady Buxton) on 26th May 1921.

The deadlock still remained between the army and Mr Daking. The tension was beginning to tell on Louisa Martindale, and at a Board of Management meeting in early June 1920 she proposed to the Board that the whole package be re-examined. The New Sussex should stay permanently in Ditchling Road, she hazarded, and Sussex House, when it eventually became vacant, should be converted into flats and let. Her rationale was that this would provide a very good source of income and, in the meantime, the land not being used by the Guardians could be let to a Mr R. E. Allen of York Avenue, who had expressed an interest in starting up a tennis club in the area. Luckily, the Board did not agree; no doubt they recognised that, as the prime mover in the scheme to re-locate the hospital, Dr Martindale was shouldering the heaviest burden and that it was the strain talking. However, unless something moved soon, the grim spectre of approaching bankruptcy would have to be faced. The

Board, however, decided to continue to wait, and their decision was good: patience and steady nerves were rewarded when the military authorities, rather more smartly than had been feared, agreed to carry out the repairs to the range. But, incredibly, a week later Mr Daking complained that not only had the kitchen range been found wanting but also other repairs to the buildings had been found to be necessary!

There was no doubt now that Mr Daking had deliberately seized this golden opportunity to get the army to pay for as many repairs to the workhouse as he possibly could and that this was the real reason for his stubborn refusal to move. Louisa Martindale, recovering from her moment of weakness now that Mr Daking's motives had become so transparent, was irate and said darkly to the Board at an emergency Board of Management meeting that a question about the delay ought to be asked in the House of Commons. Amazingly, she managed it: in July 1920 Charles Thomas-Stanford, the local Conservative MP and owner of Preston Manor, got to his feet in parliament to ask for a reply from the War Office as to when they would carry out the repairs to the Brighton Poor Law Institution. It was a personal triumph for Louisa Martindale but, as was to be expected, the reply was none too satisfactory. The military authorities replied as stolidly as might be anticipated that 'the case was being treated with all possible expedition'. Nevertheless, the point had been made, and publicly, and a warning shot fired accurately towards Mr Daking. It would not go unnoticed by his employers.

Throughout June and July the Board of Management decided to meet twice monthly. Sir Berry Cusack-Smith, inspired by Dr Martindale's success with Mr Thomas-Stanford, promptly followed up with what turned out to be an excellent idea: that the Brighton and Hove Guardians should pay a financial penalty to the owners of Sussex House as compensation for their loss of money because of the delay. The Guardians, councillors and aldermen of Brighton, businessmen and well-known women, would not be unsympathetic to the plight of a property owner and landlord being held at financial knife-point by an intransigent tenant, simply because of the condition of a kitchen range! The very notion of having to hand over a pecuniary penalty to the owners of Sussex/Windlesham House would cause Brighton Corporation to indicate serious and swift criticism to the Guardians, which serious and swift criticism would be instantly and very satisfactorily downloaded straight back to Mr Daking. Ismay FitzGerald must have felt vindicated, though possibly rather sorry that she had not thought of this herself after Mrs Cobb's riposte of the month before.

Clearly rattled, Mr Daking hastily agreed to the use of a room in Sussex House for the Board of Management to use as an office and for its meetings; no doubt Miss Green was very much looking forward to making a thorough exploratory tour of Sussex House. Having learned a long lesson from dealing with the Guardians, the Board made arrangements to quit their room at the Pioneer Club but extracted a proviso from the secretary, Mr Collings, that a monthly tenure was possible, should it ever be needed.

With the August summer holiday season well upon everyone, after a good rest energies would be re-fired, ready for the final and long-awaited move. At last, in October 1920, after a year of waiting and three months of pain the Guardians finally vacated Sussex House, probably to the deep disappointment of all inhabitants, particularly the officers in charge, Mr and Mrs Gander, whose future was now uncertain. The relief was such that, forgetting their anger and rage, in the manner that only a feminine generosity can come up with, the Board of Management waived the three months' rent owed to them by the Guardians for their long stay.

Everyone snapped into business mode. The office was opened and the boardroom set up for meetings. Mrs Scott Malden and her son, no doubt as relieved as anyone that the move was now firmly in sight, agreed that the Old Boys of Windlesham School would be asked to come up with some cash in return for the honour of a ward being named Windlesham Ward. A caretaker had to be appointed immediately and a second telephone installed, which would come in very useful for the intense planning that would be needed for a really grand opening of the New Sussex Hospital.

Notes

[1] Mrs Ralli was the widow of a rich businessman who had left money in his will for medical and community benefits. Not surprisingly Mrs Ralli was also associated with Dr Boyle and the Lady Chichester Hospital, she was an LCH council member in the 21st anniversary year.

[2] Hope Malleson was a writer, the daughter of Elizabeth Malleson (1828–1916) the teacher and campaigner. Elizabeth Malleson (née Whitehead) was the eldest of twelve children born to a Unitarian solicitor and his wife, the daughter of an army surgeon. Elizabeth campaigned against the Contagious Diseases Act; taught at the Portman Hall School in London (endowed by Barbara Bodichon); founded the Working Women's College in Bloomsbury; and also set up the Rural Nursing Association to ensure that women living in rural areas had access to district nursing care. She was married and had three daughters and one son. (Owen Stinchcombe, *Oxford Dictionary of National Biography*.)

[3] The proposal was seconded by Lady Cusack-Smith and carried, but opposed

by Mrs Scatliff and Ismay FitzGerald. They are unlikely to have agreed to Mr Colborne's suggestion, which was a reminder of bad times long abandoned in the far-off days of the Lewes Road Dispensary and may have thought that Dr Martindale was too lenient and a sterner rebuff was needed.

[4] Dentistry has always been a branch of surgery, since extraction of teeth is necessarily accompanied by the shedding of blood, and it is the Colleges of Surgery which award the LDS — the Licentiateship of Dental Surgery. The story goes that a woman medical student in Edinburgh, Miss Pearce, enquired about a basic course in dental extractions since she intended to go to India to work as a doctor and her prospective patients, in purdah and the zenana, could not allow their faces to be seen by a man other than her husband. A course was started up and the first woman subsequently to obtain the LDS (L.D.S.R.C.S.Ed) was Lilian Murray (later Lindsay) in 1895 from the Royal College of Surgeons in Edinburgh after the London Dental Hospital refused even to let her through the door. They are said to have carried out her interview on the pavement! It is rather vague, possibly even apocryphal.

In 1908 the Brighton (now Brighton and Hove) High School for Girls' magazine printed an article by Madeline Bostock, an Old Girl and a qualified dentist practising in Stafford, describing her training and extolling the virtues of a career in dentistry for women. She says that under the new [sic] regulations of the Royal College of Surgeons of England the dental student must spend four years in professional study, the first two as a pupil — either with a registered practitioner or in the mechanical laboratory of a dental hospital — and the last two at a dental and general hospital. She became a student at the National Dental College and studied anatomy and physiology — with mandatory dissection — at the London School of Medicine for Women. She obtained her LDS from the Royal College of Surgeons in Glasgow and mentions that: 'No woman has as yet received this qualification from the Royal College of Surgeons (London) but within the last few months this body has decided to admit women to their qualifications.' The 1901 Census describes Miss Bostock as aged 17 and a student governess; she must have trained and qualified between 1901 and 1907.

Dentistry was at this time very practically slanted with much of the dentist's income coming from the sale of dentures. Dental surgery was not taught at university level so the path to qualification and a licence to practice was dependent on admission to examinations of the Colleges or Faculties of Surgeons. The Enabling Act of 1877, which allowed the colleges to choose whether or not to examine women, was embraced early in Glasgow and Edinburgh which would explain Lilian Murray Lindsay's trip north and it would seem most likely that the interview on the pavement was in fact a confrontation with the Royal College of Surgeons in London about their refusal to admit women to its examinations. The College finally admitted women to examinations in 1908. From: *Brighton High School for Girls Magazine* 1908, a bound copy now at Hove Reference Library. Thanks also to the Royal College of Physicians and Surgeons in Glasgow for a copy of a speech by Margaret W. Menzies Campbell given to their dental students in 1980.

[5] Miss Verrall resigned as treasurer of the Brighton Branch after the separation since she maintained that she did not believe in a joint treasurership. She must have reconsidered, possibly after persuasion, and agreed to stay on until the first annual meeting. She was offered a vice-presidency at the New Sussex and later accepted the same honour at the Lady Chichester. However, about this time she and her sister Annette took up residence at 'The Lydd', a recently built and not unsubstantial house in Sharpethorne near West Hoathly. She may have simply decided to retire from active work.

⁶ He did not explain, and probably did not need to, Mr Daking's point of view. Mr Daking, a resolute and ungenerous man, disliked gas intensely. He considered it to be a modern and expensive invention which had no place in a workhouse, where costs had to be kept to a minimum and any hint of luxury for the inhabitants strictly stamped out. His dislike of gas continued after the return to Race Hill; in 1922 he had the gas lighting removed from the wards (dormitories) because of the expense. He did not overcome his dislike of gas until the price of coal shot up in the late 1920s and, reluctantly, gas cooking finally replaced the old range. Gooch, J. (1980) *A History of Brighton General Hospital.* Phillimore.

FUTURE OF WOMEN DOCTORS.

◆

OPPORTUNITIES AND CHECKS.

DR. LOUISA ALDRICH-BLAKE, Dean of the London (Royal Free Hospital) School of Medicine for Women (University of London), presided yesterday at the opening of the Winter Session of the School, in Hunter-street, Brunswick-square, W.C. There are 450 students, of whom 70 are new this session.

Miss LOUISA MARTINDALE, senior surgeon, New Sussex Hospital, Brighton, delivered an address on "The Woman Doctor and Her Future," and told the students that they were entering the medical profession at, perhaps, the most interesting and wonderful time of the last century. The whole question of maternity mentality required fuller investigation, and this had been arranged for under the supervision of Dr. Janet Campbell, Senior Medical Officer, Ministry of Health, and a distinguished scholar of that school. It had always seemed to her that it was especially in the case of cancer that the work of the woman doctor was most needed.

The only serious check to the career of some women practitioners was their inability to get appointments on the honorary staff of some of the more reactionary of the general hospitals, necessitating the establishment of women's hospitals entirely officered by women doctors. The time would come when gynæcology, at any rate, would fall more and more to the task of the women doctors, just as men's diseases would remain in the hands of men doctors. Within the next few years there would be many developments in the modern hospital. It might be that large clinics would be established for paying patients of all classes; it might be that more hospitals would be managed and financed by the people themselves; or it might be that our present general hospitals would be subsidized or taken over by the State. In any case, there would be ample opportunities for the woman doctor of the future.

The Times, 4 October 1921

15

THE OPENING CEREMONY

In November 1920, with the occupancy of Sussex House finally assured and, hopefully, the major dramas now in the past, Elizabeth Robins felt unable to continue as chairman of the Board, but was happy to stay on as vice-chair. A sufferer from continual poor health, she was cared for in later life by Octavia Wilberforce, whose arduous journey to qualify as a doctor she had, in part, financially supported. It was a wise move; Miss Robins lived on, a creaking but well-loved gate, until her eightieth year in 1952. Octavia Wilberforce, a handsome and happy young woman from an excellent Sussex county family, had met with severe opposition from her father upon announcing her desire to study at the London School of Medicine for Women. She was, fortunately, not without other friends, amongst them (and in particular) the Buxton family of 'Newtimber', a fine old moated red brick and tile house in its own handsome, leafy estate just outside Brighton. Charlie, Lord Buxton's eldest son by his first wife, had loved Octavia and proposed marriage to her. Uncertain, and wanting to go ahead with her determination to become a doctor, she had turned him down. Although a healthy and robust young man, he became suddenly and acutely ill with appendicitis and died three weeks later. Deeply distressed, Octavia had remained friendly with Earl and Lady Buxton, who gave their own tribute to Charlie by supporting Octavia's medical studies for several years.

Sydney, Earl Buxton, a politician fairly well up in the Liberal hierarchy and a friend of Mr Asquith, married in 1896 Mildred Smith, a young woman from a well-to-do family living at Roehampton, near Richmond Park. It was his second marriage. Sydney Buxton had a cousin, Ruth Buxton, who, two years later in 1898 married Jocelyn Pelham, Lord Stanmer, who in 1905 after the death of his father became the sixth Earl of Chichester. Mildred and Ruth were lifelong friends and would share many sorrows. Both would experience the grief of outliving both a son and a husband, no less bitter for the wealthier classes than for the poorer. In November 1920 Lady Buxton was approached and agreed to become chairman of the Board of Management at the New Sussex, replacing Elizabeth Robins (the Robins–Wilberforce connection doubtless a major channel for this prestigious and highly successful appointment) and in January 1921 she chaired her first Board of Management meeting. This took place, also a first, in the boardroom at Sussex House although, always a busy lady, she had to leave early. Apologies from Lady Rhondda were also received.

Throughout 1921 the build-up to the grand opening—which clearly had to be not just a 'Grand Opening' but a gala of epic proportions — was discussed alongside the nitty gritty details needed to ensure that routine hospital life at Ditchling Road continued smoothly. Enough money had been raised to buy the new property, but income was also needed to keep the old Brighton Branch going as well as to repay the mortgage, and there were the usual suggestions for an upsurge in fundraising activities to think about (some of which came to pass and some of which did not). On the hospital front the Board was much distressed to find out that a new medical insurance plan to help out with a sudden and unplanned-for hospital stay, the Sussex Provident Scheme, was about to be launched by Dr Gordon Dill from the Royal Sussex County Hospital. All the other local hospitals had been invited to participate, all other hospitals that is except the New Sussex: possibly an example of the invisibility frequently suffered by the female half of the population. Offended, the Board smartly sent a stern letter to Dr Dill deploring the omission. He apologised, and a courteous reply was shortly received from the secretary of the Royal Sussex, most cordially requesting that a delegate from the New Sussex attend a conference to be held at the Royal Sussex so that the rules for the Provident Scheme could be discussed. Mrs Eggar, already on the Royal Sussex County Board of Management, was clearly the natural choice to represent the New Sussex.

Decisions such as which firm to order drugs from and where to buy new equipment for the hospital clashed uncomfortably with uncertainty as to who should do the ordering and whether any expenditure should, in the first instance, be sanctioned by the finance committee. There had been a problem: the Board seems to have agreed an expenditure without prior reference to the finance committee and, clearly annoyed about this, in May 1921 Sir Berry Cusack-Smith, chairman of the finance committee, resigned. He had served the Lady Chichester/New Sussex for three years and, although his wife remained as an occasional visitor to the New Sussex Board meetings, she too seems to have left for good; both were later appointed vice-presidents at the Lady Chichester. The problem was solved tactfully by the treasurer, Mr Gribble, who proposed that indeed, 'there should be no commitments or alterations of estimates without consultation with the Finance Committee'.

The New Sussex matron, Miss Milborne, had worked at Ditchling Road for eight years at a salary of £90 a year. A rise was long overdue, particularly with all the extra duties which were rapidly coming her way. She would be living in Sussex House, so a flat and private bathroom for her sole use had to be added to the alterations and, in June 1921, her salary was increased to £129. The engagement of a new resident porter and his wife, Mr and Mrs Peters, at £2 a week plus a free flat, uniform and allowances for coal and light was straightforward but the confirmation of his duties and privileges (he would be allowed to use a garden for growing vegetables and for keeping chickens but not a pig) had to be organised.[1] Dr Martindale was most specific that the porter would have to be strong in the arms, since he might be asked to help out with lifting patients. Nurses' salaries also had to be decided, and over at Ditchling Road a sudden but serious shortage of milk for the patients had to be tackled and decisions made about changing the supplier.

The list of things to do seemed endless. An estimate to repair the dilapidations at Ditchling Road had to be obtained, and Mr Clayton's drawings for the remodelling of the interior of Sussex House to provide operating theatres, outpatients' waiting rooms, wards, bathrooms and offices, not to say consulting rooms and staff toilets, had to be carefully scrutinised by the doctors. With regard to the wards, important decisions had to be made. How many should be public and how many private; how were they going to be named and what were the charges to be? Builders' estimates for the new hospital came in, and Mr Swann gained the contract because he was the cheapest. His band of workmen moved into Sussex House in March 1921, causing the second Annual Meeting of governors — held on 1st April 1921 and chaired by Lady Otter — to be held at Dr Martindale's new house, 11 Adelaide Crescent; but in July 1921 there was a sudden scare when his work was clearly observed to be slowing down to well behind the promised schedule — a not unusual circumstance, well known today. Summoned to a Board meeting Mr Swann naturally and loquaciously blamed the delay upon a strike by his workers, as well as the general shortage of plasterers; not without qualms, the Board gave him the benefit of the doubt, since — rather luckily — his carpenter had been able to make cupboards and shelves out of some old wood found at Sussex House, a nice piece of saving and recycling. But cracks suddenly appearing in the floor of the proposed operating theatre were a serious cause of worry; they would have to be filled in, which meant more estimates to obtain and more money to be spent. The lift did not work, and all twenty-seven different suggestions for fundraising that had been received would have to be examined. To top it all, the Board had forgotten Queen Alexandra Day on 30th July and that Ditchling Road had promised to help out.[2]

There were other decisions to be made: which fuel should be used, oil or gas? should the order book for hospital linen be held by Matron or supervised at the new hospital? Which day of the week should Miss Margaret Dobson, the oculist, open her ophthalmology clinic? The Brighton Medical Officer of Health had requested that a VD clinic be set up at Sussex House, but the Board remained rather cagey about this, not wanting of offend him but not really wanting a VD clinic in the new hospital either. Should the New Sussex go along with another bright idea from the Royal Sussex County about forming a local voluntary hospital committee? Should there be a nurse permanently on duty in outpatients'? More nurses were needed now that the hospital had adopted the standards of the Royal College of Nursing with regard to off-duty times — which meant that more salaries would have to be found from somewhere. And, all the time, bills, bills, bills and money draining away in spite of the vigilance of Mr Gribble and the finance committee. No doubt once the new hospital was up and running income would be generated from its private beds, nevertheless insurance, tax, and Mr Swann's invoices still had to be paid and the estimate from Ronuk's — simply to fill in the cracks in the operating theatre — was over £137. The overdraft of over £1,000 looked gloomily as though it would accumulate rather than lose its weight.

All these dramas were not helped by the volunteer secretary, Miss Turner, clearly overworked with all the new activity, suddenly (and hardly surprisingly) demanding a holiday. Miss Smithers, who also did some voluntary, part-time work, went off on holiday without asking, saying as she disappeared that she did not plan to return as she had found a job in London. Wisely, Dr Martindale insisted that Matron should also take her long overdue holiday and, as though all that was not enough, in November Miss Green, no doubt completely exhausted, resigned. She had threatened to leave in October, had been persuaded to stay a little longer, but finally buckled under her workload. This redoubtable lady had attended over seventy meetings (plus others not at Sussex House) and had had office and paper work to keep on top of as well as entering and adding up the accounts. The Board knew well that they would lose a phenomenal worker and, somewhat desperately, begged her to stay until after the opening ceremony, even promising extra clerical help with keeping the books. But Miss Green was, as always, firm. She would leave as soon as a new secretary was found since she considered it very important that her successor be initiated into the work well before the annual meeting.[3]

The Board must have turned gratefully to the happier tasks of planning the Grand Opening ceremony. A provisional date had been chosen: 9th December 1921. From the start it had been the Board's policy that the opening ceremony would also be a fundraising and publicity occasion *par excellence*. A celebrity would be needed, but who would agree to officiate and also be popular enough to bring in the public? This too was not straightforward. Dr Martindale, well aware no doubt that the Prince and Princess of Wales had opened Dr Garrett Anderson's New Hospital back in 1890, and that HRH Queen Mary had done the honours in 1912 at Dr Chadburn's South London Hospital, suggested the Princess Royal or Princess Christian of Denmark, both daughters of the late Queen Victoria. Either would do nicely. The New Sussex was not a spanking new building dominating the quiet beaches of Brighton and Hove, nor was it tantalisingly placed inside the chic streets of London, so realistically only minor royalty might be approached. Possibly Queen Alexandra could be persuaded, added Dr Martindale hopefully. Maybe Lady Buxton might help out in the Buckingham Palace direction?

Mrs Herbert Jones was deputed to write to Lady Buxton. Time and money and energies were draining ominously away. Practical as ever, Miss Merrifield said that perhaps Lady Buxton, if she could not actually obtain the Princess Royal (probably no-one thought she could) might be given a free hand to make a choice. Miss Merrifield did add, rather doubtfully, that she thought Lady Buxton herself was keen on Lloyd George, and Mr Stafford added quickly that perhaps the Countess Lytton might do since she, if not actually royalty, had been a Lady-in-Waiting to Queen Victoria for many years. By October 1921 no important personage had been lined up. Making a rare appearance Elizabeth Robins also announced herself keen on Lloyd George (no doubt to Miss Merrifield's dismay) and went on to wonder whether Lady Rhondda, who, she declared, was one of his personal friends, might ask him. This did not go down well and in haste the Princess Royal was again tossed into the frame. This time Lady Buxton did agree to write to one of HRH's ladies. Not holding out much hope in that direction, and brushing aside a rather feeble but, no doubt, last-resort suggestion of Miss Louisa Aldrich-Blake (from Dr Martindale), Lady Buxton finally came up with the winner: might she suggest Lady Astor MP, who had done sterling service on behalf of women doctors before, was on chattering terms with the beautiful and powerful of the realm and was well known for her entertaining and pithy speeches? She might just do very well indeed.

The Princess Royal, to no-one's surprise and probably to the relief of everyone (except, possibly, Dr Martindale) indicated that she was unable to accept. Lloyd George — again no doubt to quiet satisfaction — was not sure. In November 1921, Lady Buxton was delighted — and no doubt very proud — to announce that Lady Astor had indicated that she would be happy to accept an invitation to perform the opening ceremony; furthermore, she might even be able to make an earlier, fact-finding private visit! High gear was instantly engaged.

They had a date, a celebrity and no more than a month to go.

The Board, by then experienced in these matters, instantly formed an Opening Ceremony sub-committee to take care of the outstanding details. Mrs Stafford, Mrs Scatliff and Dr Martindale volunteered to serve on it, as did Ismay FitzGerald, who as an Honourable in her own right would come in very useful. They arranged to meet five days later to start to get the last minute ideas together. A few arrangements were put in place immediately: Lady Buxton, in her capacity as chairman of the Board of Management, agreed to preside over the ceremony and be relied upon to take charge of Lady Astor and see that her needs were met. The ceremony would take place in the outpatients' hall. After their meeting the Opening Ceremony sub-committee came up with the final working programme for the day and the list of 'honoured guests' that had been drawn up. These honoured guests would be fortified by a luncheon beforehand, and then be seated at a high table or platform during the ceremony so as to have a grand view of what was happening. An initial enquiry found that a luncheon could be organised at the Prince's Hotel for 7s 6d a head and Mrs Godfree and Matron, along with Mrs Paske-Hasselford and Mrs Harrison were drafted to form a Tea sub-committee. Afternoon tea would be served to all guests (for a small sum), in the nurses' dining room. Taxis would be needed to ferry the honoured guests back to Sussex House after the luncheon and comfortable seating on a platform would have to be placed in the outpatients' hall. This created a job for the new porter, Mr Peters, who not only helpfully borrowed a suitable platform from the nearby Brighton High School for Girls, but also managed to come up with a carpet to cover it. The local girl guides would be mobilised to help out as ushers and stewards and even sell the tea tickets, if the agreement of Mrs A. O. Jennings (she was active in the Girl Guide movement) could be obtained. To provide a nice mix, a bevy of girls from Roedean School could also be on hand to help out where required, courtesy of Miss Millicent Lawrence. For general entertainment and also for the extraction of cash from guests, Miss Maule, Mrs Radcliffe and Dr Maud Griffith would organise a bazaar-type stall selling fancy goods and trinkets. Hopefully, everyone who passed by would examine and with any luck buy something. Floral decorations would be needed and an appropriate bouquet for Lady Astor bought; Mrs Stafford would approach Messrs Balchin, the local florists, for the loan of decorative plants.

The champagne and glasses needed for the traditional toasts to the health of the King and Queen and the good fortunes of the New Sussex Hospital would be supplied by the Prince's Hotel. Who would propose the toasts and who would second them caused some deep thought, since a tidy balance between precedence and experience was essential so as not to cause offence. After a small flutter about the price of the luncheon (which was finally agreed with the Prince's Hotel at just 5s a head although, charitably, only 4s 6d would be charged to the hospital) and some concern over the inexplicable omission of the fish course from the proposed menu, everything began to fall into shape. The speakers and honoured guests would get their lunch and tea free, other guests would have to buy their tickets for luncheon in advance after receipt of the invitation. The Roedean prefects could mingle amongst the crowd and push the tea tickets at a shilling a head and Miss Penelope Lawrence, the senior Lawrence sister, would be asked to sit on the platform as an honoured guest. Instead of the Girl Guides, girls from Miss Blake's school and Miss Maule's St Michael's Hall were now proposed to do the welcoming honours, and it was agreed that Matron and her nurses should all be in best uniform and presented to Lady Astor with great ceremony. After greeting her at the door they would accompany her ladyship on the essential guided tour, using the lift that had only recently been installed at great expense. It is nice to learn that Matron was given a seat on the platform during the ceremony.

Eventually all was as streamlined as could be hoped and all that was left was to wait for the day to come and to pray for fine weather. One hundred ordinary invitations (quoting the costs of luncheon and tea) had been sent to people all around Brighton and, luckily, someone had remembered to invite the press and to hand out publicity pamphlets describing the beginnings of the New Sussex Hospital at Ditchling Road.

Dr Boyle was present at the luncheon, although she appears not to have been placed on the platform as an honoured guest, nor did she speak at the luncheon or the ceremony at the hospital. Indeed in the run up to the day there had been no mention by the Opening Ceremony sub-Committee that she should be asked to do so. We cannot know whether she was asked and declined or was just excluded. Eighty years later it seems to be almost unforgivable that, for either reason, her work, and that of Dr Mabel Jones in the early years of the century, seems not to have been publicly lauded at this most prestigious event. Dr Boyle was a witty and fluent public speaker, well known and highly respected in Brighton and Hove and a public show of friendship between the Lady Chichester Hospital and the New Sussex could have been enormously valuable. Looking back it is as though a golden opportunity was put aside: a few words from her, wishing good fortune to the New Sussex and being graciously accepted would not have been difficult, even if said through gritted teeth, but it did not happen. It fell to Miss M. E. Verrall to give a brief sketch of the history of the hospital from its beginnings as an outpatient hospital at the bottom of Islingword Road, and she mentioned that it originated in the mind of Mrs Martindale. She added that the move to the present premises was made owing to lack of space and because it made for 'economy of management'.

On 9th December 1921 Viscountess Astor arrived promptly. She was met by Lady Buxton who then handed her over to Mr Gribble, nominated as her official male escort for the day, who took her to luncheon in the fine banqueting hall at the Prince's Hotel. Small tables had been arranged for those who had bought luncheon tickets, all with a good view of the high table, where the honoured guests would be fed and from which the first round of speeches would be made. At the high table Lord Buxton accompanied his wife who, as chairman of the Board and a countess, and technically the woman of highest rank present, had been chosen to propose the health of the royal family. The King! The Queen! The Prince of Wales! and the Princess Royal, who, she triumphantly announced, had just become a patron of the New Sussex Hospital. No doubt very conscious of her politician husband beside her, she also managed to throw in a comment about Ireland.[4] On the 'honoured guest' platform were also Lady Leconfield, wife of the Lord Lieutenant of West Sussex, and, very sensibly, Mr and Mrs Cushman, the Mayor and Mayoress of Hove. Dr Martindale had managed to get an invitation for Miss Louisa Aldrich-Blake, the celebrated surgeon, as an honoured guest, and Mr A. O. Jennings had brought along Sir Arthur Newsholme, a former Brighton Medical Officer of Health and President of the Brighton & Sussex Medico-Chirurgical Society. (Sir Arthur had not been on the original honoured guest list, but Mr Jennings had a previous engagement with him that day and murmured that he would be able to attend the luncheon if a place could be also found for Sir Arthur.) Mr Jennings had been given the responsibility for proposing the double toast, to Lady Astor and to the success of the hospital; he took the occasion to supplement the toast by making a small speech in which he praised the hospital, most aptly and no doubt to grim smiles of agreement, by declaring that by its very power to resist adversity the New Sussex was fit to succeed. He added that the demand for women to be treated by women doctors was real and that the New Sussex* had already received women patients from all over the country and that it had the power to attract the friendship of businessmen and of charitable trustees such as those of the Sir John

Howard estate, as well as the influence of men of substance such as the late Bishop of Lewes. This was stirring stuff.

A few words of flattery to Lady Astor followed: he congratulated her on serving as the first woman MP and raised a laugh with a quote about the House of Commons: 'She was the first whoever burst into that silent sea', remarking, to much laughter and applause, that he felt that was 'a misquotation as applied to the House of Commons'. The Mayor of Hove replied with a welcome to Lady Astor, who said she lamented that she did not fulfil the conditions of the passage in Colossians that runs: 'Let your speech be always with grace, seasoned with salt. That ye know how to answer every man.' She added, to laughter, that her speech was not graceful but that she did have to be ready to answer every man. She thanked God that she had vitality, even if she lacked eloquence, because women who wanted to do anything needed twice as much vitality as men: they had so much leeway to make up. She did not look upon herself as a pioneer but rather as a bullet shot out of a canon built by pioneers: 'I can only hope I have exploded in the right direction' she added, amid laughter. 'Although I was not a pioneer I was a natural born suffragette; not from hostility to man, but because my maternal instincts made me long to help him, seeing what a one-sided creature he be.' Recalling a previous visit during the Great War Lady Astor said that it gave her a feeling of despair then to see so many people exercising dogs on the Hove Lawns. It showed there would always be a majority of people who did not realise the needs of the world and the joy of service. With regard to Mr Jennings's reference to herself Lady Astor remarked, 'It is really comic when you think of yourself as an historical character. I get the giggles when I do.' She concluded by saying that she believed that in the future people would point with pride to the hospital and that it would be 'a beacon to the women of England'.

Dr Martindale replied gracefully to Lady Astor, paying tribute to Miss Aldrich-Blake, to Elizabeth Robins (who was unable to attend) and to her successor as chairman of the Board, Lady Buxton. Lady Rhondda, who had cancelled at the last minute, was mentioned, as was Sir Berry Cusack-Smith, Mr F. M. Cobb and Mr Gribble. At 2.30 the luncheon ended and everyone made their way to Sussex House.

The Opening Ceremony sub-Committee had done well: Sussex House was decorated with flags, and the Girl Guides, who had been re-drafted, lined up to make a blue-uniformed and wide-hatted guard of honour for Lady Astor. The outpatients' hall was crammed to bursting and the floral decorations were in need of protection as the platform party made its way forward after their tour of the hospital (probably only to carefully selected areas, avoiding rooms not quite finished and where Mr Peters would have done the cleaning and tidying of paints and ladders). Having stretched their legs, everyone settled down to listen to yet more speeches. Soon, Lady Astor got to her feet and declared the New Sussex Hospital open. She described it as a real credit to women and a glory to Brighton. She spoke also of her pleasure at being able to encourage professional women, making an oblique reference to the downturn in places offered to women medical students, then continued with a warning that, unless women were given equal opportunities with men, bitter feeling would be aroused and that the current unjust and narrow-mindedness of attempting to get women out of jobs had to be fought.[5] She finished with the obligatory appeal for funds, which were badly needed to meet the £2,000 overdraft.

To underpin this appeal, a pretty demonstration had been organised. During the run-up to the opening, collecting boxes had been wielded on street corners by everyone who could be pressured to do so, including many girls from local schools. The cash collected had been placed into purses and these were individually presented to Lady Astor, who graciously accepted them on behalf of the New Sussex. The sum total inside the purses was announced to be over £130. Matron and her nurses had also presented a Gold Purse containing £25, and at last Miss Aldrich-Blake rose to give a hearty vote of thanks to Lady Astor, nicely seconded by Miss Penelope Lawrence from Roedean.

The ceremony — called the Presentation of Purses — was a very effective piece of theatre. A similar event had been organised in London when the New Hospital for Women was opened in Marylebone Road, although Dr Elizabeth Garrett Anderson had been a little luckier in managing to attract the Prince and Princess of Wales to perform the opening ceremony. The purses had been presented to their Royal Highnesses by children, prettily dressed in white and bobbing their best curtseys. This time it would be Lady Astor receiving the purses, but no matter; not only was this a fine spectacle for the guests, it would also be a privilege for the local little girls, the nearest most would ever come to being 'presented' to royalty. Not quite the same, but nevertheless something for their proud parents to remember.[6]

It was over. Everyone went to a well-deserved tea and, no doubt admiring the fancy goods stall, drifted away so that only Mr Peters and his wife were left to clear up. It had been a great success; nothing had gone wrong. A year's hard work, frustration, fear and hope had come together at last on a December day in a building that as yet was not really finished. Lady Astor had been impressive, the luncheon had gone off well — apart from the missing fish course — and the opening ceremony had been as memorable as it had been planned to be. The Board could confidently face 1922 with renewed energies and a warm friendship between its members, most of whom would serve happily together in the years to come.

BRIGHTON'S NEW HOSPITAL.

LADY ASTOR ON OPPOSITION TO PROFESSIONAL WOMEN.

. Lady Astor opened the new Sussex Hospital·for Women and Children at Brighton yesterday.· Officered entirely by·women,· the hospital meets the needs of patients unwilling to enter.the free wards of public hospitals and unable to pay nursing·home fees.

Lady Astor said the hospital.was a .credit to women and a glory to. Brighton. She was glad to be present to encourage professional women, against whom the tide .was now flowing strongly, partly because of economic conditions and party because .people were .getting frightened of the moral pressure of women.

Before the opening Lady Astor was entertained at luncheon. Lady Buxton presided. and the guests included Lady Leconfield; Lord Buxton. Sir Arthur Newsholme, the Hon. Ismay Fitzgerald, and Miss Marie Corelli.

The Times, 10 December 1921

Notes

[1] Mr and Mrs F. Gander, who had lived at Windlesham House during the war as employees of the workhouse in charge of the old men, applied for the job but failed to get it.

[2] Queen Alexandra Day was a Flag Day: volunteers stood on street corners shaking charity collecting boxes at passers-by who, in return for their generosity, were given a little paper flag (with the name of the charity boldly displayed) which was prominently pinned onto their coat lapels. The first Queen Alexandra Day was in June 1912 and represented the celebration of the fifty years since, as Princess

Alexandra, she arrived in Great Britain from her native Denmark to marry the Prince of Wales. It was started by Queen Alexandra herself to support her favourite charities, and she requested that a rose should be given rather than a flag. Presumably the Board of Management had made a rash promise to the local organiser to chip in and provide some volunteers to shake collecting boxes but then, unfortunately, had forgotten to do so. This would have been seen as rather bad form. The Queen Alexandra Rose Day Charity continues the tradition to this day but without the flag day <www.alexandraroseday.org.uk>.

[3] Her position seems to have been taken by a Miss Lander.

[4] The Anglo—Irish Treaty, also known as the Irish Free State Agreement, had been signed in London only three days before on 6th December 1921. The agreement brought the independent Republic of Ireland into existence and was rampant headline news in all the papers.

[5] Lady Astor may have been referring to the Restoration of Pre-war Practices Act of 1919, and the Employment of Women, Young Persons and Children Act of 1920, which made it illegal to retain civilian war workers in jobs formerly carried out by skilled craftsmen. The intention was that after demobilisation ex-servicemen could return immediately to their pre-war jobs but in reality the Acts had the effect of forcing many women out of their war work and back down the ladder into unskilled and low paid jobs. The big London medical schools, which had opened some wards to women medical students for co-educational clinical instruction during the later years of the war, one by one declined to continue to do so, beginning with St George's in 1919. By 1928, apart from University College Hospital, which accepted twelve women annually, only the Royal Free Hospital would admit women to their wards for clinical instruction.

[6] The reporter from the *Sussex Daily News* was there and did the New Sussex proud in his newspaper the next day.

16

INTO THE 1920S

At the Board meeting following the exhaustions of the New Sussex opening ceremony the Board was delighted to hear that, with all bills paid, a surplus of £200 had been made which was siphoned directly into the building fund. Letters of thanks went out promptly. On the downside, the receipts from the car raffle (for which tickets had been sold at the opening ceremony) had not reached the target, only £303 having been received. Each had been priced at half a crown, no small sum, so this is not surprising. This was in spite of the efforts of Mrs Bromley Davenport, who had persuaded her husband to take a bundle of the tickets into his workplace, the Stock Exchange. Mr Cobb suggested that the raffle be stopped and the money returned to those who had bought tickets. The raffle for a gramophone had been more successful: £39 had been raised. A gramophone could be purchased for £2 12s 6d so was a good deal for both the winner and the hospital funds. The Board of Management decided that the car raffle should go ahead anyway and went ahead with the draw for the gramophone — but recommended that a permanent and professional fundraiser be employed. Miss Caroline Clarke was appointed Appeals Secretary in March 1922; however, she was either ineffective or unsuitable and, just seven months later, she was asked to resign.

The move from Ditchling Road was accomplished although, sadly, no record remains of what must have been serious upheaval, no doubt laced with much tension and drama. In the years that followed, routine, day-to-day life had to be attended to and the Board of Management got down to the everyday business of managing the life of the hospital. The solitary male at the New Sussex — the porter and caretaker Mr Peters — was, after discussion, finally allowed free use of part of the hospital grounds to cultivate his own allotment (as he had been promised), providing that his time there did not clash with his duties. Matron continued to be in charge of the Linen Guild and was given a special bank account. The advertisement for the appeals secretary brought up the sickeningly recurrent problem of the name of the hospital: would any respondent imagine that this was the Royal Sussex County that was advertising? The nurses muttered about overwork and complained about confusion as to whose job it was to open the front door and answer the telephone (surely this should be one of the porter's duties?) Even Matron, Miss Milborne, began to grumble about overwork and demanded to know exactly whose responsibility it was to organise the nurses' work — hers or the doctors'? Experienced, and by now working well together, the Board promptly despatched an observer to the South London Hospital for Women to find out how the nursing staff there were organised. Subsequently, two new staff nurses were appointed and the complaints ceased.

In March 1922 a strange dispute arose between the Lady Chichester Hospital and the New Sussex. As might be expected, the bone of contention was money; a legacy, in fact. Dr Martindale reported to the Board that Miss Annie Hall had left £1,500 in her will to 'Dr Boyle's Local Dispensary'. She had to add that the executors, in particular Sir Charles Wooley, a solicitor, had said rather ominously that in the case of a dispute the Executors 'have power to give the legacy elsewhere'. There is a strong indication here to suggest that it was well known locally that the ladies of the two hospitals would have difficulty in reaching an agreement. Mr Gribble was handed this thorny problem. He took the view, quite properly in the eyes of the New Sussex Board, that since the dispensary was no longer in existence then it would be equitable and right that the legacy should be divided equally between the two hospitals. He suggested diplomatically to the executors that the New Sussex would make no claim and would in fact agree to the £1,500 being given to Dr Boyle 'providing that she gave an undertaking to pay a portion to the New Sussex. And that the New Sussex would expect a half.' As could be forecast, the Lady Chichester objected to the suggestion.

By April 1922 Mr Gribble had backed down a little and agreed that, since Dr Boyle's name was clearly in the will then her hospital should have an immediate £200 from the legacy while the remainder, £1,300, should be divided equally. Dr Boyle still did not agree. The following month the Lady Chichester requested that it receive £1,000, while the remaining £500 was to go to the New Sussex. This was not acceptable to Mr Gribble. Realising that no solution could be arrived at, and with neither side prepared to go on negotiating, both hospitals agreed to seek an arbitrator, a sad measure of the ill-feeling between them. By July the arbitrator had made no decision, and a new shock had come the way of the New Sussex Board of Management: Lady Buxton, who had done so well as a figurehead and chairwoman of the Board, offered her resignation because, in her own words, she 'lived too far away from Brighton to do the work as a chairwoman should do.'

This was unexpected and Mr Gribble asked the Board to write to Lady Buxton to request that she defer her resignation until a replacement could be found. He, and probably all the others, may well have known what was coming up next at that same Board Meeting: the news that Dr Martindale would announce that she was leaving Brighton for pastures new in London. She, too, was not present at the meeting but her letter was read out:

> After August 1st I propose to do consultant work only having arranged with Mrs Jeffries MD to take over my general practice; I hope to continue my work at the Hospital as before, although I propose attending only 2 or possibly 3 days a week for operations ... this change in my plans will necessitate my giving up Out Patients on Thursdays, which, I need hardly say, will be with much regret.

Elizabeth Robins, as usual managing to be in the chair at such a momentous meeting, expressed:

> her deep regret, which was shared by every member of the Board, [that] the Hospital should be losing the daily help and watchful care of Dr Martindale whilst fully realising the great privilege of retaining her services as resident surgeon. [sic][1]

Louisa Martindale did pack her bags and leave Brighton, although she always maintained her links with the New Sussex, coming down to Brighton once or twice a week to operate and she stayed on for a while as a magistrate.[2] Dr Martindale lived in London for the remainder of her life, working as a consultant surgeon in the UK and abroad. When in Brighton and Hove she sat as a magistrate on the Brighton bench, later moving to the bench at East Grinstead. She was a governor of the Prison Commission of Lewes Prison, which led to her giving lectures to inmates of Holloway Prison; many other public works followed and she was later awarded the CBE. She set up a consultancy in London, and went on to become eminent in the pioneering field of using X-rays for the treatment of breast and uterine cancer. A grand portrait of her, painted by the celebrated artist Frank O. Salisbury, shows her in full academic scarlet robes, her right hand resting on an X-ray machine.

A year later, in 1923, Ismay FitzGerald also withdrew from the Board.

The work of the New Sussex continued, with interesting items noted in the Board of Management minutes concerning fire drills, inspections of drains and gullies and necessary economy in the use of gas and electric torches for the night staff. There was a crisis when a visitor waiting in the hall fell through an unlocked door down a flight of stairs and into the basement (a notice 'Private Staircase' was smartly placed on the door). Mr Swann, the builder, had left much work undone and Ismay FitzGerald was given the important task of inspecting the building in order to put together a precise list of work still to be carried out. Fundraising fêtes and tea dances abounded, decisions had to be made concerning setting up a local voluntary hospitals' committee as outlined in a Ministry of Health circular, which appeared to be of doubtful advantage and participation was to be avoided if at all possible. Mrs Eggar, still involved with the Royal Sussex Management Committee, was landed with that job; she was also volunteered to deal with a tree in the hospital garden, which had become dangerous after the summer gales.

The Provident (Insurance) Scheme set up by Dr Gordon Dill from the Royal Sussex seems to have been in trouble from its outset (receipts were less than had been hoped) and a wrangle with Hove Corporation over the siting of a directional notice — 'To the New Sussex Hospital for Women and Children' — was cleared up when the manager of the local Lloyd's Bank agreed (for the sum of one shilling) to allow the notice to be placed on the railings outside his branch. By September 1922 the Annie Hall legacy problem had still not been resolved, although the Mayor of Hove had agreed to be the arbitrator. The next month he awarded £850 to the Lady Chichester Hospital and £650 to the New Sussex. Rather diplomatically Lady Buxton (who appears to have stayed on as chairwoman for a few months), having agreed to ask Lady Cowdray to open the first day of the impending two-day New Sussex annual fête in the Brighton Dome, 'Ye Olde Sussex Fayre', to be held on 14th and 15th December 1922, suggested that she might ask Lady Chichester to open the second day. This gesture bore sweet fruit. In return the Lady Chichester Council promptly asked Lady Buxton to open the second day of the Lady Chichester Hospital's autumn extravaganza 'Ye Autumne Fayre', also in the Dome, on 19th and 20th October (see Appendices III and IV).

Looking back at the previous history of the two hospitals the proposal was a diplomatic coup for Lady Buxton, though the fact that it had to be made at all underlines the unease and tension between the two hospitals. The minutes of the following Board meeting record that Lady Buxton — who was probably diplomatically absent — had requested the Board's approval for her plan by letter, and added her hopes that the two hospitals would draw closer together in appeal work. Mrs Herbert Jones (the widow of the late Bishop of Lewes and soon to become chairwoman) was temporarily in the chair, and moved:

> That this Board welcomes the action of their chairwoman in asking
> Lady Chichester to open their fête on the second day and wish to
> put on record that they are unconscious of any bitterness between
> the two hospitals. It is reported from the Medical Committee
> that the Lady Chichester Hospital currently sends patients to the
> New Sussex for operative treatment which is itself expressing co-
> operation with their work.

She then added:

> The Board do not at present however feel their way to giving up
> appeal work on their own and form part of an amalgamation of an
> appeal for the women's hospitals.

Money, it would seem, had yet again reared its divisive head,
however, Lady Buxton must be given the credit for offering the olive
branch. Nothing more can be gleaned from the Board's minute books;
maybe Dr Martindale's removal from Brighton and Hove had been
instrumental in this move towards cordiality. In any case the Board
wrote to Lady Chichester giving her the details of the fundraising
results of a recent bazaar, to which she replied courteously with a
letter of thanks, and wished prosperity to the New Sussex. Hopefully,
an era of mistrust between the two hospitals had ended.

In November 1922 Octavia Wilberforce, by now MRCS LRCP,[3]
took up a paid post as clinical assistant in the outpatients' at the
New Sussex, and started her general practice two months later at 24
Montpelier Crescent. In buying the house she had been assisted by
a generous gift from Mrs Dolly Yates Thompson and a loan from
Lady Denman, having usefully picked up new and rich patients from
her treatment of their maids in outpatients'. In 1925 she was given
an honorary position as assistant physician at the hospital, with two
beds at her disposal.

In March 1923 distressing news arrived at the Lady Chichester
Hospital in Aldrington House. On her way from Glasgow to visit
her sister in Bexhill, Dr Mabel Jones had died after falling from an
overnight London, Midland and Scottish Railway train; her body was
found on the line near Heyford in Northamptonshire. A coroner's
inquest heard that a door had been heard to slam whilst the train was
moving and a window in the adjacent compartment was later found
to be open by the train ticket examiner. The inquest also heard that
Dr Jones was not known to have any family or financial troubles, she
had been in good spirits and was very cheerful during the journey.

A verdict of 'Accidental death whilst falling out of an express train' was recorded. However no autopsy was carried out and an inventory of her personal estate does indicate that Dr Jones was in straitened financial circumstances; she had not worked for two years.[4]

Although it had been fifteen years since Dr Jones had left the Church Road general practice and the Lewes Road Dispensary to head north and live and work in Glasgow, Helen Boyle was much shaken by this news. There is no reason to suppose that Helen Boyle and Mabel Jones had not kept up acquaintance, and Dr Boyle was at some point certainly in contact with Emma Jones, Mabel's sister. Practical as always, and with an eye to raising money and improving the hospital, Dr Boyle proposed setting up a Dr Mabel Jones Memorial Fund, the money collected to be used to add a new wing to Aldrington House, to house an observation ward; £600 was targeted as the sum needed and an appeal was launched. Regretfully, the Memorial Fund did not ever accrue much cash and it became a part of the 1926 appeal.

But more pleasant events were to come; one of them being the arrival of Dr Doris Odlum as house physician at the Lady Chichester in about 1924. A young woman at the beginning of her career as a psychiatrist, she began a long professional friendship with Dr Boyle. There was also an unexpected bequest to the hospital of a house in Westbourne Villas, only a stone's throw from Aldrington House, and this opened up new possibilities. Initially, everyone was rather dubious about the property: it was unmodernised and suffered from damp. As always, money would be needed to make it habitable. Eventually, what was necessary was done and the house came to be used as a nurses' home, no doubt to general satisfaction. Another blessing, which also turned out to be mixed, was received in 1926: the gift of a cottage in the countryside at Walton-on-Thames. Miss A. M. Clark gave the property to the Lady Chichester for use as a convalescent home, but later, in 1928, with the overdraft still running at over £2,000, the Council reluctantly decided to discontinue its use.

In 1925, at long last, the Lady Chichester Hospital Council of Management made its own successful application to the Sir John Howard legacy fund for £5,000, so that the temporary building and the old corrugated hut that had been put up rather hastily in 1920 could be replaced with a new wing. It would be called the Sir John Howard Wing, in accordance with the trustees' instructions. This greatly-improved accommodation included two more wards, each with twenty-four beds, and a sun balcony. The kitchen was extended, gas cooking apparatus installed and a new scullery built, this time with an adequate larder. A new restroom, bathroom and lavatory were added for the staff; no doubt a very welcome addition. The central heating and hot water system was overhauled and the whole hospital redecorated. It was a lot to do. The extent of the building works, which were finished around 1926, highlights the speed of the removal to Aldrington House in 1920, and does seem to confirm that very few, if any, additions and alterations had previously been carried out and that the substantial award from the Sir John Howard trust to the Brighton Branch had been a bitter pill indeed (see chapter 12).

In the event the money raised was not quite adequate to meet the extent of the building works; a sad and not unfamiliar story. Estimated originally at £7,500 the cost would, as is usual with these matters, creep up to £7,900. The final sum needed was well over the £5,000 received from the Sir John Howard trustees, and a fresh appeal was launched to raise the funds.

The appeal, titled 'Twenty-One Years of Pioneer Work', was written and launched in 1926, marking the twenty-one years since the ten-bedded hospital in Roundhill Crescent had opened, and the catchy slogan 'Coming of Age' was adopted as a potential money-spinner. It has survived in the Contemporary Medical Archives Centre at the Wellcome Institute and gives us the best possible review of Dr Boyle's work at the Lady Chichester Hospital, first at Roundhill Crescent then all the way to Aldrington House. The thirteen pages are divided up into informative paragraphs: 'The Idea', 'The Beginning of the Work', 'Work in the War', 'The Hospital Today', 'Methods of Treatment', 'The Hospital's Magazine', 'The Children's Ward', 'The Out-Patient Department', 'After-care', 'Six Typical Cases' and 'The Ideas Justified'. A summary of 'The Work' and 'The Example Followed' (details of other hospitals nationwide which had also begun outpatient work for early cases of mental illness) and 'The National Value of The Work' followed.

There is a fine drawing of Aldrington House — without the extra wing. The figures quoted on page three do not quite align with the figures quoted in the Annual Meeting Report for that year: the 'Act of Faith' is much lauded, indeed only the best intentions go into an appeal. The purchase price of Aldrington house is given as £4,900 and £900 is said to have been spent on altering and equipping it (this does not quite tally with Lady Chichester's urgent letter in the *Brighton Herald* of 23 June 1920 when baths and boilers were lacking and yet to be installed).

'Twenty-One Years of Pioneer Work' is headed up on the inside of the front page with a glittering list of illustrious patrons and council members (and shows a sprinkling of names also associated with the New Sussex, see Appendix I). The document ends conventionally and conveniently in the necessary blank bank standing order forms and a form of bequest to be appended to the donor's last will and testament. Cheerfully, it comments that the value of the hospital's freehold buildings in Hove and Walton-on-Thames, plus that of its investments, amounts to between £10,000 and £11,000. However, a list of the building needs is tactfully inserted, the grant from the Howard trust of £5,000 is mentioned but the appeal sets out a further target of another £5,000, catchily broken down into 40,000 half-crowns,* easy enough for anyone to put into a collecting box. 'Not a very large sum to ask?' when 'the population of Great Britain is over 40 million' the appeal chattily asked. But half a crown was no small sum, and the full amount needed was never raised and in the event the appeal did not reach its target.

The appeal encapsulates Dr Boyle's vision and her life's work. Many of her academic papers and bound reports of her speeches can be read today; although always stylish and entertaining they were intended for the ears of other colleagues and are sometimes difficult to read. 'The Twenty-One Years' appeal, although fairly long-winded, is more easily digestible and very much more accessible to the lay person. Dr Jones did get her memorial: the solarium, a 'sunlight' balcony with windows and a glass roof, was eventually built on the flat roof of the new wing and was named for her. (Unfortunately, some years later the roof began to leak and the solarium was removed in the late 1940s.) A framed photograph of Dr Jones, along with her La Reine Elisabeth Medal and Citation that had been awarded by the Belgian Government in 1919 for war work with Belgian refugees, was given to the Lady Chichester Hospital where, no doubt, it was prominently displayed on a wall. The photograph, citation and medal have survived and are now at Millview Hospital although, sadly, not on show.

By 1925 advances in psychiatric medicine had at last brought about a government rethink on the efficacy of the Lunacy Laws, which had been unchanged for over fifty years. A new Mental Health Act was proposed and a Royal Commission on Lunacy and Mental Disorder set up to enquire and to listen to evidence from doctors prominent in the field, and to advise the government appropriately. Dr Boyle, by now held in high esteem amongst her colleagues in the Brighton & Sussex Medico-Chirurgical Society, made a very public appearance by giving evidence to the Royal Commission on Lunacy. She was accompanied by Lady Chichester.[5]

---

* A handsome, silver coin worth 2s 6d. There were eight half-crowns in a pound.

On Sunday, 2nd December 1928, the nation heard about the Lady Chichester Hospital when, courtesy of the BBC, Lady Chichester herself made a broadcast appeal on the radio. Followed up by a letter to *The Times*, it must have been successful because letters of support were received and new subscribers recruited. As might have been expected, a greater number of potential patients asked for more information.

In 1929 a long-held dream came to pass; however it, too, was a mixed blessing, having a brace of stings in its tail. Dr Harper Smith, Superintendent of the Brighton County Asylum at Hayward's Heath and Honorary Consultant Psychiatrist at the Royal Sussex County Hospital, approached Dr Boyle and the Lady Chichester Hospital with a startling new offer. The new Mental Health Act, so long awaited, had at last brought into law the 'voluntary patient' who, for the first time, would be able to obtain psychiatric treatment without being certified insane. Dr Harper Smith was anxious to establish a Department of Early Mental Diseases and a corresponding outpatients' department, at the Royal Sussex County. He offered Helen Boyle an appointment as honorary medical officer, jointly in charge. Twenty years previously, when Mabel Jones had been in joint practice with her at 37 Church Road,[6] Dr Boyle had approached the Sussex County Hospital with a proposal that an outpatients' clinic for treating early nervous disorders might be formed. Her offer had been immediately and brusquely declined, and this she had never forgotten. However, in 1930 Helen Boyle took the decision to co-operate with Dr Harper Smith, which would mean that, at last, a woman doctor would take up an honorary appointment at the Royal Sussex. There was, however, a troublesome downside to the offer. While the agreement would give Dr Boyle what she had so long desired — an almost free hand with women callers at the new outpatients' clinic — there were two unpleasant provisos: six borderland male patients were to be admitted to the Lady Chichester Hospital for treatment and the necessary building alterations would have to be at the Lady Chichester's expense. This meant crossing a Rubicon, because the hospital would then cease to be purely for women and children.

The admission of male patients into treatment at the Lady Chichester would leave the New Sussex as the only women's hospital in the two towns. It is difficult to imagine how Dr Boyle felt but for many years there had been a greater masculine involvement, with Sir Robert Armstrong-Jones as honorary consulting physician, Mr H. Nethersole Fletcher as dentist and Mr C. H. Bryant as oculist, as well as the businessmen serving as members of the Council of

Management. A mile or so away the New Sussex had also made use of businessmen and town councillors on its Board, but, remaining true to its principles, did not ever accept male patients. Only towards the end of its days under the National Health Service would it come to appoint male medical staff, and for nearly all the many years of its life the only man on the New Sussex staff was the porter.

However, the two hospitals had long since gone their separate ways and the New Sussex was not in any way dependent on the Royal Sussex County for patronage or patients. It had its own well-placed and seemingly endless pool of medical women to work as honorary consultants and house physicians, clinical assistants, pathologists, dentists and oculists and Dr Boyle may well have paid the penalty for being a pioneer in her field, for she had no wide reserve of prominent women psychiatrists interested in early nervous disorders to fall back upon. Two — Dr Odlum and Dr Lamorna Hingston — were up and coming but there was not an endless source. Dr Boyle may well have felt that she had no real option other than to abandon the long-held 'women and children only' principle of the Lady Chichester, and that it would all be for the best.

By the 1930s it was sixty years since women doctors had underpinned their claim to enter the medical profession by insisting that it was women themselves who needed and would prefer a woman doctor. The Great War and the heady times of the twenties had merged the demarcation lines that had existed between the sexes and brought men and women together as never before. What is more, many hospitals were beginning to offer more paid jobs to young women just out of medical school — as long as they were not married. University medical schools had begun to re-open their doors to women students across the nation after the war had slipped into the past, and the 1919 Sex Disqualification (Removal) Act had started to bite. Their teachers — who were also practising doctors in the hospitals attached to the medical schools — began to acquire a real interest in seeing their star women students take up paid professional work. Women doctors had also become keen to begin to treat patients of both sexes, seeing no reason in those modern days of jazz, fast motor cars and the silver screen why they should be restricted to their own. They wanted to be accepted as respected colleagues, to be able to apply for jobs in any hospital, and to be welcomed onto any ward. The opening of the Lady Chichester Hospital to male patients would have made a good deal of sense politically to the ambitions of many women medical students and was possibly, for them, a welcome reform sweeping alongside the wave of the long-awaited parliamentary vote.

A reform, maybe — but in the meantime, where to put the men? Circumstances were kind: number 5 Rutland Gardens, one of two nicely positioned, semi-detached houses backing onto the garden at Aldrington House, suddenly became vacant. It was purchased and, in 1930, six men were moved in. The arrangement was most satisfactory: male patients could be accommodated separately but very close to the main building. A few years later number 7 also came up for sale and was purchased.[7] The transactions, as usual, were costly and the profits from the hospital's investments had a struggle to keep up. After building the new wing and purchasing 5 Rutland Gardens, the overdraft for the Lady Chichester climbed to an all-time high of £5,465.

In 1932, after first joining its ranks way back in 1910, Dr Helen Boyle was the recipient of a considerable local honour: she was elected as the first woman president of the Brighton Medico-Chirurgical Society. Of all her appointments, this was likely to have been the sweetest. She was followed in later years by three women doctors who have also appeared in this narrative.[8]

In 1937 a glossy pamphlet publishing details of the New Sussex was published. Beginning with a short history it describes the new wing built in 1928, and in 1931 and 1932 the addition of two more wards — the Sir John Howard Ward and the Marie Corbett Ward — all by courtesy of the seemingly fathomless fund of the Sir John Howard Memorial Trust. This gave the hospital a total capacity of sixty beds. A new nurses' home was added in 1936. There is a fine photograph of the operating theatre and another of the new wards, looking out over the trim garden and lawn.[9]

It is a measure of Brighton and Hove's historical taste for individuality, and its pride in the innovative endeavours continually poured out by its people, that two women's hospitals (albeit one with a few male patients on the side) survived as long as they did. By 1939 and the sickening arrival of the Second World War, only three other women's hospitals were open in the UK; two in London — the Elizabeth Garrett Anderson and the South London, and one in Edinburgh — the Elsie Inglis Memorial Hospital. All others had withered away, memories only, and those fading fast.

In Brighton and Hove the deep conservative vein which runs so obstinately and so contrarily close to the tumultuous surface of life was possibly the reason for the reluctance of the townspeople to let their women's hospitals go. But their days were diminishing: in 1945 a Labour government detonated into power and three years later the welfare state became a reality.

Notes

[1] East Sussex Records Office HB 12/4.

[2] Two years previously, in 1920, Louisa Martindale had moved her practice from 10 Marlborough Place in Brighton to genteel 11 Adelaide Crescent in Hove, the one-time home of Sir Arthur O. Jennings, a Board member of the New Sussex and local magistrate. She was the first doctor to put up her brass plate in the Crescent (it cost her £100 for the privilege) and although she liked the house well enough was never really happy there, preferring the liveliness of cramped but central Brighton to the quiet composure of Regency Hove. Those who know the geography of Hove (see map, page 194) will instantly come to realise that Dr Martindale's new home and practice was within a stone's throw of Dr Boyle's residence at 37 Church Road and her rooms at 9 The Drive. It was however much nearer to the New Sussex and other women doctors were also gravitating to Hove. She gives no explanation for her choice and one can only surmise Dr Boyle's reaction.

[3] Member of the Royal College of Surgeons; Licentiate of the Royal College of Physicians. She had no London matriculation and did not ever gain her MD.

[4] *Northampton Mercury* 30 March 1923 and *The Evening Times* (Glasgow) 28 March 1923.

[5] A summary of Dr Boyle's evidence to the Royal Commission:

1. General hospitals should establish clinics to treat early nervous disorders.

2. There should be no compulsory detention in clinics.

3. A social service should be developed to co-ordinate the work between the mental hospitals, clinics and aftercare organisations.

4. There should be no obvious connection between the mental hospitals, clinics, Boards of Control and asylums etc.

5. The clinics should be supported on the same lines as the VD clinics.

6. Supervision should be in the hands of the Ministry of Health.

From Westwood, L. (2003) *A Quiet Revolution in Brighton: Dr Helen Boyle's Pioneering approach to Mental Health care 1899—1939.* Society for the Social History of Medicine.

[6] When Dr Boyle and Dr Jones first moved to Hove in 1898 they seem to have leased the whole house and retained a servant (1901 Census). The house was then numbered 3 Palmeira Terrace. Some time later the house (re-numbered 37 Church Road) was divided into flats by the landlord Messrs Osman Ward, the solicitors who had bought it from the trustees in about 1890. The firm remains the landlord of the house to this day. Dr Boyle remained in residence in a flat on the first floor until she eventually retired to a cottage in Pyecombe with her secretary, Miss Rita Gore-Lindsay. No doubt this was financially advantageous.

[7] Both houses remain part of the Aldrington House complex to this day.

[8] Florence M. Edmonds, 1934; Lillias M. Jeffries, 1948; Gladys M. Wauchope, 1954.

[9] The pamphlet survives and is held at Brighton Local Studies Library. Interestingly it does not boast quite the heavy list of grandees that the Lady Chichester appeal of some years earlier manages to put up front, but the President, HRH The Princess Louise, Duchess of Argyll (a daughter of Queen Victoria) was a high profile catch (see Appendix II).

17

Epilogue

The story ends here, partly because further records of both hospitals become a long and not always inspiring list of everyday management struggles over small details, differences of opinion and minor dramas such as the state of the old brownish varnish inside the front door of Aldrington House, which ought to be replaced and how long would this take? All these concerns shrank into a minor key with the impending arrival of the National Health Service and its inevitable radical changes. The hospitals in Brighton and Hove would all be absorbed into its matrix.[1]

By the 1940s the profile of hospitals throughout Great Britain had changed. Most were now municipal hospitals; the old workhouse infirmaries liberated by the abolition of the Poor Laws into the full-time care of the local authorities. There was a municipal hospital (large, medium, or cottage) in or near every town; modern, up-to-date, comfortably accessible. Voluntary hospitals remained but they were fewer in number; they were autonomous, their independent funds were sunk in trusts, they were often larger than the municipal hospitals and frequently supported a medical school. In both the consultants and the matron were very much in charge. When the National Health Service was founded in the late 1940s the greatest change it imposed was that in future all hospitals, municipal or voluntary, were to be funded by central government and managed by a nationwide network of regional hospital boards. The hospital administrator, springing fully formed like Athene from the head of Zeus, was born.

Hospitals were grouped under their regional boards, not necessarily by area but by specialist function and the Lady Chichester, to Dr Boyle's distress, became part of the separate St Francis group of psychiatric hospitals, cut off from the local general hospital regional board. She had always insisted on an holistic view of mental illness, that her hospital should be just another part of the local health care system, and now near retirement, fought a long — and unsuccessful — battle to keep her hospital away from the St Francis group.

The New Sussex was absorbed but left alone, its funds swallowed but its debts paid, its doctors salaried but its patients still coming. Louisa Martindale continued as a high profile visiting surgeon until she, too, retired to her London home in the 1950s.

The task of assimilating all the hospitals in the UK under one gigantic umbrella system took more than a few years; the nationwide administrative system was (and still is) constantly tinkered with as costs continue to soar yearly with the new scientific advances in surgery and medication demanded by members of the public. Nothing much has changed except that the yearly shortfall between money in and money out has become even larger. Unravelling the constant shifts in the structure of the NHS over the years — from regional boards through area health authorities and independent trusts, which might or might not be geographically based, has become almost a source of academic study in its complexity and has no place here; however, in 1974 yet another massive shake-up was put in place. This time the reorganisation would include the closure of the remaining women's hospitals. The New Sussex, the smallest and furthest away from London, was the first to suffer gradual extinction and began, as might well be expected, to ease out the women and to introduce men onto the staff. In about 1957 the first male member of staff ever to put foot in the hospital, other than the traditional porter, was radiologist Mr Mike Fisher, and in 1963 Mr Bryan Measday was appointed as a gynaecologist. In 1966, upon her retirement, the senior gynaecologist Dr Margaret Neal-Edwards was replaced by Mr Herbert Melville MD. Around that time Nigel Porter became a general surgeon and Dr John Wagstaff a general physician.[2] In 1980, although only after much local opposition, the health authority further wielded the axe and the final closure of the New Sussex was carried out in classic style and with whimsical echoes of past events.[3]

Even in dissolution the Lady Chichester and the New Sussex retained their years of uneasy relationship. In October 1980, the East Sussex Area Health Authority announced that the New Sussex would be closed temporarily for refurbishment and modernisation. Assurances were given to the complaining public that the closure would not be permanent and that medical and surgical treatment for women would in the interim be transferred to the Brighton General Hospital at Race Hill (the old workhouse infirmary and by then Brighton Municipal Hospital). A year later the health authority smoothly declared that the cost of modernisation had proved too high and that the pressure to find accommodation for patients suffering from mental and emotional disorders was, at the same time, seriously pressing (health authorities by then had responsibility for psychiatric patients). They proposed that Sussex House be re-opened as a psychiatric hospital for short-term care patients, who would be removed thence away from the Lady Chichester in New

Church Road. Long-term patients from the Lady Chichester would also be removed to Brighton General Hospital. The two houses in Rutland Gardens would become a part of a day centre to be built in the grounds of Aldrington House. Protests and severe accusations of broken promises were to no avail.[5] Interestingly, later statistics showed that after the move there was a noticeable decline in the waiting lists for women awaiting gynaecological operations. The health authority, naturally, was pleased by this result, deeming that its choice had been proved correct. That many women might have chosen to suffer a little longer rather than go up the hill to the gaunt old workhouse infirmary with its male doctors would not have occurred to them.

In 1982 the *Brighton & Hove Gazette* carried an article headed 'Question over £90,000 hospital bequests', which queried the whereabouts of monies bequeathed to the New Sussex by Brighton and Hove residents in their wills. Concern was expressed, and was not allayed by the health authority, which blamed the delay on the Charity Commissioners. It added that the money would probably go to the Royal Sussex County and to the Bevendean Geriatric Hospital.

In 1986 Aldrington House was targeted. This time new plans would move any remaining short-term, acute in-patients to Sussex House, which would be enlarged if required. Aldrington House itself would be refurbished and used this time solely as an outpatients' centre and to accommodate a day-care centre for elderly people suffering mental illness, who would continue to live in the local community. Fewer beds would be needed, the two houses in Rutland Gardens and the main house would combine to reopen as one day-care centre. The health authority was excited and enthusiastic about its plans, but local people were not impressed. More protests followed but, again, to no avail. The Lady Chichester Hospital no longer exists, although Aldrington Day Centre stands on its shadow, behind Helen Boyle's inviting, tree-lined garden and wide gravel path which still sweeps up to the imposing porch.

By 2001 Sussex House had been vacated and sold off to a developer. Work started on conversion of the hospital into modern flats after planning permission was granted in 1999. The name has been changed to Temple Heights and the garden has been destroyed, having been built over with a rather insubstantial-looking yellow block of flats known as York House. In its place Millview Hospital, a brand-new, concrete built psychiatric hospital for short-term patients, mostly youngsters, has been built in the residential area around Neville Road in the northern regions of Hove and Brighton. It stands next to the Hove Polyclinic, a day centre for medical and surgical cases with no overnight beds, which has some rather formal greenery, plenty of sunshine, but no particular charm. Both are publicly accessible by one rather sluggish bus route and what was once a wildlife area has recently been replaced by a new hotel.

In the late forties, although officially retired, Dr Boyle continued to work part time at the Lady Chichester and remained on the management committee: her last recorded attendance at a meeting was in February 1957. She is reputed to have continued to see patients up to the day before her death: she died overnight, in her bed, from a heart attack on 20th November 1957. Dr Boyle was eighty-eight years old, and had been in robust health for her age, still walking daily out on the downs, high in the green and breezy hills of Clayton, near Brighton, where she lived with her companion and secretary since 1929, Miss Rita Gore-Lindsay, who survived her for several years. A memorial service was held at All Saints' Church in Hove on 4th December 1957; the church was full and the service widely reported in both the national and local press. Many obituaries were published and can be easily accessed, although they contain very much the same information about her life.

The Honourable Ismay FitzGerald died in 1946, having lived with Louisa Martindale for more than thirty years. Thereafter, the retired Dr Martindale seems to have lived alone, looked after by a housekeeper. She died in London in 1966 at the great age of ninety-three and her death certificate gives the causes of death as pneumonia, thrombosis and arteriosclerosis. It was noted that she had a carcinoma of the right breast and glaucoma in both eyes, which had resulted in blindness. In her autobiography of 1951 she writes ruefully that the dangers of working closely with X-rays were little understood in the early days. Inside Millview Hospital her portrait looks down strangely from the boardroom wall. She stares out at the world through her *pince-nez*, her hands still resting lightly on her X-ray equipment.

> Not Heaven itself over the past hath power,
> But what has been has been, and I have had my hour.[5]

MISS LOUISA MARTINDALE

Miss Louisa Martindale, C.B.E., J.P., M.D., B.S., F.R.C.O.G., who died on Saturday at her home in London at the age of 93, was a pioneer among medical women.

Qualifying as M.B., B.S. London in 1899, she obtained the M.D. in 1907 and was elected F.R.C.O.G. in 1933. During 1906-07 she acted as Medical Officer to Hull Education Committee and as honorary Medical Officer to the Lees Walk Home for Girls. She became Medical Officer to Roedean School and to the Brighton and Hove High School; at the same time she carried on a consulting practice in Harley Street as a gynaecologist and held the appointment of Consulting Surgeon to the Marie Curie Hospital, and the New Sussex Hospital at Brighton.

She was a former president of the Medical Women's International Association, and of the Medical Women's Federation. Her professional writings included books on *The Woman Doctor and her Future* (1922) and *The Prevention of Venereal Disease* (1945). She was awarded the C.B.E. in 1931 and was a Justice of the Peace.

Obituaries from *The Times*, (above) 7 February 1966 and (right) 22 November 1959.

DR. HELEN BOYLE

TREATMENT OF NERVOUS DISORDERS

Dr. Helen Boyle, who died at her home at Pyecombe, Sussex, on Wednesday, the day after her 88th birthday, had been for many years a leader in early treatment of functional nervous disorders.

Her work started over 50 years ago when the medical and psychological treatment of such disorders was almost unknown, and it continued up to the time of her death in a time when the medical profession recognized such treatment as vitally important.

Her most outstanding public services were the founding of the Lady Chichester Hospital for Functional Nervous Disorders and the National Council for Mental Hygiene, now the National Council for Mental Health. She first realized the urgent need for the treatment of nervous breakdown when working as medical superintendent of the Canning Town Mission Hospital, and in 1905 she founded the Lady Chichester Hospital. There was then no hospital provision for early nervous disorders and for mild uncertifiable mental illness. For over 50 years she was the mainspring of its work.

In 1920 at the request of several societies in Canada and the U.S.A. she crossed the Atlantic to speak. On her return she interested Sir Maurice Craig in her work, and together, in 1923, they founded the National Council for Mental Hygiene with the idea of improving the mental health of the community.

Clifford Beers, the founder and secretary of the National Committee for Mental Hygiene in the U.S.A., and the founder of the international movement, later spoke of the inspiration that Dr. Boyle had been to him and the debt which the movement owed her.

She was the first woman to be elected as a member of the honorary medical staff of the Royal Sussex County Hospital, of which she was elected honorary consultant for nervous disorders, and in 1939 she became president of the Royal Medico-Psychological Association. She was the first, and so far has been the only, woman to hold the presidency. In 1953 she was elected a member of the committee of honour of the World Federation for Mental Health as " a distinguished pioneer in the field of mental health."

At the request of Archbishop Temple she became one of the original members of the Churches' Council of Healing, and continued to serve on the working committee. In the war of 1914-18 she served in Serbia with the Royal Free Hospital unit and received the Order of St. Sava.

Notes

[1] The Royal Sussex County Hospital, Hove General Hospital, Brighton General Hospital, Sussex Maternity Hospital, Sussex Eye Hospital, Royal Alexandra Hospital for Sick Children, Sussex Throat and Ear Hospital, Foredown Hospital for Infectious Diseases, Bevendean Sanatorium, Lady Chichester Hospital, New Sussex Hospital. Lauste, L. W. MD, FRCS, 'Hospitals in Brighton and Hove', *Proceedings of the Royal Society of Medicine Vol. 65* February 1972, pp 221–6.

[2] Personal communication with Herbert Melville, 6 January 2006.

[3] The Elizabeth Garrett Anderson Hospital faced closure in 1975, but strong action, which included strike threats by nurses, porters and cleaners, kept it open but with a change of name to the Elizabeth Garrett Anderson and Obstetric Hospital. In 2006 it will shrink into the Elizabeth Garrett Anderson Ward at the University College Hospital Trust's new hospital. The South London Hospital for Women was closed in 1984 and a nine-month protest occupation by women followed. The occupation was forcibly ended by police action in 1985 (forty women police officers were sent in.) In Edinburgh the Elsie Inglis Memorial Hospital (officially the Elsie Inglis Memorial Maternity Hospital) became part of the Edinburgh Southern Hospitals under the Scottish South Eastern Regional Hospital Board with the arrival of the NHS in 1948. The hospital became part of the Royal Infirmary of Edinburgh and Associated Hospitals Unit in 1984 and closed in 1988.

[4] For a considerable amount of further information about the NHS see Rivett, G. *History of the National Health Service*, at <www.nhshistory.net>.

[5] John Dryden. Quoted in Louisa Martindale's *A Woman Surgeon*.

From the 1926 Appeal

'TWENTY-ONE YEARS OF PIONEER WORK'

THE LADY CHICHESTER HOSPITAL

FOR EARLY NERVOUS AND BORDERLAND
CASES AMONG WOMEN AND CHILDREN
HOVE, BRIGHTON
SUSSEX

A Record and an Appeal

President:
THE RIGHT HON. THE COUNTESS OF CHICHESTER.

Vice-Presidents:
DAME HENRIETTA BARNETT D.B.E.   MISS M.E. VERRALL.

Patrons:
THE DOWAGER MARCHIONESS OF DUFFERIN AND AVA.
THE LADY ST. HELIER.
THE LADY BETTY BALFOUR.
THE LADY FRANCES BALFOUR.
LADY EMMOTT.   LADY BYLES.
LADY BATTERSEA.   THE COUNTESS LYTTON.
VIOLET, THE LADY BEAUMONT.
KATHLEEN, VISCOUNTESS FALMOUTH.
MISS OLIVE BOYLE.
MRS GEO. CADBURY O.B.E.
MRS LYDIA KLEIN.
SIR MAURICE CRAIG C.B.E., M.D.

Council:
MRS BADCOCK.   MRS BYRON.   MISS A.M. CHUBB.
MRS CORAM.   MRS CULVERHOUSE.
MRS HANKEY.   MISS ISAACSON.
THE COUNTESS OF LISTOWEL.   MRS MORRIS.
THE HON. MRS CLIVE PEARSON.
THE LADY ELIZABETH PELHAM.
MRS STEPHEN RALLI.   LADY SCHNIFFNER.
SIR BERRY CUSACK-SMITH.   F.B. STEVENS Esq.
MRS LANGMUIR WATT.   COL. LANGMUIR WATT C.M.G.

Hon. Treasurer: E.W. RICHARDSON Esq.
Hon. Financial Adviser: MISS GORDON HOLMES.
Organising Secretary: MISS G. LAWIS.

Secretary:
Mr A.F. GRAVES F.C.I.S., F.L.A.A.,
117 NORTH STREET, BRIGHTON.

APPENDIX II

From a promotional pamphlet, 1937

THE NEW SUSSEX HOSPITAL FOR WOMEN AND CHILDREN BRIGHTON (Incorporated)

PAST PATRONESS AND CHAIRMEN

Patroness: H.R.H THE PRINCESS ROYAL   1918–1929

Chairmen: THE COUNTESS BUXTON G.B.E., J.P.,   1920–1922
MRS HERBERT JONES   1923–1924
LADY RAWSON   1925–1931

President:
H.R.H. THE PRINCESS LOUISE DUCHESS OF ARGYLL

Chairman of the Council of Management
LADY CAMPION

Vice Chairman
E.D. STAFFORD Esq.

Vice-Presidents:
THE MAYOR AND MAYORESS OF BRIGHTON
THE MAYOR AND MAYORESS OF HOVE
THE COUNTESS BUXTON G.B.E., J.P.,
THE LADY DENMAM G.B.E.   THE LADY LECONFIELD
LADY VERNON
MRS EGGAR   MRS HENSON INFIELD
MISS ELIZABETH ROBINS   MRS IRENE VANBURGH

Hon. Treasurers
THE VISCOUNTESS RHONDDA   J.B. STURGIS Esq.,

Hon Secretary: Miss D. GORE-BROWN

Council of Management

Miss E.C. BEVAN	Miss A MARION JACOBS
Mrs BOGLE-SMITH	Mrs BLACKETT-JEFFRIES M.D.
Col. T. M. BOOTH C.M.G.,	B.S.(Lond.)
D.S.O., J.P.	Mrs LOGAN-HOME
Hon. Mrs WALTER BURRELL	Mrs ALAN MARGETSON
Lady CAMPION	Miss MARTINDALE C.B.E., J.P., M.D.,
Mrs ADRIAN CORBETT	B.S., (Lond) F.C.O.G
Mrs DALE	HENRY D. ROBERTS Esq. M.B.E.,
Mrs DUNLOP	Mrs SCATLIFF M.S. (Lond),
Lady EDWARDS	E.D. STAFFORD Esq.,
Miss B.M.J. GRAHAM-LEES	J.B. STURGIS Esq.,
Mrs ALEC HOLDEN	Miss OCTAVIA WILBERFORCE
	M.R.C.S., L.R.C.P.

Secretary: PERCY F. SPOONER, F.C.I.S., F.H.O.A.

Appeal Secretary: Miss D.W. HARPER.

Matron: Miss M.P. ASHBEE.

Almoner: Miss M.S. WILDBLOOD A.I.H.A.

Sussex Daily News 19th October 1922 (Day 1)

YE AUTUMNE FAYRE

A Host of Attractions

AT HOVE TOWN HALL

Aiding The Lady Chichester Hospital

It seems almost incredible that autumn's group of bazaars and charitable functions is again with us. Yesterday these led off with an annual event "Ye Autumne Fayre" on behalf of The Lady Chichester Hospital for Women and Children, which, as in the past, was held at Hove Town Hall. A very beautiful picture of autumn colouring met the eye on entering. Clever hands had been at work and the transformation was complete. The opening ceremony was performed by Violet Lady Beaumont with Dr Hobhouse in the chair. On the platform were many interested and associated with the hospital including the Mayoress of Hove (Mrs F. W. A. Cushman) the Countess of Chichester, Lady Schiffner, Dr Helen Boyle, Mrs Coram and others. With a few encouraging words Lady Beaumont expressed the great pleasure it gave her to be present and warmly congratulated the helpers on their wonderful achievement. "It is the prettiest bazaar I have ever been to" she said as she declared it open and wished it the greatest possible success. A bouquet of lovely tawny chrysanthemums was sweetly presented by the Mayoress's little daughter, pretty Miss Eileen Cushman, who received warm thanks. Lady Chichester, in moving a vote of thanks to Lady Beaumont for her presence, dwelt on the excellence of the work at the Hospital, and begged all would make it known as far as they possibly could. She thanked everyone for their generous help — Lady Schiffner seconded. Mrs Coram proposed a vote of thanks to Dr Hobhouse, and at the same time mentioned the names of many tradespeople and others whose support they deeply valued, not forgetting the Girl Guides, who had lined the entrance on the arrival of Lady Beaumont.

A RIOT OF COLOUR ·

Quite impossible of description were the masses of autumn flowers, grasses and brilliantly shaded foliage which so fittingly gave the name to the Fayre. The platform was a high bank wherein sunflowers and shaded hollyhocks reared their stately heads from bronze hued boughs, berries and autumn flowerets. This hid the Fairy Grotto so beautifully designed, made and arranged by Miss Ethel Onslow, the whole thing being her handiwork. Inside all was a gorgeous vista of golden trees lit with the glow of a thousand soft-toned lights and fantastic decoration, serving to throw up the wonders of the magic cauldron, where Mrs Alfred Morris sat in her mysterious eastern dress and told fortunes, and where the lovely little granddaughter of Mrs Poole held sway in her Magic House crowned with dazzling jewels. The Magic Golden Goose had a corner to himself [sic], and loudly he cackled when for sixpence or a shilling a golden egg was laid. Helping in charming costumes were Mrs Creswick and Mrs Rowe whose duty it was to see to this remarkable bird. All was magic in this Aladdin's Grove of wonders, and Mrs Steyning-Beard and her three pretty girls, Barbara, Ursula and Ruth, with the help of Miss Ashford-Ayre had a magic basket of Peacehaven sweets, specially sent from that enchanted spot where the beautiful little seaside bungalow is to be the property of some lucky person for the sum of 2s 6d [half a crown], the price of the tickets, which people flocked to buy for the benefit of the Hospital. This is proving a huge draw. The Magic Well in the precincts of the Grotto was looked after by Miss Hudson, and Miss Onslow in her eastern gleaming glittering robes was a veritable Queen of Sheba.

HUMAN SPIDER &c

Another wonderful side show, also most cleverly provided by Miss Onslow, was the illusion "The Human Spider." This represented a spider's body with the sweet laughing face of a real little girl, and must be seen to be appreciated. A Cinderella competition which was run by Mrs Sydney Herbert and Miss K. Fenner was an entirely original venture. The lucky person whose foot fitted the various shoes — or one — in Cinderella's Parlour gained a prize, 10s or £1, for the payment of 6d. It was impossible to find or think of anything not on sale in the way of attractive goods at the Fayre. For the amusement of all who spent their money in the good cause was an arts and crafts stall looked after by Mrs Culverhouse and Mrs Paske-Nazelfoot. Toys and crackers and beautiful dolls, including a dream of loveliness which was being drawn for at 1s a ticket were at a stall of which Mrs de Pinna Weil, Miss Rowlandson and

Miss Richardson were in charge. Cakes of the most delicious order were sold by Mrs Arnold Marks and Mrs Hayman. Sweets in tempting array were offered by Mrs Thacker and Miss Docking, and handkerchiefs by Dr Lillian Harris, Mrs Crow, Miss Harris and Dr Nora Crow. Besides these the most imposing and largest stall of any, which occupied a big centre place, was in [the] charge of Mrs Langmuir Watt, Mrs Odling, Mrs Spratling, and others, and the most beautiful produce was sold which included fruit, vegetables, flowers, eggs, birds dead and live chickens and ducks, also jams, pickles and every sort of delicious and dainty food to stock a larder with. Small wonder a big trade was done.

OTHER SALEABLE GOODS

The Drive stall, with all sorts of fancy needlework and charming things, was in the charge of Sister Smith, Miss Chubb, Miss Billett and Nurse Marrable; Hospital stall, the Matron and nurses; hosiery, Miss Gibson; stationery and dainty fancy knickknacks, Lady Lange; tobacco stall Lady Schiffner, Miss Carter, and Miss Turner; vanity stall Lady Chichester and Lady Monk-Bretton; palmistry and card-reading Mrs Legge-Wilkinson and Miss Mead; magic fish pond, Miss Andre Lange; houp-la, Miss Parry; competitions Miss Clarke; and guessing the weight of cake and ham, Mrs Fletcher. Refreshments were served in a charming enclosure hedged in beneath the gallery with grasses and flowers. Over this department Mrs Burt Brill preside with valuable help forthcoming from Mrs Harrison, Miss Lennard, Miss Pierce, and a bevy of pretty girls to wait on everyone. Included among them were Miss Gladys Rainford, Miss Crawford, the Misses Muriel and Iris Dilke, Miss Marsden, Miss Harrison, Miss Pape, Miss Knight and others, Mrs Leslie Parker being busy selling tea tickets. Side-shows too numerous to mention, were everywhere, and a most wonderful elephant, cleverly made by Miss Edith Onslow, collected pennies for the Hospital. Others who gave special service to the very worthy object were Mr and Mrs Roberts, Miss Elsie Plante, Miss Jessie Stewart, Mr Rowden, Miss Longdon, and Mrs Poole, all helping Miss Onslow in the Fairy Grotto and elsewhere, and a host of others including Colonel Langmuir Watt who everywhere worked with a will to make the Fayre the Great success it was. The heartiest thanks and congratulations went to Mrs Thacker, who was responsible for the whole of the artistic and unique decorations. One of the greatest attractions is the wireless [radio] concert arranged by Messrs Galliers, while the excellent music supplied by Miss Padfield's Band and "Our Orchestra" made the proceedings of the most bright and lively order. The Fayre will be open today and tomorrow.

YE AUTUMNE FAYRE

Mayor-elect of Hove Presides at
Opening Ceremony

A most interesting little ceremony marked the second day's opening of "Ye Autumne Fayre" at the Hove Town Hall, yesterday, which does so much to swell the funds of The Lady Chichester Hospital. The chair was taken by the Mayor elect of Hove, Alderman Jago, who won all hearts with an excellent little speech. He introduced Lady Ellenborough, who charmingly performed the opening ceremony, and whose forthcoming interest in the hospital is a matter for congratulation. She was presented with a bouquet of bronze red chrysanthemums by tiny Miss Viola Leaver, the grand-daughter of Mrs Poole, who is giving valuable help to the bazaar. Lady Chichester expressed the warmest thanks to Lady Ellenborough in the name of everyone for so kindly coming at the last moment in place of Lady Buxton, who was prevented by the indisposition of her husband from carrying out her engagement.*

THE MAYOR'S EULOGIES

The Mayor of Hove, Councillor F.W.A. Cushman eulogised, not only the work for the object in view, but the interest the Chairman was taking in the function when moving a vote of thanks, and interesting facts came from Dr Helen Boyle and Mrs Coram who also spoke. Others present included Lady Schiffner in black and steel, Lady Elizabeth Pelham wearing a black wrap and costume with large rosette adorning a close fitting hat. Lady West was in brown, Lady Ellenborough wearing a becoming tone [sic] of pale grey with drooping grey feathers in a hat to match, with skunk furs and a long diamond neckchain. Lady Chichester wore a smart beaver wrap, trimmed with beaver fur, her toque set off at one side with dark coq's plumage. These any many more well-known people were present. The Fayre will be held again today.

---

* It is perhaps one of the sadder moments of the story of the two hospitals that Lady Buxton was apparently, after all, unable to open the second day of the Lady Chichester Hospital's 'Autumne Fayre'; but the thought was there.

Sussex Daily News 14ᵗʰ December 1922 (Day 1)

YE OLDE SUSSEX FAYRE

A Beautiful Tudor Village

BRIGHTON DOME TRANSFORMED

Aid for New Sussex Hospital

It would be impossible to estimate how much time, thought, taste and real work has been expended on the interior of The Dome to produce the beautiful effect which met the eye there yesterday. It had been transformed, by fairy hands it would seem, into a lively Tudor Village, the inhabitants of which were making merry with Ye Olde Sussex Fayre. Bright blue skies, a vista of lovely green trees and hill sides, with fine old Tudor buildings, a winding river with pleasure and fishing boats, were all round in a panorama of picturesque beauty. And, if all this does not attract thousands to buy at charming stalls, surely no effort on behalf of charity or really worthy institutions has a chance. The Fayre is to help the funds of the New Sussex Hospital for Women and Children, Brighton and Hove, which is offered by women doctors, and has the Princess Royal as its patron.

THE OPENING

It was opened by Mrs Cooper Rawson, wife of the Junior M.P. for Brighton & Hove, who made one of her characteristically charming little speeches, Viscountess [sic] Buxton presiding. Also on the platform, which gave a splendid view of the village, with its booths and stalls, were Miss Vernon (organiser), Mr and Mrs Cobb, Dr Helen Webb (who took the place of Dr Martindale), Mr Stafford, Mrs Eggar (the Secretary of the hospital) and others. Introducing Mrs Cooper Rawson Lady Buxton dwelt on the work of the hospital, and explained the necessity for the Fayre. Warmly admiring the beautiful surroundings, she stated that in all her experience of bazaars, that was the prettiest she had ever seen. Dr Helen Webb, who followed, mentioned Mrs Martindale, Dr Martindale's mother, as one whose interest had done much in furthering hospital work. The New Sussex Hospital was unique, for patients could come there and be looked after as though they were in their own homes, with every comfort. The Matron was at all times glad to shew anyone over the wards. She hoped its growth would be considerable, and looked forward to the time when the present vacant land they owned would be covered with hospital buildings.

BRIGHTON M.P'S AS PATIENTS!

Apologising for the absence of her husband, who was unable to leave his parliamentary duties, Mrs Cooper Rawson remarked that both members in Brighton would soon require hospital treatment if their strenuous life continued. She congratulated all those who had taken part in producing the Fayre. Her knowledge of hospitals and their needs led her to believe that if there were double the number of beds in this particular hospital they would not be good enough. They had a good nursing staff and a first rate Matron, and she thought them lucky people. The debt to be cleared was £1000 and she made an earnest appeal for more subscribers and finished by saying "Health is the greatest blessing in the world, and on behalf of the sick and suffering, I ask you of your loving charity to do everything you can to make this bazaar a success." Votes of thanks were proposed by Mr Stafford, seconded by Mrs Eggar and carried unanimously. All round, the stalls were set out in most attractive style, and purchasers must have been hard to please if they could not find anything to engage their fancy. It was a busy scene and picturesqueness was added by the charming old English dresses of all the helpers, the number of whom was considerable.

WHO COULD RESIST

Pretty faces in quaint sun bonnets and lace caps, and floral patterned gowns with panniers and puffs, vended a host of tempting goods and mingling here and there were real Sussex smock frocks on some of the boys, while the serviceable dress of the farm girl struck a note of utility and up-to-dateness which was strange in old world Tudor surroundings. All however, made up a picture which has never been excelled in Brighton for charm. Delightful music by the Hove School of Music Orchestra, and conducted by Mr E. Dupont, made things lively and bright. A tour of the stalls was made by Mrs Cooper Rawson and Viscountess [sic] Buxton, who were immensely interested in everything. Something out of the common has to attract visitors to fairs and bazaars these days and people were crowding to the great Reel Competition – a giant indeed wound with string. Guessing to the nearest correct length of the string ensures the winner of a ten days tour (for two) in Switzerland. Other beautiful prizes were set out on a special stall, and included all sorts of antique and valuable articles, also seats for theatres and places of amusement, by no means the least attractive being a dinner for two at a local restaurant.

HARD WORKERS AT THE STALLS

One of the biggest stalls was the Traders', in front of the platform, and looked after by Mrs Mackenzie, with Mrs Hadlow, the helpers being Miss Bucknell, Mrs Gilbert, Mrs Hutchinson, Mrs Jacob, Mrs Lang, Miss Ronpell, Miss Sheppard and Miss Steen. There was beautiful food, household requisites, a wonderful basket of fruit, kitchen utensils, mistletoe and holly, hats and a most exquisite young person in pink, who held out her pretty doll's arms to entreat someone to purchase her. The Matron of the Hospital sold charming white woollen garments, besides numerous other delightful things, bath crystals being shewn in many shades and colours. The helpers were Sisters Aylott, Clayton, and Freeman, and nurses assisted by Mrs Bowden, Miss Braidish, and Miss Chatfield. They kept to their trim nurses' uniform and very cool and nice they looked. Books, antiques and curios were sold by Miss A.E. Nellen, and she had some lively bargains to dispose of. Miss Maule, Miss Betty Ionides, Miss Mabel Roll and Mrs and Miss Reynolds all helped to bring grist to the mill. Mrs Andrade and Miss Grey presided over a cigarette and tobacco stall, with help from the Misses Blumfield, Mrs Gray and Mrs Williams.

TO PLEASE THE EYE

Charming goods were displayed on the stall of Mrs Jack Butler, who was assisted by Miss Butler, Miss Ellis and Miss Swainson. Here charming cushions and fancy work, cute little mascots and all sorts of attractive goods. Bags and baskets, delightfully assorted, were sold by Mrs Herbert Carden, helped by Miss Grace Carden, Mrs S. Colston Garrett, Mrs Fabian Rice and Miss Peggy Whitelaw. Lady Lange with Mrs Andree Lange and Miss Lange was [sic] well occupied selling balloons, crackers, and fascinating toys and Christmas gifts. Mrs Stafford had charge of the Hassocks stall and sold leatherware and lavender with [illegible] underwear, dolls, and many pretty things. Mrs W. H. Eggar and Mrs

Feltham helped her. The Baker's oven and village well were novelties in charge of Mrs Roland Smeed and Miss Higgins, with the Misses Pruett helping, and beautiful greengrocery and provisions were offered by Miss Willett, Miss Gardiner and Mrs Bonnick, and Mrs E. Hall, with the assistance of Mrs Corbett, Miss Marten, and Miss Matherson. Mrs Wolfe did a good trade with her toys at her Tiny Tots stall, where Mrs Bound, Mrs Davis, Miss Fry, Miss Grimer and Mrs Plumb were all busy, and Miss Cobb with her delicious sweets and willing helpers was another who was not idle. Her assistants included the Misses M. Hull, Peters and Waghorn.

DELIGHTFUL ART POTTERY

Miss Vernon has some charmingly pretty things on her stall, the colourful art pottery being delightful. Many of her attractive goods were made by disabled ex-Servicemen, and she was backed by Miss Harris, Mrs Hewetson, Mrs Hordern, the Misses Rand, Miss Simpkings, Mrs Vernon and Mrs Dindor. Handkerchiefs, toilet requisites, soaps, perfumes &c, were cold by Mrs Cuthbert Radcliffe, with Mrs Alston, Miss Morley, and Miss Spinney, while tempting dairy produce found many customers at the stall presided over by Mrs Warne and Miss Bacon. Those assisting were Miss Field, Mrs Gauntlett, Miss Kendall, Miss Kerrick, Miss Jose Wellborne, and the Misses Wilkinson. One of the most interesting was the farmyard stall with its livestock. Mrs and Miss Olliver (Patcham) and Miss Aylwin looked after fat geese, ducks and chicken, who did not fail to make themselves heard. Meek eyed rabbits nibbled cabbages in their cages, and two beautiful sheep dogs slumbered in peace and comfort. All were for sale. Viscount Selby and the Misses Vernon arranged raffles, and Mrs Davenport and Mrs Jeboult supplied paper and string.

FOR THIRSTY FOLK

Besides these there was the picturesque 'Ye Olde Fryco Inne' [sic] where bottles of delightful drink gleamed in the electric light together with fruit cordials and ginger wine. There was also a stall groaning with delicious cakes in the charge of Lady Otter, with the help of Miss Colett, Miss Jacob, Miss Belle Parrots, Miss Prior, Miss Rolandi, Mrs Thacker, and Miss Woodward. Additional enterprises for the purpose of raising money included Palmistry by Miss Percival and Lady Mercer with the Misses Barnes, Mrs Fraser, Miss E. Hume, and Miss L. Percival assisting. Under the able organisation of Mrs Sidney Herbert the following side-shows proved ......attraction; Houp La....Lucky Wheel.....' The smallest and fiercest.....in the world......the property of an Indian Potentate' Mrs Albert Willey. [Sadly an elderly piece of sellotape has obscured the text here!] Smelling Competition, Miss Hollis; Lucky Arrow, Miss Snelling; Hidden treasure, Miss Fenner; The Bird that Loves Children, Mrs Jackson; Lucky Bowl, Mr Halford; Candle Competition, Mrs Reginald Carter; Bombardo. Mr R. Cushman; various competitions Mr Stapleton Moore and Mrs Clarke; Bunty Pulls the Strings, Mrs Packer.

HELPERS WITH TEA

Tea and refreshments were served in the wide corridor, and very delicious looking were many of the dainties presented by kindly supporters of The Fayre. This was in charge of Mrs Dale and Mrs Paddon who had as helpers: Mrs Aitchison, Mrs Barnard, the Misses Barnard, F. Barry, Blatch, Bradley, [sic] Mrs Dutt, Miss Carr, Miss Carver, Mrs Conran, Mrs Humble-Crofts, the Misses Felgate, Gibbon, Gosling, Holt,, Mrs Howe, Miss A. Jones, Mrs King, Miss Mogridge, Miss Morris, Mrs Parham, the Misses Parry, Philip Recks, Mrs Robinson, Mrs Ruddiman, the Misses Sherrard, Smyth and Voller.

Others giving valuable help were:-

Cloakroom attendants: Mrs Rose and Mrs Pack; Stewards: Master Butler, Messrs Chambers, B. Field, F.C. Evitt, Gearing, W. Graham, A.G. Hatton, Jacobs, Moss, F. Pruett, A. Palmer, Russell, P. Round, T. Starling, Roland Smeed, and Williamson. Programme sellers: the Misses Breach, Sheila Boniface, Jean Marshall (per Miss Jacob), Brown, Edna Davie, Judy Firth, Margery Foskett, A. Gornold, Humphrey, Joyce Hoodless, Betty Kendall, Marjory Langton, Elsie Langton, Joan Longley, Yvonne Mather, Orbell, Swaine, Joan Horton-Stephens, Margaret Smith, B. Scatliff, Master G. Scatliff, the Misses Tillstone, Winsome Thorogood, Sylvia Ward and Williams.

Music was supplied by the Municipal Secondary School Orchestra, conducted by Mr. G. H. Whitcomb. The Fayre will be opened today by the Countess of Chichester.

Sussex Daily News 15th December 1922 (Day 2)

YE OLDE SUSSEX FAYRE

Reopened by the Countess of Chichester

SPEAKERS' AMUSING CONTEST
WITH THE FARMYARD

Yesterday Lady Buxton again presided at the opening ceremony of "Ye Olde Sussex Fayre" in aid of The New Sussex Hospital for Women and Children, which was gracefully performed by the Countess of Chichester. Supporting them on the platform were the Mayor and Mayoress of Hove (Alderman Jago J. P. and Mrs Jago,) Canon Hordern, Lady Otter, Miss Elizabeth Robins, Mr Gribble, Mr Cobb, Mr Stafford, Miss Merrifield and others. The Chairman called on Miss Elizabeth Robins to speak on behalf of the Hospital, first of all remarking that they felt greatly indebted to Lady Chichester for her presence. Lady Chichester's interests were with her own Hospital, but she felt they could mutually work together, one looking after the needs of the body and the other the mind. Miss Elizabeth Robins in a long speech emphasised many points put before everyone on the first day's opening, and dwelt on the skill of women doctors and the strides their work had made. She announced the offers of £10 from two different sources provided others would come forward with similar sums. (It is understood that other promises have been forthcoming). Lady Chichester warmly eulogised the work of the New Women's Hospital [sic] and was emphatic in her praise of the charming appearance of the Fayre, hoping its Financial success would be as great as its artistic one. The Mayor of Hove moved a very hearty vote of thanks to her ladyship, and coupled it with all the good wishes of the season. In the place of the vicar of Brighton, who was prevented from attending, Canon Hordern seconded and extended sincere thanks to Lady Buxton, Miss Vernon and all the ladies who had worked so untiringly for the Fayre.

INTERRUPTIONS FROM THE FARMYARD

The denizens of the farmyard, probably annoyed at their close confinement, set up an altercation of their own, and now and then entirely drowned the voices of the speakers, who at times, amid roars of laughter, were forced to subside. All thoroughly enjoyed the unrehearsed effect, which was a most amusing episode of the afternoon [sic]. The feathered company, however, relapsed into silence when Miss Adele Jouanno's Orchestra struck up and provided a lively and festive atmosphere. Though the first day's takings were disappointing, the stalls shewed distinct signs of thinning, and it was anticipated things would brighten up towards the close. The great excitement of yesterday was the unwinding of the giant reel and discovery of the winner. Among valuable prizes was a handsome antique chest of drawers presented by Lady Leconfield, and many who had taken tickets for the competition hoped they might win this instead of the Switzerland trip. Lady Buxton gave a charming tea service for this same competition and Mrs Yates Thompson a gold slave bangle, a silver entree dish came from Lady Rhondda, and many other beautiful gifts were added.

OLDE WORLDE FROCKS

Many were the real old English gowns worn at the Fayre, some being exceedingly valuable. Miss Chester, one of the helpers, was charming in her cotton frock and sunbonnet, and wore a beautiful old lace fichu, an heirloom from an ancestress. Mrs Sidney Herbert looked most picturesque in her old-world dress of an elderly lady with white net cap and fichu and quaint black gown figured with white, big horn spectacles giving a curious realism. A word of thanks is due to Miss M.C. Lander, Secretary to the Hospital, who also worked very hard to ensure the success of the undertaking.

TIMELINE

1898 Dr Boyle and Dr Jones arrive in Hove at 3 Palmeira Terrace.

1899 Lewes Road Dispensary for Women & Children opens at 145 Islingword Road.

1905 Lewes Road Hospital for Early Nervous Diseases of Women & Children opens at 101 Roundhill Crescent. Sixth Lord Chichester inherits his title and his wife becomes the patron of the hospital. The Dispensary stays in Islingword Road.

1907–8 Dr Martindale sets up practice in Brighton and joins the Dispensary staff. Dr Jones moves to Glasgow. Dr Boyle ceases attending the Dispensary.

1911 The Dispensary moves to 4 Ditchling Road; both Hospital and Dispensary are known jointly as the Chichester Hospital and Dispensary for Women and Children.

1912 6 Ditchling Road is added and opens as a small medical and surgical hospital. The Dispensary is known as the Outpatients'. Both are known jointly as the Lady Chichester Hospital and Dispensary.

1913 LCH moves from Roundhill Crescent to 70 Brunswick Place and is named the LCH Hove Branch. At Ditchling Road number 8 is added to 4 and 6, and named the LCH Brighton Branch.

1918 The branches separate into two independent hospitals. Brighton Branch (Ditchling Road) renamed temporarily New Sussex Hospital (NSH) has its own Board of Management: Hove Branch retains name Lady Chichester Hospital (LCH). Lady Chichester stays with the latter as president and chairman of its Council of Management.

1920 LCH moves to Aldrington House, Hove.

1921 NSH moves to Windlesham House, Brighton. Lady Buxton becomes president and chairman of the Board of Management.

1922 Dr Martindale leaves Brighton but stays as surgeon at the NSH.

1923 Death of Dr Jones.

1948 Both hospitals absorbed into the NHS. LCH into the St Francis group, the NSH under the East Sussex Area Health Authority.

1955 Death of Mildred, Lady Buxton.

1957 Death of Dr Boyle.

1965 Death of Ruth, Lady Chichester.

1966 Death of Dr Martindale.

1980s Closure of the NSH and LCH. Sussex House becomes a psychiatric hospital. Aldrington House becomes day centre for psychiatric patients.

2002–3 Sussex House is converted into flats as 'Temple Heights.'

APPENDIX VI

PLACES, PEOPLE AND CONNECTIONS

These are some of the women and men whose lives had influence either directly or indirectly upon the LCH and NSH. Many lived or worked locally, others considerably further afield. These accounts are not meant to be exhaustive, this would be impossible, but they are meant to highlight the widespread academic, social, business and professional connections that two little hospitals in a small town in Sussex could call upon to nourish their existence.

ABBREVIATIONS

b: born, BOM: Board of Management, Bt: baronet, c: *circa*, d: died, hon: honorary (unpaid/ awarded as honour), LCH: Lady Chichester Hospital, m: married, NSH: New Sussex Hospital, WW1/2: The First/Second World Wars.

BAO/BAORUI: Bachelor of the Art of Obstetrics/Royal University of Ireland. MB: Bachelor of Medicine. BCh/S: Bachelor of Surgery. B&S Med-Chirg Soc: Brighton & Sussex Medico-Chirurgical Society. CH: Order of the Companions of Honour. CI: Lady of the Imperial Order of the Crown of India. CMG: Companion of St Michael & St George. CBE: Commander of the Order of British Empire. DBE: Dame Commander of the Order of British Empire. GBE: Dame Grand Cross of the Order of British Empire. GCVO: Dame Grand Cross of the Royal Victorian Order. GG: Governor General. FRCP: Fellow of the Royal College of Physicians. FRCS: Fellow of the Royal College of Surgeons. LDS: Licentiate Dental Surgery. LKQCPI: Licentiate of the King and Queen's College of Physicians Ireland. LRCPI: Licentiate of the Royal College of Physicians Ireland. LRCP: Licentiate of the Royal College of Physicians. LRCS: Licentiate of the Royal College of Surgeons. LSA/LMSSA: Licentiate in Medicine & Surgery of the Society of Apothecaries. LSMW: London School of Medicine for Women: MB: Bachelor of Medicine. MBE: Member of the Order of British Empire. MD: Doctor of Medicine. MS: Master of Surgery. OBE: Officer of the Order of the British Empire. RAMC: Royal Army Medical Corps. RRC: Lady of the Royal Red Cross. SPR: Society for Psychical Research. VA: Lady of the Royal Order of Victoria & Albert. YWCA: Young Women's Christian Association.

The London School of Medicine for Women

The LSMW was founded by Sophia Jex-Blake and opened in 1874 at 30 Henrietta Street (later Handel Street), London. There were fourteen students. In 1892 it was rebuilt at 8–11 Hunter Street, and in 1898 changed its name to the London (Royal Free Hospital) School of Medicine for Women, although the full title was rarely used. A new block of laboratories was added in 1897 (the students lost their tennis courts) and a lecture theatre, biological department and administrative office were added in 1899. The students' common rooms, the refectory and library were ready in 1900. The LSMW became a school of the university in 1900, styled the London (Royal Free Hospital) School of Medicine for Women (University of London). Elizabeth Garrett Anderson was Dean 1893–1903, then Dr Julia Cock 1903–1914 and Miss Aldrich-Blake 1914–1925. All three were associated with the LCH at various times. Miss Aldrich-Blake was followed as dean by Florence, Lady Barrett MD, a friend of Louisa Martindale. The LSMW finally became co-educational in 1948 with the arrival of the NHS, and was re-named the Royal Free School of Medicine.

Newnham College, Cambridge

Newnham College was opened in rooms in Regent Street, Cambridge in 1871 by Henry Sidgwick (1838–1900), a don at Trinity College, later moving to Merton Hall on Northampton Street. It was rebuilt as Newnham Hall in 1875. Special classes were devised which avoided the traditional classical studies taught at Girton College. Women were admitted to Cambridge University examinations in 1881 and graduates were given a certificate which indicated that, had a degree been awarded, it would have been of such-and-such a class; however, women did not become full members of the university until 1947. One of the first five Newnham students was Edith Creak, who in 1876 became the first headmistress of Brighton High School for Girls.

The Society for Psychical Research

Henry Sidgwick (1838–1900) was also the first President of the Society for Psychical Research in 1882. His wife Eleanor (née Balfour) was the second Principal of Newnham College; she was a sister-in-law of Lady Frances Balfour. Margaret de Gaudrion Verrall (née Merrifield) was a lecturer at Newnham and a prominent medium in the P.S.R; she was from Brighton, the sister of Flora Merrifield. Mrs Verrall was married to Professor Arthur Verrall of Trinity College Cambridge, also a Brightonian. Mr and Mrs Henry Yates-Thompson, wealthy art collectors, endowed the Champneys Library at Newnham in 1897; Mrs Yates-Thompson (Dolly) was a friend of Elizabeth Robins, the Campion family, Octavia Wilberforce, and Leonard and Virginia Woolf. Florence Lady Barrett MD was married to Sir William Barrett, a prominent founder member of the SPR; Edward Benson, Archbishop of Canterbury whose widow Minnie was a friend of Mrs Martindale at Horsted Keynes, was a cousin of Henry Sidgwick.

Backsettown

Backsettown was a convalescent rest home started by Dr Octavia Wilberforce and Dr Marjorie Hubert in 1927 at 'Backset', Miss Robins's 15th century farmhouse home in Henfield, West Sussex. It provided a 'rest pause', where country sunshine and tranquillity, along with home grown vegetables and fresh dairy produce, could restore health and vigour to tired single professional women and mothers. Many NSH patients went there for convalescence. Patrons included Lady Buxton, Lady Denman and Mrs Yates-Thompson. After Dr Wilberforce's death in 1963, Backsettown became a trust, but financial losses led to its closure in 1988. The Royal United Kingdom Beneficent Association took over the trust, and 'Backset', along with Dr Wilberforce's nearby bungalow, was sold privately in 1991.

People

Aldrich-Blake Louisa Brandreth DBE. 1865–1925. MB BS (Lond.) 1893, MD (Lond.) 1894, MS (Lond.) 1895. b Chingford, the daughter of a clergyman. As a schoolgirl she was known as 'Harry' and preferred cricket and boxing to piano classes and needlework. She was Dean of the LSMW in 1914 until her death in 1925. Miss Aldrich-Blake was a consulting surgeon at the New Hospital for Women, the Royal Free Hospital and hon. surgeon at the NSH. During WW1 she served with the SWH at Royaumont Abbey in France. There is a memorial to her in Tavistock Square Gardens, London, by the BMA. Address: 17 Nottingham Place, London W1.

Astor Viscountess, Nancy (née Langhorne) D. Litt (hon) CH. 1879–1964. b Virginia USA. m 1906 Waldorf, 2nd Viscount Astor (her 2nd marriage). MP for Plymouth Sutton, the first woman MP to take her seat. Lady Astor was famous for her wit, style and couture. Addresses: 4 St James's Square, London; Cliveden House, Bucks.

Balfour, Lady Frances (née Campbell) D. Litt (hon). 1858–1931. b Scotland, daughter of the 8th Duke of Argyll. m Eustace Balfour, a brother of Prime Minister Arthur Balfour. Lady Frances was a writer and suffragist; she was the first chair of the Lyceum Club, President of the Scottish Churches' League for Women's Suffrage and the author of a biography of Dr Elsie Inglis. She attended at least one BOM meeting at the NSH, and was a Council member of the LCH during its 25th anniversary year. Lady Frances was known for her bright red hair. Address: 32 Addison Road, Kensington, London W14.

Barnett Mrs, Henrietta Octavia (née Rowland) DBE. 1851–1936. Vice-president of the LCH during its 25th anniversary year. Dame Henrietta was deeply involved with improving the lives of poor women and children in London. She retired to Hove and is buried in St Helen's churchyard, Hangleton. Addresses: 1 South Square, Hampstead, London NW; 45 Wish Road, Hove.

Boyle Sir Alexander CMG CBE. 1872–1943. Brother of Helen Boyle. A diplomat, he became Provincial Commissar in East Uganda and Lieutenant Governor of Nigeria 1913–1920. At an afternoon fundraising garden party in Hayward's Heath in 1920, he was an honoured guest along with Dr Robert Armstrong-Jones and Lady Chichester, Address: High Barn, Limington, Yeovil, Somerset.

Boyle Mrs, Alice Mary (née Chambers). 1844–1920. Helen Boyle's mother. m 1868 Richard Warneford Boyle of Dublin; two sons and two daughters. The marriage ended in separation and Mrs Boyle moved first to Bristol then to Somerset. Addresses: The Cliffs, Sutton, Co. Dublin; 46 Alma Vale, Clifton, Bristol.

Buxton Countess, Mildred Anne (née Smith) GBE. 1866–1955. m Sydney, Earl Buxton, (his second wife) 1896 and accompanied him to South Africa on his appointment as GG. They had twins (a son and a daughter) and another daughter. Lady Buxton supported the demand for votes for women but disliked Mrs Pankhurst and the WSPU. She was related to Lady Chichester and served as Chairman of the NSH BOM 1920–1923. Address: Newtimber House, Nr Brighton.

Campion Sir William Robert DSO, Colonel. 1870–1951. Conservative MP for Lewes. m 1894 Katherine Byron; two sons and two daughters. Lady Campion was associated with the Barclay Home for the Blind in Brighton, and the Sunshine Home for Convalescents in Hurstpierpoint. She was Chair of the NSH BOM in the 1930s. Miss Jean Campion, the Colonel's sister was a friend of Octavia Wilberforce. Address: 'Danny', Hassocks, West Sussex (now apartments for retired people.)

Cayzer Lady, Ina Frances (née Stancomb) b c1870–1935. m 1904 Sir August Cayzer Bt. Chairman of Clan Line Steamers Ltd (Cayzer, Irvine & Co., Ltd). Lady Cayzer was associated with the NSH, offering fundraising support and activities. Address: Roffey Park, Forest Road, Horsham (now a business college and part of Sussex University.)

Chambers George Wilton JP. 1812–1904. Elder brother of Dr Thomas King Chambers and father of Alice Mary Boyle. m Anne Worthington, 1840; four sons and four daughters. He was a wealthy Yorkshire businessman with interests in coal, ironworks, railways and banking. He took a special interest in the West Riding South Yorkshire Pauper Lunatic Asylum at Wadsley. Address: Clough House, Clough Road, Rotherham, Yorks.

Chambers Thomas King. Doctor. 1817–1889. MB 1842, MD 1846. m Henrietta Maitland; two daughters: Lucy and Alberta. Elected FRCP in 1848, he served as censor, councillor, Lumleian lecturer, Goulstonian lecturer, Harveian Orator, and was honoured by being invited to accompany HRH the Prince of Wales on a visit to Italy as his personal physician. He was physician and lecturer at St Mary's Hospital in London, carrying out honorary work at the LSMW, the House of Charity in Rose Street, and the Working Men's College. Dr Chambers died in 1889 after a long illness. Address: Shrubs Hill House, Shrubs Hill, Egham, Surrey.

Chichester 6th Earl, Jocelyn Brudenall Pelham OBE. 1871–1926. He succeeded his father in 1905. The Earls of Chichester held the voluntary positions of President of the Royal Alexandra Hospital for Children, President of the Surgical Aid Society, President of the Albion Home for Female Penitents and Patron of the Home for Orphan Boys in Brighton and Hove. Lord Chichester was also a Public Works Loan Commissioner. He died from influenza in 1926; his elder son, the 7th Earl, also died from influenza two weeks later. After the death of the 8th Earl in 1945, Stanmer Estate was sold and Sussex University built in Stanmer Park. The present Lord Chichester lives in Wiltshire.

Chichester Countess, Ruth (née Buxton). 1875–1965. m 1898 Jocelyn Brudenall Pelham; two sons and two daughters. President of the LCH 1905–1948; President of Brighton YWCA. She is buried alongside her family in Stanmer churchyard. Address: Stanmer House, Stanmer Park, Nr Brighton.

Clayton Charles Edward JP. Architect. 1855–1923. Partner of Clayton & Black Architects, 10 Prince Albert Street, Brighton and responsible for the alterations to Windlesham House. He was a Quaker and m Alice, daughter of Thomas and Phoebe Glaisyer, also members of Brighton Meeting: Glaisyer and Kemp are still trading as chemists in Western Road, Brighton. He was an early subscriber to the Lewes Road Dispensary and Sister Clayton of the NSH was one of his five children. Address: 'Holmbush', Fulking, East Sussex.

Cowdray Viscountess, Annie (née Cass) GBE. 1860–1932. m 1881 Weetman, 1st Viscount Cowdray. She was President of the Horsham Suffrage Society. The Cowdray (Pearson) family members were well known in Brighton and West Sussex as benefactors and supporters of voluntary organisations Address: 'Paddockhurst', Worth, West Sussex.

Cusack-Smith Sir Berry Bt., 1859–1929. b Dublin. Sir Berry was a lawyer and diplomat, spending many years in the Pacific islands and Mexico. During WW1 he served in Mesopotamia and India as a Colonel in the Territorial Field Artillery. Sir Berry and his (2nd) wife Jane served on the NSH finance committee and BOM, moving later to the LCH. He is buried in Woodvale Cemetery, Lewes Road, Brighton. Addresses: Copsale Court, Horsham; Furze Hill, Hove.

Denman Baroness, the Honourable Gertrude Mary (née Pearson) DBE. 1884–1954. Daughter of Lord Cowdray. m 1903 3rd Baron Denman. She was a member of the Executive Committee of the Women's National Federation, Chairman of the National Federation of Women's Institutes, President of the Ladies' Golf Union, Chairman and Hon Director of the Women's Land Army and a vice-president of the NSH. Address: Balcombe Place, Balcombe, Hayward's Heath.

Dormer Pierce Francis. Clergyman. 1869–1923. Rev. Prebendary and Canon of the Church of England and Vicar of Brighton (St Peter's Parish Church) 1917–1923. Canon Pierce gave an oratory at Charles Clayton's memorial service on 1st December 1923; the following day he boarded a tram at Seven Dials on his way to St Peter's Church and was later found dead in his seat. (*Sussex Daily News* 28 November, and 1 & 3 December 1923.) Addresses: The Old Vicarage, Victoria Road, Brighton; Clifton Lodge, 3 Dyke Road, Brighton.

Dufferin and Ava Dowager Marchioness, Harriot Georgina (née Hamilton) VA CI DBE. c1843–1936. m 1862 1st Marquess of Dufferin and Ava, Viceroy of India 1884–1888. As Vicereine Lady Dufferin was asked by Queen Victoria to become patron of a fund to endow hospitals for women and children in India and to train Indian women as doctors, nurses and midwives. The Dufferin Fund is still in existence in India but now supports both sexes. In her later years Lady Dufferin was a patron of the LCH. Address: Clandeboye Estate, Nr Bangor, Northern Ireland. Maureen (née Guinness), the (divorced) wife of the 4th Marquess, lived at 'The Owl House Gardens', Lamberhurst, Kent, a 16th century cottage with gardens currently open to the public. <www.owlhouse.com>

Edmonds Florence Mary JP. Doctor. 1879–1974. MB BS (Lond.) 1911, MD (Lond.) 1914. Assistant to Dr Murdoch in Hull before setting up in general practice in Hove about 1912. Dr Edmonds was hon physician at the Queen Alexandra Hospital for Children, Brighton, and at the NSH, where she was also a BOM member. She was the hon financial secretary of the B&S Med-Chirg Soc 1931–32, and elected president for 1934–35. Addresses: 5 Brunswick Place, Hove; 61 South Way, Lewes.

Eggar Mrs, Katherine. 1849–1939. NSH BOM member. m Thomas Eggar, a solicitor. She was a member of committee of the National Union of Women Workers and with Mrs Uhthoff (wife of Dr B Uhtoff, President of the B&S Med-Chirg Soc in 1895) founded the local branch of the Queen's Nurses. She was organiser of the Linen Guild and a member of the BOM at the RSCH. Address: 30 Brunswick Road, Hove.

Fair Blanche OBE JP. Miss Fair was a subscriber to the Lewes Road Dispensary and hon divisional secretary of the (Brighton) Red Cross. Her sister Alice was organising secretary of the Brighton & Hove branch of the RSPCA Fund for Sick and Wounded Horses. Addresses: 16 Montpelier Villas, Brighton; 35 Vernon Terrace, Brighton.

FitzGerald the Honourable Ismay. c1875-1946. Daughter of Lord FitzGerald of Kilmarnock (2nd marriage). She was a companion and friend to Dr Martindale for thirty-five years and an NSH BOM member. Addresses: 10 Marlborough Place, Brighton; 28 Loudoun Road, St John's Wood, London NW8; Little Rystwood, Forest Row, Sussex.

Garrett Anderson Mrs, Elizabeth. Doctor. 1836–1917. LSA 1866, MD (Paris) 1870. m 1871 Skelton Anderson. Dr Garrett Anderson was the second woman to be admitted to the medical register (the first was Elizabeth Blackwell in 1859). She founded St Mary's Dispensary in 1866 at 69 (now 72) Seymour Place, London W1, and in 1872 opened a hospital for women, the New Hospital, in rooms above which moved to Marylebone Road in 1890. She was a lecturer at the LSMW from its inception in 1874 then Dean from 1883 to 1903. For a time in 1905 she was vice-president of Lewes Road Hospital and Dispensary. After retirement she took up local politics in Aldeburgh and, following the death of her husband, was elected Britain's first woman mayor. Millicent Garrett Fawcett (Mrs Henry Fawcett), Elizabeth's youngest sister, was the President of the NUWSS for many years. Address: 4 Upper Berkeley Street, Portman Square, London W1; Alde House, Aldeburgh, Suffolk.

Gentle Sir William Benjamin JP. Chief Constable of Brighton Police. Address: 6 Chichester Terrace, Kemp Town, Brighton.

Godfree Mrs. BOM member at the LCH Brighton Branch, then NSH. m George Godfree, solicitor, of 13 Pavilion Parade, Brighton. Mr Godfree was Chairman of the Board of Guardians in 1918. Addresses: 4 Lorne Villas, Preston Park, Brighton; 23 Goldsmid Road, Hove.

Gribble Edwin Frank. Banker. b 1859. A former accountant, Mr Gribble was manager of the London County & Westminster Bank at 8–11 Pavilion Buildings, Brighton. He was a councillor and alderman of Hove and served on the BOM at the NSH, becoming joint treasurer with Lady Rhondda. Address: 7 Salisbury Road, Hove.

Griffith Mrs, Elsie Maud. Doctor. MB BS (Lond.) 1918. m Dr John Richard Griffith MD, a doctor and surgeon at the RSCH. They had a joint general practice in Hove. Dr Elsie Griffith was physician at the NSH for many years. Dr John Griffith was elected President of the B&S Med-Chirg Soc in 1943. Address: 13 Brunswick Square, Hove.

Harper Smith George. Doctor. MA (Cantab.) 1904, MRCS LRCP (Lond.) 1910, MD 1913. Dr Harper Smith was assistant medical officer at Claybury Asylum and during WW1 was a captain in the RAMC. He was a member of the Medico-Psychological Association and the B&S Med-Chirg Soc. For many years he was the senior medical officer at Brighton County Asylum at Hayward's Heath (estb. 1859 with 937 beds, the County Asylums Act 1845 had made it mandatory for each borough and county to provide adequate asylum accommodation for its 'pauper lunatic' population). Addresses: 47 Church Road, Hove; Fir Cottage, Hayward's Heath.

Harris Mrs, Lilian Maude (née Cummins). Doctor. b 1872. LRCPI (Dublin) 1897. m 1903 Dr Henry Arthur Clifton Harris, a homeopathic physician. She was physician at LCH — both Hove Branch and Aldrington House — for many years, physician to the Girl's Friendly Society and Examiner for the Sussex Red Cross. Addresses: 12 Buckingham Place, Brighton; 32 Vernon Terrace, Brighton; 20 Dyke Road, Brighton; 'Appledram', Ditchling, Sussex.

Hingston Cecily Lamorna MBE. Doctor. 1894–1989. MRCS LRCP (Lond.) 1930. b Cornwall. She served as a nurse during WW1 then came to Hove as Helen Boyle's driver and secretary. Becoming deeply interested in Dr Boyle's work she determined to study medicine, and Dr Boyle assisted her through her medical studies offering her a position at the LCH after she qualified. Dr Hingston specialised in child psychology and established a Child Guidance Clinic at the LCH in 1935. In 1937 she became a consultant psychiatrist at the RSCH. When Dr Boyle retired in 1948 Dr Hingston became senior psychiatrist at the LCH until retiring in 1960. Addresses: 56 Shirley Drive, Hove; Flat 1, 9 Third Avenue, Hove.

Holmes-Siedle Mrs, Rosa (née Harse). BA (Cardiff), LDS RCS (Eng.), m 1919 Bertram Adolph Holmes-Siedle LDS R.C.S (Eng.) at Golder's Green Roman Catholic Church; they had two sons and two daughters. Mr and Mrs Holmes-Siedle set up their dental practice and home in Brighton in about 1920, retiring in the 1960s. Mrs Holmes-Siedle was the consulting dentist at the NSH. Address: 6 St George's Place, Brighton. Mrs Holmes-Siedle's sister Dr Eleanor Harse OBE (1971), MRCS LRCP (1921), lived for a short time at 'The Garth', Black Rock, Brighton, probably after obtaining her Diploma in Public Health in 1924. Dr Harse became a missionary to Japan until her death in Tokyo in 1990 aged 95: she worked for seventy years as Medical Director of the Seibo Byoin International Catholic Hospital.

Howard Sir John. 1830–1917. b Liverpool. An engineer and businessman who constructed the Palace Pier in 1899. He founded the Howard Charity to give weekly assistance to elderly people in need, and endowed the Howard Convalescent Home for Poor Women in Black Rock (used for wounded soldiers in WWI) and twenty-four cottage homes for sick nurses in Kemp Town. He was known locally as 'the octogenarian philanthropist' and was knighted in 1916. In his will Sir John left a large sum of money to be put into a legacy trust to be used for medical purposes in Brighton and Hove. The net value of his personal estate at his death was £275, 215 16s 6d. He is buried in Florence Place Cemetery, Ditchling Road. Address: 'Burnford', 171 Preston Road, Brighton.

Jeffries Mrs, Lillias (née Blackett). Doctor. MB BS (Lond.) 1908, MD (Lond.) 1915. Dr Jeffries bought Dr Martindale's general practice in 1921 and worked as a gynaecologist at the NSH, the LCH and the workhouse infirmary. She was elected President of the B&S Med-Chirg Soc in 1948. Mr Jeffries was a member of the Indian Civil Service. Address: 11 Adelaide Crescent, Hove.

Jennings (later Sir) Arthur Oldham MBE. c1864–1934 Mr Jennings was a lawyer and a judge; he was Registrar and High Bailiff of the Sussex County and the Bankruptcy Courts and District Registrar of the High Court of Justice. Mrs Mabel Jennings was Divisional Commissioner of the Brighton & Hove District Girl Guides. Both were BOM members of the NSH. Address: 29 Adelaide Crescent, Hove.

Jones Lillie Mabel Agnes. Doctor. c1870–1923. MB (Honours in Medicine and Obstetrics) BS (Lond.) 1893, MD (Lond.) 1895. b Newfoundland. She worked at the New Hospital for Women, the Royal Free Hospital (as an anaesthetist) and the Victoria Hospital for Sick Children in Hull, then moved to Hove into general practice with Helen Boyle in 1898. About 1908 she became medical officer at the Glasgow Institute for Orphans and Destitute Girls, medical assistant and anaesthetist at Glasgow Women's Private Hospital and assistant surgeon at Glasgow Female Lock Hospital. During WW1 she worked with refugees from Belgium and was awarded La Medaille de la Reine Elisabeth. She retired in 1921 and died in 1923. Addresses: 37 Church Road Hove; 143 Hyndland Road, Glasgow; 2 Alfred Terrace, Hillshead, Glasgow.

Lawrence Millicent. 1863–1925. Trustee and BOM member of the NSH. Millicent was one of the seven Lawrence sisters of Roedean School. Her elder sisters Penelope and Dorothy attended Newnham College but family funds did not allow Millicent to follow them; she attended a teacher training course at Maria Grey College. Address: Roedean School, Roedean Way, Brighton.

Leconfield Baroness, Violet Beatrice (née Lawson). 1892–1956. m 1911 Charles, 3rd Baron Leconfield, Lord Lieut. of West Sussex 1917–49. Lady Leconfield was vice-president of the NSH and opened the new wing in 1928. 'The Leconfield Arms' public house is at 116 Edward Street, Brighton. Address: Petworth House, Pulborough, West Sussex.

Loder Lady Louise (née Beauclerk). 1869–1958. Daughter of the 10th Duke of St. Albans. m 1890 Gerald Loder 1st Baron Wakehurst, Conservative MP for Brighton 1889–1905. Lady Louise was patron of the NSH, Brighton YWCA, and President of the Brighton Lying-In Institution. Addresses: Abinger House, 142 Kings Road, Hove; Wakehurst Place, Ardingly, West Sussex.

Louise Caroline Alberta HRH, Duchess of Argyll, VA CI GCVO GBE RRC. 1848–1939. 4th Daughter of Queen Victoria. m 1871 the Marquess of Lorne (later 9th Duke of Argyll), eldest brother of Lady Frances Balfour. Lorne was a GG of Canada. The Duchess was patron of several voluntary societies in Brighton and patroness and President of the NSH. Address: Invararay Castle, Argyll, Scotland.

Malleson Hope. BA (Cantab.) 1863–1933. Hope Malleson was a BOM member and governor of the NSH. She was a daughter of Elizabeth Malleson, a teacher and feminist who founded the Rural District Nursing

Association (district nurses). She lived in Rome with her friend M.A.R Tuker, a contemporary from Newnham College. Miss Malleson was the author of *A Woman Doctor, Mary Murdoch of Hull.* Her father, Frank Malleson, was born in Hove c1829.

Martindale Mrs, Louisa (née Spicer). 1839–1914. Mother of Louisa and Hilda. m 1872 William Martindale, a businessman in the paper trade. Her father was also a paper merchant. Two of her sisters married into the Unwin family of Unwin & Allen, publishers. Mrs Martindale retired to Horsted Keynes, where she became friendly with Minnie Benson, who lived in 'Tremens,' a nearby house. Mrs Benson was the widow of Edward Benson, Archbishop of Canterbury 1882–1896 and the mother of the writer E. F. Benson, who lived in Rye. Mrs Martindale is buried in Horsted Keynes churchyard. Address: 'Cheelys', Horsted Keynes, West Sussex.

Maule Miss. Member of the NSH BOM. Daughter of Lt. Col. G.E. Maule of Brunswick Square. Miss Maule was the co-proprietor, with Miss Isaacson, of a boarding school for girls in Landsdowne Road. Miss Isaacson was a member of the LCH council c1926. Address: St Michael's Lodge, Landsdowne Road, Brighton.

Merrifield Flora de Gaudrion. 1860–1943. Younger daughter of Frederic Merrifield, barrister and lawyer, Clerk of the Peace and of the County Court for East and West Sussex, and his wife Anne (née de Gaudrion). Miss Merrifield was amongst other things hon secretary of the Brighton Women's Suffrage Society and chairman of the Special Committee of the local NUWSS branch. She was a member of council and treasurer of the LCH Brighton Branch and the NSH. Addresses: 14 Clifton Terrace, Brighton; 24 Vernon Terrace, Brighton.

Murdoch Mary Charlotte (known as 'Murdie'). Doctor. 1864–1916. LRCP&S (Edin.) LRFCS (Glas.) 1892. b Elgin, Scotland, daughter of a lawyer. Dr Murdoch worked as clinical assistant at the New Hospital for Women alongside Dr Helen Webb, then as clinical assistant at the Brompton Hospital and the East London Hospital for Children. She moved to Hull and was house surgeon in the Victoria Hospital for Children and the Tottenham Fever Hospital, before setting up her own general practice. During WW1 when Hull was bombed Dr Murdoch became ill with pleurisy, after walking through the snow to answer a night call, and died on 20th March 1916. Her memorial service was conducted by the Bishop of Hull and thousands of mourners gathered. Her body was cremated and placed in the Lady Chapel at All Saints' Church. Address: 102 Beverley Road, Hull.

Odlum Doris. Doctor. 1890–1964. MA (Oxon) 1921, BA (Lond.) MRCS LRCP 1924. Resident Medical Officer and Physician at the LCH 1928–1948, Physician of Nervous Disorders at the Royal Victoria and West Hants Hospital, Consultant Emeritus Bournemouth and East Dorset Hospital Group 1955–1964. Fellow Royal Society of Medicine, Member Royal Medical Psychological Association, member and joint hon Secretary Council of Mental Hygiene. Addresses: 29 Poole Road, Bournemouth; Ardmor, Cliff Drive, Canford Cliffs (1959).

Otter Lady, Elizabeth Audrey (née Woodard). d. 1925. m Sir John Otter JP, councillor, alderman, Mayor of Brighton 1913–15. Lady Otter did much voluntary work, she was *inter alia* chairman of the Brighton Red Cross Working Party 1918 and chairman of the Imperial Club for Nurses' Committee. She was a member of the NSH BOM during the 1920s, then a patron. Address: 16 Vernon Terrace, Brighton.

Ouless Walter William RA. Portrait artist. 1848–1933. b Jersey moved to London in 1874. m 1878 Lucy Chambers, elder daughter of Dr Thomas King Chambers. Two of his works hang in the National Portrait Gallery. Mrs Ouless gave donations to the Lewes Road Dispensary. Address: 12 Bryanston Square, London W1.

Pickworth Florence. Teacher of music. Hon secretary of Brighton & Hove Women's Franchise Society, committee member of Brighton Homeopathic Dispensary, hon secretary to the dispenser at Lewes Road Dispensary until 1905. Probably related to Frederick Pickworth a 'professor of violin' and conductor of the Palace Pier orchestra.

Ralli Mrs, Marcella. 1838–1922. Lady of the Order of St John of Jerusalem. Widow of Stephen Ralli (1829–1902), a Greek cotton merchant whose family fled from the island of Chios in 1822 after an uprising against the Turks. The Ralli family set up Ralli Brothers in London in 1826, and became international cotton and wheat traders with offices in Marseilles, Constantinople, Odessa and St Petersburg. Mrs Ralli endowed the Ralli Pathology Laboratory at the RSCH and built the Ralli Memorial Hall near Hove station (the commemorative plaque can still be seen). Addresses: 37 Park Lane, London; St Catherine's Lodge 9, 10 St Catherine's Terrace, Hove.

Rhondda 2nd Viscountess, Margaret Haig Thomas. 1883–1958. Daughter of David Alfred Thomas 1st Viscount Rhondda. m 1908 Humphrey Mackworth (div). She succeeded to her father's fortune and his title under special remainder; her attempt to take her seat in the House of

Lords was blocked by the other lords. She was a WSPU member, and the owner and editor of the magazine *Time and Tide*. Lady Rhondda was hon treasurer of the NSH 1921–23, then vice-president. Addresses: 1b Baytree Lodge, Frognal, Hampstead, London NW3; 503 Keyes House, Dolphin Square, London SW1; Churt Halewell, Shere, Surrey.

Robins Elizabeth. 1862–1952. b Louisville, Kentucky. American actress who came to England in the 1890s from Norway. She translated the plays of Ibsen and introduced them to the London stage playing the leading roles. Miss Robins then gave up acting to begin a second career as a writer of plays and novels; a suffragette and friend of Mrs Pankhurst she wrote the highly acclaimed play 'Votes For Women' in 1907. Miss Robins served as chairman of the NSH BOM for many years and wrote the LCH Brighton Branch pamphlet *What Can I Do?* in 1915. Addresses: 'Backset', Henfield, West Sussex; 36 Albion Street, Hyde Park, London W1.

Roth Mrs, Anne Elizabeth. m Bernard Roth JP, treasurer of the Brighton Liberal and Radical Association. Mrs Roth was an original council member at Lewes Road Dispensary in 1899 and a close friend of Mrs Thorne. Addresses: 'Wayside', 1 Preston Park Avenue, Brighton; 'Kingswood', Enfield, Middx.

Rukhmabai. Doctor. 1864–1955. LRCP&S (Edin.) LRFCS (Glas.) 1893, MD (Brux.) 1894. b Bombay (now Mumbai), India. Rukhmabai was married as a child but as an adult fought a long battle in the Indian and English law courts to free herself from the marriage. She was helped by many English and Indian social reformers, and with the aid of the Dufferin Fund entered the LSMW c1889. She returned to India in 1895 becoming Chief Medical Officer of Hospitals in Surat and Rajkot. Address: French Bridge, Bombay, India.

Ryle Mrs, Catherine. Mrs Ryle was an NSH BOM member for many years. m Dr Reginald John Ryle BA (Oxon.), MD (Lond.) hon surgeon at Sussex Eye Hospital, President of the B&S Med-Chirg Soc 1914 and Medical Superintendent of the Home for Inebriate Women. Address: 15 German Place, Brighton.

Scatliff Mrs, Helen Mary (née Collen). Doctor. 1878–1978. MB (Lond.) 1904. b Bath. m Harold Ellerton Scatliff MA (Oxon.) a surgeon. Mrs Scatliff was hon physician at the LCH Brighton Branch the NSH, also serving on the NSH BOM. Mr Scatliff was consulting surgeon at the Brighton, Hove & Sussex Throat and Ear Hospital (founded 1879). Addresses: 11 Charlotte St, Brighton; 46 Marine Parade, Brighton.

Scharlieb Mrs, Mary (née Dacomb) DBE. Doctor. 1845–1930. Licentiate of Medicine, Surgery and Midwifery Madras (now Chenna), India 1878, MB BS (Lond.) 1881, MD (Lond.) 1888, MS (Lond.) 1897. Dame Mary travelled to India with her barrister husband: she studied midwifery and diseases of women at Madras Medical College then with her two sons returned to England and entered the LSMW in 1879. After qualifying in 1881 she went back to India as lecturer in forensic medicine, midwifery and the diseases of women at Madras Medical College and University. She returned again to England to study for her MD and did not go back to India. Address: 149 Harley Street, London W1.

Spicer Sir Albert Bt. MP. Brother of Mrs Martindale and a friend of William Martindale; he served with Dame Henrietta Barnett on the Committee of the State Children's Association. He made donations to the Lewes Road Dispensary and Hospital. Address: 10 Lancaster Gate, London W1.

Spicer Sir Evan MP. Brother of Mrs Martindale. Sir Evan fully supported equality for women, his wife Lady Spicer made donations to the Canning Town Women's Hospital in London. Address: 'Belair', Dulwich, Surrey.

Thorne Mrs, Isabel (née Pryer). 1834–1910. m Joseph Thorne, businessman, Master of the Worshipful Company of Cutlers (the Cutlers' Company has had a long connection with the manufacture of surgical instruments). They had four sons and two daughters. Mrs Thorne went with Sophia Jex-Blake to Edinburgh in 1869 to seek training as doctors. She did not ever qualify, becoming Secretary of the LSMW in 1877. Mr Thorne retired to Lewes and served as Mayor from 1884–85. After her husband's death Mrs Thorne moved to London where she lived with Dr Attwood Thorne (her son) and Dr May Thorne (her daughter). Her elder daughter Isabel m 1890 Frank Verrall, the son of Francis Verrall of Southover Manor, proprietor of Southover Brewery. Mrs Thorne is buried with her husband in the churchyard at St John's Church, Southover, Lewes. Addresses: The Grange, Southover, Lewes; 10 Nottingham Terrace, London NW1.

Thorne May OBE. Doctor. 1861–1951. LSA 1895, FRCS 1902. Younger daughter of Mrs Isabel Thorne. She became secretary of the LSMW after the death of her mother in 1910. Dr Thorne was associated with the Elizabeth Garrett Anderson Hospital and the Royal Free Hospital in London; during WW1 she served in Malta with the RAMC. Address: 148 Harley Street, London W1.

Vance Mrs, Grace. Doctor. MB BCh. (Belfast) 1916. m 1916 John Hazlett Vance MB BCh (Belfast), BAO 1916. They seem to have been students together at the Queens College Belfast, marrying immediately after qualification. Dr Vance worked as an anaesthetist at NSH, the Drs Vance probably shared a joint practice at 57 Richmond Buildings. Address: 2 Richmond Terrace, Brighton.

Verrall Marian E. MBE. b 1857. Miss Verrall was a council member at the Lewes Road Dispensary in 1899, in 1905 she became hon treasurer. She remained as hon treasurer to the LCH Brighton & Hove Branches but resigned after the separation although staying as a BOM member at the NSH. Miss Verrall went on to be vice-president of the LCH and was *inter alia* hon secretary to the Ladies' Association for the Care of Friendless Girls and the Girls' Friendly Society in Brighton. She lived with her sister Annette Sarah Verrall; their brothers were Dr (later Sir) Thomas Verrall MD, President of the B&S Med-Chirg Soc 1894; Hugh Verrall, a solicitor, Chairman of Committee at the Brighton Lying-In Hospital; and Arthur Verrall, Professor of Poetry at Trinity College, Cambridge. Addresses: 26 Gloucester Place, Brighton; 'The Lydd', West Hoathly, East Sussex.

Wauchope Gladys Mary. Doctor. 1889–1966. BSc. 1919 (St Andrews), MRCS (Eng.) LRCP (Lond.) 1921, MD (Lond.) 1926. Dr Wauchope served as a VAD nurse for two years during WW1. She came to Hove in 1925 as an assistant to Dr Florence Edmonds then set up her own general practice. She was elected FRCP in 1946 and President of the B&S Med-Chirg Soc in 1954. Dr Wauchope was a physician at the NSH for many years. Addresses: 5 Brunswick Place, Hove; 64 Wilbury Road, Hove; Brook Cottage, Ripe, East Sussex.

Webb Helen. Doctor. d 1925. LSA 1888, MB (Lond.) 1888. Dr Webb was from a Quaker family. She was physician at the New Hospital London, Medical Inspector at St Paul's Girl's School, Consultant at the Children's Hospital, Harrow Road, London, Demonstrator in Anatomy at the LSMW. She came to Brighton c1919 and was a member of the site and building committee then BOM at the NSH. Address: 12 Clifton Terrace, Brighton.

Wilberforce Octavia. Doctor. 1888–1963. LRCP LRCS 1920. Dr Wilberforce was from a prominent Sussex county family who opposed her desire to become a doctor; she managed to enter the LSMW in 1915 with financial help from Lord and Lady Buxton, Elizabeth Robins, and Dolly Yates-Thompson. She worked as clinical assistant at Graylingwell Mental Hospital (formerly West Sussex County Lunatic Asylum) then came to Brighton in 1923 as GP and hon physician at the NSH. Address: 24 Montpelier Crescent, Brighton.

Brighton & Hove

1: The Dispensary 2: Lewes Road Hospital 3: LCH Brighton Branch
4: Dr Martindale's house 5: New Sussex 6: LCH Hove Branch
7: Dr Boyle's house 8: To LCH Aldrington House 9: To the Workhouse
10: To the RSCH

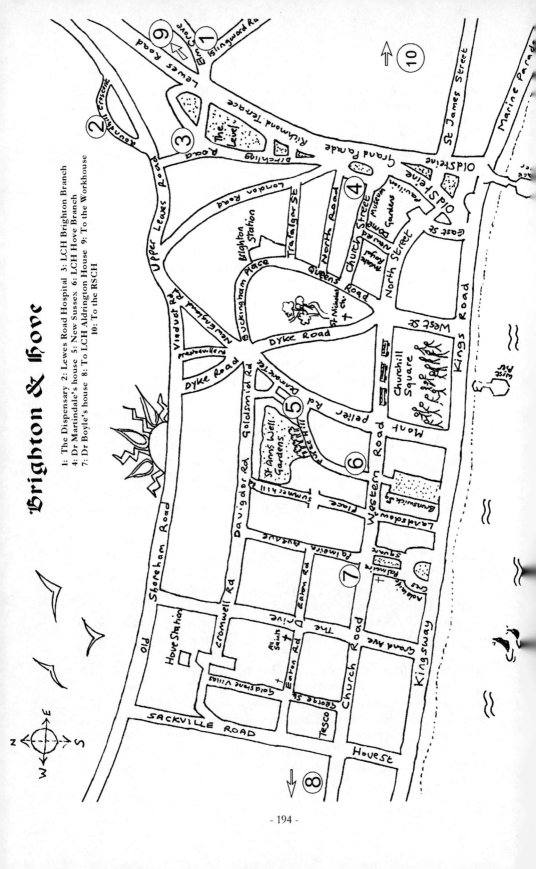

SOURCES

From works by Helen Boyle

'Account of an Attempt of the early Treatment of Mental and Nervous Case (with Special Reference to The Poor)'. *Journal of Mental Science*, October 1909.
'Early Nervous and Borderland Conditions'. From a paper read at St Mary's Hospital Medical Society, 28th January 1920. *St Mary's Hospital Gazette* April 1940. Reprinted by the Southern Publishing Company, 130 North Street, Brighton.
'Family Life: Some Difficulties and Dangers'. Summary of a lecture given under the auspices of the National Council for Mental Hygiene at the Royal Pavilion, Brighton, 8th November 1934.
'Some Points in the Early Treatment of Mental and Nervous Cases (with Special Reference to The Poor)'. *Journal of Mental Science*, October 1905.
'The Mental Hygiene Movement'. Address given at a special meeting of the National Council for Mental Hygiene on the occasion of the visit of the President, HRH The Duchess of Kent, at Manson House, Portland Place, W1, 26th April 1944.
'Watchman, what of the night? The night is departing, the day is approaching'. (Isaiah 21:11/12 KJV). Presidential address delivered at the Ninety-eighth Annual meeting of the Royal Medico-Psychological Association, held at Brighton, 12th July 1939. Published in the *Journal of Mental Science* September, 1939.

Sources for the Martindale Family:

A Woman Surgeon by Louisa Martindale CBE. Victor Gollancz, 1951.
From One Generation to Another 1839–1944. A Book of Memoirs by Hilda Martindale CBE. George Allen & Unwin, 1944.

Other sources:

A Quiet Revolution in Brighton: Dr Helen Boyle's Pioneering Approach to Mental Health Care 1899–1939. Louise Westwood 2001, published by the Society for the Social History of Medicine.
A Story of a Red Cross Unit in Serbia by Dr James Berry. J. & A. Churchill, 1916.
A Woman Doctor, Mary Murdoch of Hull by Hope Malleson BA. Sidgwick & Jackson, 1918.
A Woman Physician by G. M. Wauchope. John Wright & Sons, 1963.
Brighton and Hove High School 1876–1952 by M. G. Mills. Brighton Herald Ltd, 1953.
Brighton General Hospital by Janet Gooch. Phillimore, 1980.
Dr Elsie Inglis by Lady Frances Balfour. Hodder and Stoughton, 1918.
'Driving Ambitions: Women in Pursuit of a medical education 1890–1939' by Carol Dyhouse, *Women's Historical Review* Vol.7 No. 3, 1998.
Edith Pechey-Phipson MD by Edythe Lutzker. Exposition, New York, 1973.
Elizabeth Garrett Anderson by Jo Manton. Methuen, 1965.

Encyclopaedia of Hove by Judy Middleton. Middleton, 1991.

English Feminism 1780–1980 by Barbara Caine. OUP, 1997.

English Medical Women by A. H. Bennett. Isaac Pitman, 1915.

'History of the National Health Service' by G. Rivett <www.nhshistory.net>.

'History of Mental Health Law and Practice' by Clive Unsworth, in *The Politics of Mental Health Legislation*. Oxford, 1987 <www.imhl.com/history.htm>.

'Home and Away: The Feminist Remapping of Public and Private Space in Victorian London' by Lynne Walker, in *New Frontiers of Space, Bodies and Gender*. Ed. Rosa Ainley. Routledge, 1998.

Hospitals in Brighton & Hove by L. W. Lauste MD FRCS. Proceedings, Royal Soc. Med. Vol. 65 February 1972.

In Love With Life: A Pioneer Career Woman's Story by Miss Gordon Holmes. Hollis and Carter, 1944.

Memoirs of a Doctor in War and Peace by Isabel Hutton MD. Heinemann, 1960.

Mildred Buxton: A Memoir based upon her Letters. Arranged by Margaret Cropper and William Barnes. Orpington Press, 1966.

Octavia Wilberforce: The Autobiography of a Pioneer Women Doctor. Edited by Pat Jalland. Cassell,1989.

Sophia Jex-Blake: A Woman Pioneer in Nineteenth Century Medical Reform by Shirley Roberts. Routledge, 1993.

Storming the Citadel: The Rise of the Woman Doctor. E. Moberley Bell. Constable, 1953.

Tales of Old Hove Schools by Judy Middleton. Middleton, 1991.

The Charge of the Parasols by Catriona Blake. Women's Press, 1990.

The Hidden History of Glasgow's Women by Elspeth King. Mainstream, 1993.

The Hospitals by B. Abel-Smith. Heinemann, 1964.

The Medical Profession in Mid Victorian London by M. J. Peterson. University of California Press, 1978.

The Life and Rebellious Times of Cecily Hamilton by Lis Whitelaw. Women's Press, 1990.

The Virago Book of Women and the Great War. Edited by Joyce Marlow. Virago, 1999.

The Wagners of Brighton by Anthony Wagner and Antony Dale. Phillimore, 1983.

Windlesham House School Roll by Henry C. Malden. Printed by H & C Treacher, North Street, Brighton, 1887. Local History Studies Collection, Brighton Museum.

With the Scottish Nurses in Roumania by Yvonne Fitzgerald. John Murray, 1918.

Women Gain a Place in Medicine by Edythe Lutzker. McGraw-Hill, 1969.

The Theatre Royal, Brighton by Antony Dale. Oriel, 1980.

Lady Chichester Hospital Annual Reports. East Sussex Record Office, Lewes. HB63

New Sussex Hospital Annual Reports and minutes of the Site and Building Committee and Board of Management. East Sussex Record Office, Lewes. HB12

Sussex Daily News and *Brighton & Hove Herald* archive copies. Kelly's street directories. Pike's street directories. Originals and microfiche at East Sussex Records Office and Hove Reference Library.

INDEX

Aldrich-Blake, Louisa 31, 39–40, 51–2, 75, 139, 142, 144, 180–1

Annie Hall Legacy 148, 150

Armstrong-Jones, Sir Robert 30, 36, 74, 105, 155

Astor, Lady 127, 140–6, 181

Blackwell, Dr Elizabeth 37, 185

Bondfield, Margaret 15, 69

Boyle, Rev A Vicars 35, 107

Boyle, Helen: early years 8, 28, attachment to family 35, qualification 8, 29, work at Claybury Asylum 29–30, work at Canning Town 30, borderland disorder 30, moves to Hove 3, 5, 158, personality 105, 142, war service 66–7, parts from Dr Jones 47, relationship with Dr Martindale 100–2, sets up Mabel Jones Fund 152, gives evidence to Royal Commission 158, published works 195, death 162

Boyle, Olive 25, 107, 165

Boyle, Richard Warneford 28, 182

Boyle, Sophia 35

Brighton and Hove Dispensary 1–2, 8

Brighton and Hove Franchise Society 55, 68, 85, 190

Brighton General Hospital 112, 119, 134, 160–1, 164, 195

Brighton Guardians of the Poor 111–4, 120, 122, 124–7, 129–32, 186

Brighton High School for Girls 15, 18, 38, 98, 123, 133, 140, 180, 195

Brighton Lying-In Institution 16, 18, 20, 26

Brighton & Sussex Medico–Chirurgical Society 5, 104, 107–8, 143, 154, 157

Brighton & Sussex Mutual Provident Society 22

British Medical Association 37, 59

Brunswick Pl 51–2, 56, 78, 83–4, 95, 178

Buxton, Lady 135, 139–40, 144, 148, 150–1, 170–2, 176–8, 181–2

Canning Town Women's Settlement 30, 61, 192

Chambers, Alice Mary 28, 182

Chambers, George Wilton 28, 183

Chambers, Thomas King 29, 183

Chichester General Infirmary 54, 80

Chichester, Lord (6th Earl) 52, 182

Chichester, Ruth, Countess (wife of 6th Earl) 24, 46, 50, 52, 56, 60, 76–8

Claybury Hospital and Asylum 29–30, 35–6, 105, 186

Clayton Miss 54, 60, 75, 128, 173

Clayton, Mr C. E. 82–3, 85–9, 91–6, 98, 116–17, 124, 137, 183

Cock, Julia 33, 43, 75, 180

'Colin Godman's' 73, 100, 109

College of Surgeons, Edinburgh 7, 16, 29, 37

Contagious Diseases Act 12, 17, 132

Craig, Sir Maurice 105, 108, 165

Daking, Mr and Mrs 112, 125, 129–32, 134

Ditchling Road 4–8 45–7, 50

Dormer Pierce, Canon 92–3, 95–6, 110, 113, 184

Elsie Inglis Hospital 61, 157, 164

Enabling Act (1877) vii, 7–8, 133

Faculty (Royal) of Physicians and Surgeons, Glasgow 7–8, 16, 29, 35, 37

Fawcett, Mrs Millicent Garrett 5, 49, 63–4, 70, 123, 185

FitzGerald, Ismay 38, 41, 49–50, 72, 85, 87–8, 94, 96, 100–1, 116, 118–19, 123, 128, 130–1, 133, 140, 149–50, 162, 185

Gander, Mr and Mrs 126, 132, 146

Garrett Anderson, Elizabeth vii, 6, 8, 13, 23, 27–9, 35, 37, 43, 45–6, 49, 61, 145, 180, 185

Garrett Anderson, Louisa 65, 70

Garrett, Newson 10–1

Gentle, Sir William 82, 89, 91, 185

Green, Miss Ruth 97, 118, 120–5, 127, 129, 132, 138–9

Gore-Lindsay, Rita 100, 158, 162

Hamilton, Cecily 67, 71, 196

Harper-Smith, Dr George 155, 186

Harris, Mrs Clifton 55, 60, 74, 78, 102, 105–6, 169, 186

Hingston, Cecily Lamorna 60, 100, 104, 109, 156, 186–7

Holmes-Siedle, Mrs 127, 187

Horsted Keynes 31, 36, 53–4, 60, 72, 180, 189

House of Commons 131, 143, 190

Howard, Sir John 82–3, 89, 187

Howard, Sir John legacy trust 84, 86–7, 91, 93, 95, 99, 109, 114, 116–7, 126, 128, 143, 152–4, 157

Inglis, Elsie 23, 65–7, 181, 195

Jex-Blake, Sophia vii, 8, 13–14, 23, 29, 179, 192, 196

Jones, Lillie Mabel Agnes: sets up practice with Helen Boyle 3, 158, dispensary 101, medal 154, 189, moves to Glasgow 47, death 151–2, memorial sunlight balcony 154

King and Queen's College, Dublin 7, 37

Lady Chichester Hosp. Aldrington House 99–109, 152–3, 157–9, 161

Lewes Road Dispensary 8, 16, 23–6, 31–5, 40, 41–6, 50
Lewes Road Hosp. Roundhill Cres 28, 32, 35, 42–4, 47–8, 50–1, 60, 86, 153, 185
London School of Medicine for Women 3, 7, 9, 13–18, 28–9, 33, 37–43, 53, 65, 75, 101–2, 133, 135, 179–81, 183, 185, 191–3
London, University of 15–16, 18, 29, 35, 37, 40, 79
Lunacy Act 106, 154
Marriage bar 59, 61
Martindale, Hilda 13, 15, 18, 25, 39–40, 59, 195
Martindale, Dr Louisa: birth 12, childhood 12–16, student life 16, 37–9, qualification 17, 39, working in Hull 35, 40–1, practice in Brighton 41–3, meets Ismay FitzGerald 49, war service 67–8, moves to London 149, death 162
Martindale, Mrs Louisa: birth 10, marriage 12, widowed 13, moves to Lewes 13, moves to Brighton 15, moves to Horsted Keynes 31, moves to London 39, death 72
Martindale, William 12–13, 189, 92
Medical Act, 1858 6
Medical Register 7–8, 29, 185
Medical Women's Federation 46, 59, 108
Merrifield, Miss F. de G. 49, 55, 85, 87, 89, 92–4, 96–7, 118–19, 124–5, 127, 139, 176, 189
Milborne, Miss 54, 60, 137, 147
Murdoch, Mary 15–16, 23, 35, 40, 46, 60, 72, 101, 122, 185, 189, 195
Murray, Flora 65, 70
National Health Service viii, 156, 159, 164, 196
National Union of Women's Suffrage Societies 63–5, 69–70, 88, 94, 123, 185, 189
New Hospital for Women 57, 61, 82, 139, 145, 181, 185, 188–9, 193
Newnham College, Cambridge 15, 88–9, 180, 188–9
Outpatients' Clinics, St Thomas', Charing Cross and Euston Rd Hosps 31
Paget, Lady 64
Pankhurst, Mrs 49, 55, 63, 65, 69–72, 122, 182, 191
Percy & Wagner Almshouses 1
Peters, Mr 137, 140, 144–5, 147, 174
Pharmacy Act, 1868 27
Pioneer Club 55, 78–80, 88, 125–6, 132, 151
Poona Medical School, India 9
Pound Day 43
Qualification of Women Act (1907) 46
Queen Alexandra Rose Day 146

Red Cross 64–7, 70, 185–6, 190, 195
Rhondda, Lady 94, 98, 116–17, 127–8, 136, 139, 144, 172, 186, 190–1
Robins, Elizabeth 54, 57, 66, 76–7, 83, 85, 88, 93–4, 97, 109, 115, 121–3, 127–8, 135, 139, 144, 149, 176, 180–1, 191, 193
'Rock Rose' 100, 109
Roedean School 88, 117, 141, 144, 188
Royal College of Physicians 7, 37, 158
Royal College of Surgeons 7, 37, 133
Royal Society of Apothecaries 6, 8, 11
Royal Sussex County Hosp. 5, 21–2, 26, 52–3, 55, 60, 78, 91, 109–10, 120–1, 125, 135–6, 138, 147, 155–6, 161, 164, 187, 193
Royaumont Abbey 39, 66–8, 81, 181
Scatliff, Mrs Harold 45, 50, 60, 76, 84–5, 87–8, 94, 102, 124, 128, 133, 140, 166, 191
Scharlieb Dr Mary 8–9, 18, 46, 122, 192
Scottish Women's Hospitals 65–9, 181
Serbia 64, 66–8, 70–1, 74, 81, 195
Sex Disqualification (Removal) Act (1919) 7, 156
South London Hospital for Women 61, 82, 89, 91, 139, 148, 157, 164
Spicer. Sir Albert 192
Spicer, Sir Evan 45
Spicer, James 10, 12
Stobart, Mrs St Clair 64, 70
Swann, Mr 137–8, 150
Thomas-Stanford, Charles 77, 131
Thorne, Isabel 14, 16–18, 32, 37, 192
Thorne, Joseph 14, 17–18
Thorne, May 18, 122, 192
Verrall Miss M. E. 24, 32, 34, 36, 52–3, 55–6, 85–6, 88–90, 94, 104, 116, 127–8, 133, 142, 165, 193
Vicarage, the Old 18, 91–8, 110, 113–14, 184
Vrnjatchka Banja 66, 68
'What Can I Do?' Appeal 76, 83, 191
Wilberforce, Octavia 37, 60–1, 77, 109, 122, 135, 151, 166, 180–2, 193, 196
Windlesham School 92, 97–8
Women dentists vii, 127, 133, 156, 187
Women pharmacists 27
Women's Social and Political Union 63–66, 69, 71, 182, 190
Woodhead, Grace Eyre 106
Workhouse, Brighton 26, 46, 60, 78, 110–14, 118–19, 124–7, 129, 131, 134, 146, 159–61, 187

☀ Hastings Press Books

Women of Victorian Sussex
Their Status, Occupations & Dealings with the Law
by Helena Wojtczak £9.99

Matilda Betham-Edwards
Novelist, Travel Writer and Francophile
by Joan Rees £9.99

Railwaywomen
Exploitation, Betrayal and Triumph in the Workplace
by Helena Wojtczak
Hardback £20 CD-ROM £7

Notable Women of Victorian Hastings
A Collection of Nine Mini-Biographies
by Helena Wojtczak £5.99

Alf Cobb: Mugsborough Rebel
The Struggle for Justice in Edwardian Hastings
by Mike Matthews £7.99

The Decline of Hastings as a Fashionable Resort
Some Edwardian Explanations
by Mike Matthews (Booklet) £2

Captain Swing in Sussex and Kent
Rural Rebellion in 1830
by Mike Matthews £7.99

Panic, Anxiety and Sugar
What's the Connection?
Booklet £2

Our books are kept in stock at many retail outlets; they can be ordered at any bookshop or bought direct from us, post-free, from the address overleaf.

Forthcoming books

Planned for 2007–8

Poor Cottages and Proud Palaces
The Life & Work of Thomas Sockett
By Sheila Haines and Leigh Lawson £9.99

Notable Women of Victorian Sussex
A Collection of Mini-Biographies
by Val Brown & Helena Wojtczak £9.99

W. N. P. Barbellion and His Critics
An Essay in Historical Method
By Eric Bond Hutton £9.99

Footplate to Footpath
The Lost Railways of the Isle of Wight
by Adrian C. Hancock £12

HASTINGS PUBLISHING SERVICES

The Hastings Press is an independent publisher of non-fiction. Submissions are invited on themes of local history. We also offer a range of services to self-publishing authors, from typesetting and cover design to a complete publishing and marketing service.

☀ HASTINGS PRESS

P. O. Box 96, Hastings, TN34 1GQ
Phone 0845 45 85 947
Fax 0871 253 4923
Hastings.Press@virgin.net

www.hastingspress.co.uk